THE SUPER COPS

THE SUPER COPS

The true story of the cops called

Batman and Robin

L. H. WHITTEMORE

STEIN AND DAY/*Publishers*/New York

First published in 1973
Copyright © 1973 by L. H. Whittemore
Library of Congress Catalog Card No. 72-96377
All rights reserved
Published simultaneously in Canada by Saunders of Toronto, Ltd.
Designed by David Miller
Printed in the United States of America
Stein and Day/*Publishers*/7 East 48 Street, New York, N.Y. 10017
ISBN 0-8128-1538-6

I would like to thank
John and Robbin Hawkins
Dave and Irene Greenberg
Robert Hantz
Jean Divney
Marguerite Cannavaro
Mary Solberg
and to dedicate this book
to Gloria.

—*L. H. Whittemore*

BOOK

1

1

David Greenberg was up early, roaming around his apartment. He sat down at the kitchen table and puffed at a cigarette while his wife, Irene, served breakfast. But he didn't have much appetite. He pushed away the food, sipped some coffee, took out another cigarette.

Today he was going to become a cop. He was going to go down to the Police Academy and get himself a gun and a shield, and then he was going to go out and do something terrific. He crushed out the cigarette and got up quickly.

"Are you taking the subway?"

The question startled him. He thought of the long ride from Brooklyn into Manhattan and then back out again.

"Hey," he said, "I'm twenty-four years old!"

"What's that got to do with anything? You're supposed to use public transportation!"

"I know, I know."

"So you're taking the subway, right?"

Without answering he slipped into a gray windbreaker and left the apartment, hurrying downstairs and into the street. He stood still for a moment, then walked to where his brown Rambler was parked, jumped inside, and closed the door.

Already he could imagine himself at the wheel of a radio car. Even better, in an unmarked detective's car. There was no way he wouldn't become more than just an ordinary policeman, not if he used his brain and his body the right way.

He drove across the Brooklyn Bridge into Manhattan and went down Twentieth Street to the Police Academy. No parking space.

He went around the block again, but still nowhere to park. Up ahead on the left was a spot in front of a hydrant. He swerved the car in and left it there. The worst they could do was tow it away.

Just walking into the building gave him an uneasy feeling, a vague combination of excitement and fear. As he moved down the corridor with several other young men, probably new recruits like himself, he had the odd sensation that he was walking back into the Navy. Worse, the place resembled an institution of some sort.

He walked into the huge gymnasium and pushed through the crowd of nearly a thousand other young men. A voice boomed over the commotion.

"All right! All you guys from the Bronx, line up down at this end of the gym! From Queens, over here! Brooklyn, next! Staten Island—"

Dave Greenberg headed toward the Brooklyn group.

"According to height!" came a new command. "Let's go, line up according to the tallest down to the shortest. Tallest guys in the front row! Come on, come on! Anybody six three? All those over six one, get in front. Others, fall in behind!"

He hesitated. There were quite a few guys who were at least six one or six two. Dave himself was no taller than six feet. But he strolled casually into the front line, jockeying for position, and stood there on his toes.

A sergeant was taking roll call. Dave glanced to his right, at the recruit standing next to him. Something made him look down— hey, this guy is also on his toes! The young man gave his name as Hantz. Robert Hantz.

The gymnasium echoed with the voices of all nine hundred recruits taking the oath of service as patrolmen on probation.

Dave moved with the crowd, fighting the impulse to rush out of the building and into the street as a cop. He hoped the first thing they would do was teach him how to handle the new gun. He imagined you could draw the gun too soon or too late—in either case, a total disaster. Well, he would learn to use his weapon in just the right way.

He purchased a gray uniform and took it home with him, but the next day he could not put it on. He would become a spectacle, moving target. People would know he was just getting his feet wet. They might even laugh at him. He put the gray uniform on the back seat of his car and, once inside the Academy building, found the sergeants' locker room and changed clothes there.

Then he reported to his assigned classroom and joined thirty-five other young men who were told they would have classes for nine weeks. Dave's spirits sank. He tried to remember a single occasion when he had learned something worthwhile in a school situation. No, he had gained almost all his knowledge, had developed almost all his abilities, on his own. He squinted at the students, who were leaning toward the instructor.

The instructor, a lieutenant, did not seem like such a bad fellow. For all Dave knew, the guy had been ordered to teach the class. So the absurdity of their having to sit in a room for nine weeks was not really the lieutenant's fault. Even so, he thought, at least the man could have the guts to admit it was going to be pretty much of a farce. How could you develop your reactions to situations on the street by listening to some officer read out of a book?

He had slid down in his seat, legs stretched out in front of him, and now he realized he had broken into a sweat. He was one of three dozen guys in gray monkey suits, trapped in a schoolroom, getting nowhere. He glanced sideways and noticed, for the first time, that Robert Hantz was right next to him again. Hantz, too, seemed bored and impatient. Dave turned his gaze frontward again.

When the session was over, he stomped out of the classroom, telling himself things would get better. But each day it was only more of the same—discussion and theory without any actual experience. The other students were inching their seats forward to hear the instructor while Dave kept moving his own chair backward. Bob Hantz was doing the same thing.

His impatience to get some firsthand experience grew over the next few weeks until, at home one Saturday morning, he decided that he could stand it no longer. He slipped into his windbreaker. Exactly what he could get involved in as a cop was unclear. The students had been told not to go looking for trouble; only if you accidentally stumbled upon a crime were you supposed to take any action. Well, he would go to a section of Brooklyn where he knew a lot of crime took place, and he would stand right in the middle of it until something happened.

Now, Dave thought as he left the apartment, now it begins.

He parked his car on a side street and, joining the crowds on the sidewalk, walked toward the busy intersection of Atlantic and Fourth Avenues. He paused to window-shop and stood on the different corners, looking as if he might be waiting for a friend. It took time for him to feel comfortable. Even though he was wearing street clothes, he found it difficult to avoid being self-conscious about his identity as a cop. When people looked at him, did they know why he was here?

At one point, while standing under the marquee of a movie theater, he saw a man walk by with a gun stuck in his belt. The man quickly pulled his jacket over the gun, but Dave had seen it. Should he now rush up behind the man and collar him? The gun probably had been stolen or purchased illegally. But Dave could not move; the whole business was too risky.

He had left his own gun in the apartment. It might have been a mistake—but the Academy still hadn't taught him how to use it. He could visualize reaching for it and winding up in a shootout, wounding all sorts of bystanders and maybe getting himself killed in the process.

As time passed, his confidence sank lower and lower. He joined several people waiting for a light to change, so he could cross the street and find a new location to stand and watch and wait. Just then a small voice—a man's voice, foreign—said something from just behind his right shoulder.

Dave looked around. A stocky man with spectacles was smiling at him. "What was that?" Dave said.

"French films."

"What?"

"You like to buy French films?"

"I dunno," Dave said.

The man held up a leather satchel and motioned for him to move back from the curb. Dave's heart began to pound as he followed the man toward a storefront. French films? Was there a law against selling dirty pictures? He wished he knew the legalities. If anything went wrong, the Police Department would probably throw him out. He shouldn't have come here on this mission in the first place; whatever he wound up doing had to be just exactly right.

The man lingered in front of a record shop and motioned for Dave to come closer. "I got three films in here," the man said. "Three very good French films. Worth a hundred dollars apiece. I give all of 'em to ya for seventy-five."

Dave felt his knees weaken. If he brought this guy into a police station on the wrong charges and then had to turn him loose, the other cops would never stop laughing. They would find out that he was just an Academy student, a gung-ho rookie still on probation. Besides, what if the guy pulled out a gun?

"Look," he said, "I don't want any films."

The man grabbed the sleeve of Dave's windbreaker. "Please, I need the money. I give 'em to ya for fifty dollars. How's that?"

"Forget it."

"Please!"

"Hey," Dave said. "Let go of me." He could feel the heat in his neck and face.

"Thirty dollars, how's that?"

"Get lost," he whispered. "Bug off!"

But now the man was becoming hysterical. "You buy!" he shouted. "You buy! Need money! Good films!"

Several people were watching the scene by now. "Now, *listen* to me," Dave said, "I'm a police officer. Got that? If you don't stop this, I'm gonna lock you up for pornography!"

He shook free of the man's grip and walked off toward the corner. His chest was heaving and he clenched his teeth. Shit! That could have really gotten out of hand! Lock him up for *pornography?* What a half-assed, incompetent statement!

"Ahhhh! Ahhhhh!"

The scream was bloodcurdling. He looked up quickly. The woman coming toward him was pointing her arm right in his direction!

Dave turned his head sideways and saw the round-faced man flying at him from behind like an oncoming train. Dave felt himself falling as the man came upward over him with a knife raised in one hand and already on its way down. Dave poised himself for one desperate effort. His legs pushed him up and his right fist smashed into the man's jaw.

The whole world began to spin. Dave's punch had snapped the

attacker's head back. The man had gone backward off his feet, the knife flying out of his hand at the last second. Dave had fallen to his knees. The world was still spinning. There were feet and legs, dozens of legs, all around him, and sirens like the woman's screams pounded into his skull.

He tried to focus on something but the spinning continued, so he moved a hand over his head and face and looked at it to see if there was blood. No blood. What the hell had happened?

"What happened? What happened?"

At first he thought it was his own voice, but then he saw the legs of a policeman and the gun on the holster, the uniform, the hard face of a Brooklyn cop. Dave felt himself being lifted to his feet. Still more sirens. Conversation and shouting. More spinning. Dazed, he was walking through the crowd. He saw the open rear door of a squad car. He ducked down and got in. The door closed. Next to him, handcuffed and weeping, was the man who had tried to sell him the French films and who had tried to kill him. Dave shut his eyes as the car lurched forward, siren blaring.

The radio car jerked to a halt. Dave opened his eyes. The door opened and he was pulled outside and pushed up some steps and taken by the arm into the station house. He faced a white-haired lieutenant behind the desk.

"What happened?" the lieutenant asked. "This man try to kill you with that knife?"

"Yeah."

"What's your name?"

"Greenberg. David Greenberg. I'm a policeman."

"What?"

Dave took a breath. Hey, he thought, I'm a policeman! I've made an arrest!

"I'm on probation," he said, suddenly excited. "I've been at the Academy a few weeks. Dave Greenberg, probationary patrolman."

The lieutenant stood up. "What were you doing out there on Atlantic Avenue?"

"I—"

"Speak up, kid!"

"I was visiting a friend. Just came from seeing a friend, and this man approaches me and offers to sell me some French films. I ignored him. Then I turn my back and he comes down on me with a knife. So I wiped him out."

"Oh, yeah? Why the hell didn't you draw your gun?"

"My gun?"

"Gun! Your gun!"

Dave tried to look him in the eye. "I don't know how to use one, so I don't carry my gun."

"Don't you know you're required to carry that weapon at all times?"

"Yessir, but I don't know how to *use* it, so—"

"Listen, Greenberg! Do you know the regulations or do you not?"

"Yessir, I do."

"Then you *deliberately* weren't carrying your gun!"

"That's right, but—"

"Greenberg, you're in trouble. You've made an arrest, here, but I'm informing you right now that a disciplinary action may be forthcoming in regard to your failure to carry your gun."

The lieutenant's lips kept moving, but Dave Greenberg heard nothing at all.

Bob Hantz sat near the back of the room, noticing that he and Greenberg had separated themselves physically from the rest of the class. He wondered when they would finally speak to each other. They had been carrying on a kind of contest to see who would break the ice.

"Over the weekend," the instructor was saying, "there was a little activity going on."

Bob noticed that Greenberg, to his left, had taken a deep breath.

"One of the guys in this room made an arrest," the instructor continued. "It was the first arrest by any of the students in this session of the Academy. Dave, why don't you tell us about it?"

Well, Bob thought, it *was* him! Greenberg began slowly. He's playing it down, Bob thought; he's going slowly, trying to control his enthusiasm.

"The guy turned out to be a known cop-hater," Greenberg concluded.

"Okay," the instructor said. "Don't sit down yet, Dave."

Bob got ready to hear the discussion. So Greenberg went out and did something!

"Let's have questions," the instructor said. "Anybody think he might have handled it differently?"

No response. Bob shifted uneasily in his seat.

"Anything about what Dave said that's unclear?"

Silence.

"Anybody have anything to say at all?"

Nothing. Bob looked down at his desk and clenched his teeth. Jesus, we should at least react to this!

"There's *no interest here* about an arrest made by one of your own classmates?"

Suddenly Bob heard his own voice: "What was the very first thing you did?"

No reply. Bob was staring toward the front of the room, but he could feel Greenberg's eyes on him.

"Dave," the instructor called. "You gonna answer his question?"

"Hell, no. That's all I have to say to this class."

The instructor said something in return, but Bob wasn't listening. He heard Greenberg sit down next to him. The class resumed. He turned sideways and, for the first time, spoke to Dave directly. "Go on. Tell me about it, man."

"You want to hear it?"

"Yeah. From the beginning," Bob said.

Dave started to talk in a low voice.

"When I went out there," Dave was saying, "I saw stuff going on all around me. I saw a guy with a gun—he walked right *by* me. I knew if I walked up to this guy and tried to take his gun away, I'd get myself killed. In the back of my mind, I was thinking I needed somebody with me. If I'd had a partner, we could've cleaned up!"

Bob took it all in, probing and giving his own reactions. When Dave came up with a way the two of them could have arrested the man with the gun, Bob nodded vigorously.

They left the Academy together that day. Bob, who was single, accepted a ride with Dave back to Brooklyn. Each day after that, Dave came by in his brown Rambler and they rode into

Manhattan, changing into their gray uniforms in the sergeants' locker room and taking their seats in the rear of the classroom, continuing their discussions and hardly ever listening to the instructor. At lunchtime, they would change back into civilian clothes before leaving the building.

"Everybody's going along with the program except us," Bob would say.

"The Academy is nothing but school," Dave would answer. "It's just bullshit!"

He felt more and more cocky when he and Bob were together. When they got caught not wearing their gray uniforms or for smoking in the hallways or for breaking some other rule, he let it be known that he didn't care, that he actually enjoyed such confrontations.

One thing they did like about the Academy was the training in the gymnasium. The gym teacher's demonstrations of various methods of handling situations on the street made a deep impression on them.

"There's one way to get an advantage over people," he said, "and that's to scare the shit out of them! When you walk up to a guy and you say to him, 'Drop your gun,' the guy's liable to shoot you. But if you go up to the guy and scream, *'Drop your gun,'* he'll drop it just out of fear!"

The teacher would jump all over the floor of the gym, bouncing and yelling to make his point.

"Be a psycho!" he shouted. "Make the other guy think you're crazy! Listen, you come to a job at eight in the morning? You want to be able to go home at four o'clock the way you came!"

Some of the students were amused over this advice, laughing and mimicking the instructor, but Dave and Bob were right up front with intense expressions on their faces, begging to get involved in the demonstrations.

Rumors began to circulate through the Academy building that all probationary patrolmen would be dumped out on the street. Dr. Martin Luther King, Jr., had been assassinated. Various sections around the city had erupted in rioting, burning, and looting, and more manpower was needed. When the speculation turned out to be true, Dave and Bob walked into the classroom like schoolboys about to be let out on the playground for the rest of the year. Dave had visions of stopping wild mobs in Harlem with just the authority in his voice. He would become a hero overnight, decorated by the Mayor at City Hall!

"You're all getting blue uniforms," the instructor announced. "You guys in my class are being assigned, as a group, to traffic duty."

Dave felt nauseated.

"You're to report to Safety Unit B," the instructor went on. "That's the Sixteenth Precinct in midtown Manhattan."

They watched glumly while the other students cheered the news that they had received the softest assignments possible. *"Traffic,"* Dave muttered. "How can they *do* this?"

He and Bob went to the locker room, hurriedly changed into their regular clothes, and left the building.

"The nearest bar," Dave said. "We're gonna become the two most drunken cops in this city."

Dave Greenberg looked around at the dark shadows and neon lights of Times Square, trying to get used to his new uniform. Now he carried a gun, a nightstick, bullets, and handcuffs, but the older cop with him was trying to teach him how to direct traffic. Dave stood there at the corner of Forty-second Street and Broadway, scowling. For God's sake, he thought, the riot is just up the block!

Dave could hear the screaming of the rioters, who had actually come into the midtown area. They were storming down in groups of up to three hundred people, breaking windows and looting the stores. Right on Broadway!

"Duffy? Shouldn't we get over there?"

"Ah, not on your life."

"But they probably *need* us!"

"Hey, kid, don't worry! We're covered! They gave us *this* post."

"But the action is right up the street!"

"Listen, Greenberg, do *you* want to go over there and get yourself killed? Fine with me, you wise-assed punk! Go ahead!"

"All right! That's what I'm doing! I'm going!"

He headed up the sidewalk along Broadway. It was close to midnight. The streets were nearly empty because of the trouble.

He passed one block and looked to his left. He saw some cops herding rioters into a subway entrance, pushing them down the stairs. Members of the tactical squad would be waiting for them when they got to the bottom.

Up ahead of him, about ten men were standing outside a storefront, helping a few other guys out of a broken plate-glass window with a television set! Dave got a grip on his new club, paused for a moment, then strode up the block after them.

His voice trembled, "You guys are under arrest!"

The men turned, startled, and began rushing toward him. He lifted his club up high, planted his feet on the pavement, and when the first man got close enough he brought the stick crashing down on his head. The club split at the handle and half of it fell behind the man. The man grabbed the broken nightstick and swung it against Dave's face. As he was falling he heard sirens and the crowd suddenly broke loose, leaving him sprawled on the sidewalk, his head throbbing with pain.

He managed to find his way back to the traffic post at Forty-second Street, but Officer Duffy was gone. It was midnight, time to go home. Dave wandered over to the station house several blocks away. When he got there, Bob was waiting for him at the door.

As they changed into civilian clothes, Dave gave a detailed account of his misfortune. There were no cuts on his face, but his head was still sore from the nightstick. He was angry; if Bob had been with him, surely the outcome would have been different.

On the way home in Dave's Rambler, Bob described his own experience on traffic duty that night.

"I was up on Madison Avenue," Bob was saying. "At Fifty-fourth Street. And this mob was storming a hotel! I go over there to help out and I find myself alone, trying to hold back about twenty people! Thought I was doing the right thing, but it didn't work out that way. I mean, the rioters—they just weren't *listening* to me, you know? And I said to myself, 'Hey, this can't work, there's no *cooperation* here.' See, when I first got to the place, there were about four or five other cops on each side of me. When the mob started to push, they left! They left—and I stayed, like a schmuck! These people just didn't want to listen. 'Can't you guys see I have a uniform on?' That didn't help at all. They *trampled* me. Down and under! They walked all over me. My hat was busted, my suit got ripped . . ."

At this point Dave was laughing so hard he nearly went off the road. Then, suddenly, he fell silent. The immediate future looked bleak; he was assigned to traffic duty for God only knew how long, and the only way to rise above the situation was to use his own initiative.

One thing was certain—he would never be able to do it alone. If he came up with any sort of a plan he would need a partner.

He and Bob could have been cut from the same mold. They were close in age—Bob was twenty-three, a year younger than Dave. Both were six feet tall and physically strong, weighing about one seventy-five each. Both were Jewish, although religion was not an important factor in either of their lives. Each had been in the service, Dave in the Navy for four years and Bob in the Army in Vietnam. But the overriding similarity was their common background in the Coney Island section of Brooklyn.

Strange, that they had never met during those years of growing up in the sprawling, tough streets of the working-class neighborhood. At different times both had gone to Lincoln High School and been thrown out. Each, in his own way, had been held back down the line—surviving only by conning, bluffing, stealing, fighting, acting on his own instincts, always searching for ways to develop whatever talents or abilities he possessed; and each had gone into the service. Now they were cops: on probation, still green and unsure of themselves, but willing to try almost anything to excel.

He stopped the car in front of Bob's place. "I think I've got a plan. You wanna hear it?"

"Yeah."

Drugs.

That was the answer. Dave had kept it in the back of his mind until now. To stand out in the crowd, he would have to do something important. And what crime was always in the newspapers and on television? Drugs, drugs, drugs. A cop who arrested someone for selling drugs was automatically a hero and a saint.

But there was more to it than that. Drugs had killed some of his friends in Coney Island. Many of the kids from his neighborhood were blacks and Puerto Ricans whose parents had moved into two-family homes and housing projects in the area. Dave had joined their gangs and had spent most of his boyhood getting into trouble with them—for fighting, for stealing cars, for simply trying to stay alive.

He had opened up a weight-lifting gym in the basement of his grandmother's house. It came to be known as Dave's Club, and the toughest guys in the neighborhood were members. Many were his heroes. They were magnificent athletes by the time they were fifteen or sixteen, but they never had a chance to develop. Most of them dropped out of school by the tenth grade, mainly because their families were broken up or too poor to keep them and they were forced to support themselves. They were told they weren't old enough to work; but they were too young to be on their own. How could they fight back?

Most could not. Beaten back before they could really begin their lives, they turned to crime and to drugs and then to more crime. When Dave got to high school, at least a dozen of his friends were already in jail. Charlie was behind bars for armed robbery. Mike was in the hospital with hepatitis and the cops were looking to bust him when he got out. The best basketball players were wasting away on drugs. One of them, Eddie Sands, was dead. Only a few of the guys still had their heads above water. Total disaster.

Dave Greenberg himself went through four high schools, avoiding the drug scene, but struggling against the same forces that were bringing down his friends. At the age of seventeen, he chose the Navy over what well might have been drugs and crime and jail.

Even when he got out, at twenty-one, he toyed with the idea of becoming a big-time criminal. Why not? What else was he good for? He decided that if you were on the wrong side of society, they would find ways to take everything from you in the end. Better to see what he could do with society's approval, first. And having decided to become a cop, why not become the best?

He had a natural intelligence. On the entrance exam for the Navy, he had scored one of the highest marks ever recorded. He took a high school equivalency test in the service and, without ever studying, he earned one of the top five grades. His I.Q. was judged to be one-sixty. When he came home and tried the police exam, he achieved the third highest mark out of nearly five thousand who had taken the test.

So why did they seem to be holding him back? Was the Police Department just an extension, or another form, of the outside world he had fought against all his life? Instead of being allowed to use his capabilities, would he first have to scheme and connive and break all sorts of rules? There seemed to be no other choice.

"The way I see it," he said to Bob, "we just go out and try to make an arrest. On our own time. We might get in trouble, maybe get thrown off the job. But at least we'll have done something."

For weeks they had worked twelve-hour shifts, doing nothing but standing on corners at night. Now they were on day tours, but still on traffic duty. Dave's nerve had grown and his patience had run out. It was evening; they were meeting in a Times Square coffee shop, and he figured it was time to act.

"It might as well be a drug collar," he went on. "If we're gonna be wrong anyway, let's do it *really* wrong. But if it *does* work out, they'll have to say, 'Well, you weren't supposed to be there, but you did a good job—you got somebody selling dope.' Maybe that'll eliminate the repercussions."

He was talking himself into it.

"Now, my thought is we go out to Coney Island, because that's where we know about best. I might be able to find some junkie who still remembers me from before. And we could get him to lead us to a guy who'll sell us some heroin. What do you say?"

Bob Hantz had a lot to say. Yes, he wanted to go out and make a narcotics arrest. Yes, their motivations were almost the same. Bob had come on the job looking for a challenge. But he had never expected the challenge to come in quite this form. The challenge was Dave Greenberg himself.

2

Dave Greenberg brought his car to a stop in the darkness. He looked up at the lights of the Coney Island amusement park and then glanced at his friend Bob Hantz. They were both dressed in green Texaco uniforms, disguised as automobile mechanics. Now there was no turning back.

"This guy runs one of the rides in Astroland," Dave said. "Nickname is Angel. Puerto Rican. Haven't seen him in years."

He almost hoped that Angel would not be there. They got out of the car and walked into the park, strolling among the crowds, not speaking. Then Dave saw him.

He was a young man, dark-skinned, wearing a long white T-shirt. Dave thought he looked about ten years older than his actual age. Angel was sitting next to a metal lever while the contraption behind him was spinning around, the riders screaming.

Dave walked up to him. "Hey, I thought it was you," he said. "How you been, man?"

Angel said he was okay.

"This here's a friend of mine," Dave said. "Bobby Hantz. We're mechanics on Fulton Street."

"Yeah?" Angel squinted at Bob. "He ain't no mechanic, man."

"What d'ya mean? He works with me in the garage!"

"Bullshit," Angel said. "He's too clean."

"Clean?"

Angel shook his head. "Mechanics don't have fingernails like that. Too clean, man."

Dave glanced at Bob's fingernails, which were spotless. It was true; he looked completely out of character for a mechanic, not to mention a drug user. Bob had grown up in a more middle-class section of Coney Island; he neither looked nor acted like a guy who had spent a lot of time in the street. It was going to require some fast talking to convince Angel otherwise.

"Listen," Dave said, "this guy is a good friend of mine. He pulled off three bank jobs before I met him."

"Where'd you meet him?"

"In the joint."

"What joint?"

"Elmira."

"Yeah? You do time up there?"

"Sure, man. Pulled a little stickup and got busted. So I met him up there. We just got out a while back."

Angel seemed impressed. He stopped the ride and let the people off, checked the new customers' tickets, and then wandered back to the lever, where he started up the ride again.

"Let me tell you something," Dave said. He leaned over and spoke in a low voice. "I've been using junk, now and then."

"You have?"

"Yeah, man. Not too heavy—about three, four times a week. But the guy I've been getting it from, he just got busted. So things are uptight, you know?"

"Right, I dig it."

"You don't suppose you could help us out, do you?"

"I dunno, man. All depends. When you want it?"

"Right away, man. Tonight."

Angel thought it over for a moment. "Okay. I can get time off in about an hour. Come back then. Maybe I'll take you to my connection."

They wandered through the amusement park, killing time. Dave tried to imagine what would happen when they met with Angel's "connection." He wished he knew more about the specifics of drugs. He knew the general behavior and attitude of addicts on the street, and he knew the basic tools of shooting dope, but not the latest terminology. Bob had mentioned that he knew a few terms; even so, Dave now felt that they had gone into this with too little preparation.

"Hey, Bob," he said. "You ever meet a 'connection' before?"

"Nope."

"Think he's a big shot?"

"I dunno."

"We gonna get killed?"

"Probably."

When they returned to Astroland an hour later, Angel was waiting for them. "You guys got a car?"

"Yeah," Dave said.

"Come on, I'll take you to my connection. He's on Twenty-fifth Street."

Dave led the way to his car. He ushered Angel into the back seat. Bob got into the front by the passenger window again. Dave took the wheel and cruised through the streets until Angel told him to slow down at a corner.

"Wait here," Angel said.

In the darkness on the sidewalk were at least a hundred blacks and Puerto Ricans. Dave didn't see anyone he knew. He reached for a cigarette and turned to Bob.

"If they make us as cops, we're dead."

Suddenly Angel's face appeared in the window.

"What's up?" Bob said.

"Outside."

They got out of the car. The man standing beside Angel was short and well built. One of the greasiest characters Dave had ever seen. Angel said the man's name was Carlos.

"Well," Carlos said, "how much you want?"

"Whatcha got?"

"I got shit."

"Well," Dave said, "we don't want any shit. I mean, we want some *dope*, you know?"

Bob's foot came smashing into the side of his leg.

"Don't mind him," Bob was saying. "That's what we want—shit."

Dave suddenly realized that "shit" meant heroin.

"How much you want?"

"How much is it?" Dave asked.

"Nickel a bag."

"Ten bags for half a dollar?"

His leg was kicked again—harder, and in the same place. Bob was forcing a smile. "As I said, don't mind him. He likes to kid around. Listen, we'll take ten nickel bags for fifty bucks."

Carlos looked at Angel and said something in Spanish, his expression indicating that he wanted no part of the deal. Then he started to walk off.

"Hey," Dave yelled. "Come back."

He was aware that the crowd on the sidewalk was watching, but he went after Carlos and stopped him. "Hey, man. What's this jive? We asked for a little favor. You don't wanna do it? Okay, then—fuck you! Blow off, baby! You ain't the only dude in the world who's doing something. We might've given you some big business, man!"

"What school you go to?" Carlos said.

"School? Shit, I ran with Charlie and Lawrence!"

"You know Charlie and Lawrence?"

"They're friends of mine!"

"Yeah? Well, they're over at the poolroom. Let me go call 'em and see what they say about you."

"Go ahead!" Dave shouted. "And after you do that, I'm gonna beat your motherfucking ass for calling me a liar!"

He turned and walked back to the car. Bob had broken off his conversation with Angel and he, too, was on his way back. If nothing else, Dave thought, we're working well as a team.

The crowd on the sidewalk was openly staring at them. Carlos and Angel had begun arguing back and forth in Spanish.

Angel approached them. "We'll be back in a little while," he said. "You want ten bags?"

"Right," Dave said.

"Okay. Wait here."

He watched them disappear in the darkness. Now what? He leaned against the car, keeping an eye on the crowd, trying to appear relaxed.

"What are we doing here?" Dave whispered. "Those dudes are just looking to jump us, man. If they find out we're cops, nobody'll ever hear from us again."

"You're right," Bob answered under his breath. "And if you keep talking the way you were doing before, you'll be signing a *contract* on us. Man, are you naïve!"

"Shit!"

"You know what I'm really worried about?"

"What?"

"That we can't get to our guns."

Dave had thought of that already. They had strapped their heavy guns to their bodies under the Texaco shirts.

"If we need 'em," Bob was saying, "we're never gonna get to 'em, man."

They fell silent. Dave had to admit the mistake. Still, he was beginning to feel oddly confident. There was no doubt in his mind that Bob would stick with him.

"What if one of them had pulled out a knife?" he said. "Which one would you have gone for?"

"Angel."

"That's what I thought. I figured you'd nail him, so I was ready to take the other one."

By this time the people on the corner had become restless. A young girl stepped forward from the crowd. "Hey, whitey! Whatcha doin' here?"

Dave stiffened. The choice was to say nothing and seem afraid, or to shout back and bluff. "Bitch!" he yelled. "Beat it!"

"Hey!" a man called. "Don't talk to the lady like that!"

A couple of dozen hostile faces began moving toward them.

Suddenly Angel and Carlos appeared from the shadows. The crowd held back, watching.

"Got the stuff?" Dave asked.

"Yeah," Carlos said.

"Let's see it."

Carlos showed him the ten glassine bags of heroin and asked for his fifty dollars. Dave had seen heroin before, and he had seen plenty of junkies, but how could he make sure it was real? Maybe Bob could tell the difference.

"Let us test it," Dave said.

Carlos was annoyed. "All right, but hurry up."

Dave took a bag from Carlos and passed it to Bob. "Test it, Bobby."

Bob looked at him as if he were crazy. He didn't know that much about heroin either.

"Sure," Bob said with a smirk. He jumped into the back seat of the car with the bag and disappeared below window level. A minute or two passed. Suddenly Bob got out of the car again. "Good stuff," he said.

Astonished, Dave played along. "Great," he said.

But what to do now? If they flashed their badges and made the collar right here, Angel and Carlos would start screaming and the crowd would go crazy. They'd be killed in a second. He frantically searched his mind for a way out, at least to stall for time. Maybe they should ask for some marijuana.

Then he heard Bob's voice: "Do you have any marijuana?"

Carlos, holding the bag of heroin again, had become increasingly impatient. "You guys wanna do some grass?"

"Yeah," Dave said. "We're having a party tonight."

Carlos was nearing his limit. "Okay, okay. We know a guy who does grass. Ten blocks up that way."

"Fine, let's go," Dave said. "Hop in the car."

He noticed that Bob had put his back against the front passenger door so he could watch the two men in the rear seat. Bob had told him that what he had feared most in Vietnam was getting killed by a sniper. "It just wasn't cricket, getting blown away without a chance to fight back."

Good, Dave thought. He could drive now without worrying about what was behind him. For the first time in his memory, he was entrusting his life to someone else.

Now it was time to get it over with. He could pull over and they could make the collar right away. But he kept driving, thinking that he might as well play it out some more, see where it led. If Bob makes a move, fine; but he seems to be leaving it up to me.

He drove slowly, because Angel and Carlos had begun to talk about their scene—drugs, weapons, cops, jail; pulling off burglaries, robberies; their fear of getting busted. Dave listened carefully to their language, sure that Bob was doing likewise. The word "cop," he noted, referred to the process of buying dope; "hacks" meant prison guards; to "take off" was to beat up or rob; "the man" was the term for police.

Dave decided to try it all out in one brilliant monologue: "I was copping some good shit, man, but my connection got busted. Then the man got me, too. Met Bobby up in the joint. Fucking hacks up there were tough. They took us off all the time."

This, he thought, is the only way to learn. He looked over at Bob, who was grinning.

At Thirty-fifth Street and Mermaid Avenue, still in the Coney Island section, he pulled the car to a stop. By his watch, it was ten thirty.

"Wait for us," Carlos said. "We'll go get the guy with the grass."

The two of them got out of the back seat and left. Dave jumped out to see where they went.

"Think they got guns?" he said as he watched them disappear into a nearby building.

"Maybe."

Bob was reaching inside his Texaco shirt and unstrapping his gun. He shoved it under his thigh. Dave leaned into the car and removed his own gun and tucked it beneath the driver's seat.

Three men came out of the building—Angel, Carlos, and another Puerto Rican. Dave stepped forward to meet them.

"This here's Jimmy," said Carlos.

"Grass?"

"Yeah," Jimmy said. "Five nickel bags."

"Okay, fine." Man, he thought, three bad-assed characters, selling me junk and grass. Best thing to do is get them all in the car, off the street. "Listen," he said, "hop in and we'll drive around awhile."

Carlos nearly shouted at him. "What for, man?"

"Hey, cool down. Far as I'm concerned, me and my friend want to buy a lot more stuff in the future. You dig? And we'd like to know more about the guys we're dealing with."

"All right," Carlos told him. "But hurry up."

The three of them got into the back seat. As Dave climbed behind the wheel, he reached down and grabbed his gun off the floor and sat on it as Bob was doing.

He started the car and drove off, wondering where he would go. He crossed one dark street, took a right turn, and just cruised along. When was a good time to nail them? In the car? No, that would be awkward. Any mistake could not only get him and Bob hurt, it could also cost them their jobs.

Carlos was talking about how he had pulled off a store robbery a while back. That was good—it meant they weren't just capturing some lightweights.

"How long you been doing shit?" Dave asked.

"Five years," Carlos said.

That was even better; this guy had probably ruined a lot of lives, selling drugs. Well, Dave thought, Bobby and I are doing something to stop him.

Suddenly he realized that he had driven right back to the corner where they had met Carlos. He stopped the car. The crowd was still there. What a mistake!

Bob was looking at him, bewildered; Dave took a deep breath and shook his head.

"Give us the money," Carlos said. "We'll give you the stuff and we'll split, man. Let's go, come on!"

Dave turned to his three passengers in the back seat. "Listen," he said, "we can't make any deal right here. Too many people."

"Then where?" Carlos shouted. "Let's cut out the bullshit, man!"

"Right, right," Dave said, pulling away from the curb. The question was, where to go? Then he got an idea. "We'll go to the Sea Gate. There's no cops in that place."

"Hurry up," Carlos said.

He picked up speed, suddenly confident. He should have thought of this before! The Sea Gate was a private, fenced-in section of homes and apartments at the end of Surf Avenue. His father had taken a first-floor apartment in one of the buildings— perfect for an arrest.

"No cops there," he repeated. "Only private police. We can make our deal without any trouble."

Then Dave realized that Bob had no knowledge of his father's apartment. He undoubtedly knew about the Sea Gate, so he was probably wondering how they were going to get through the entrance. Residents of the place all had green stickers on their car windows or license plates so the guard would lift the gate, allowing them onto the grounds. Dave had no sticker, but he was sure that the guard would recognize him and let him right in.

As they approached the Sea Gate entrance, he could sense Bob was tensing up. He headed for the guardhouse and saw Bob reach under his leg for his gun. The car's headlights shone on the gate, but Dave kept going. He heard Bob's gun being cocked and saw him rising up, ready to make the bust. Dave nodded to the guard and the gate flew upward and he continued driving into the grounds without slowing down. Bob let out a deep breath.

The three passengers in the back seat were beginning to stir. "Where you taking us?" Carlos yelled.

"Yeah," Angel said. "What is this place?"

"No sweat," Dave answered. "I got a pad in here."

"Right," Bob said. "We'll get into Dave's pad and make the deal. Then, if you want, you can try the shit with us."

Dave pulled up in front of the building where his father lived.

"In there," he said. "And don't worry—if we didn't trust you, we wouldn't be taking you into our pad, would we?"

The three passengers were silent. Dave, still sitting on his gun, wondered how in hell he was going to get out of the car with it. He opened the door, making a noise, and at the same time he let the gun fall to the floor. He got out and walked around the car and opened the back door for Angel and Carlos and Jimmy. Meanwhile, he noticed Bob pick up the gun and slide out the driver's side.

He directed the three men toward the building. With Bob behind him, he moved his arm backward and felt the gun being slipped into his hand. The three guys were walking in front of them through the door and into the foyer. Dave paused and looked at Bob. A vision of the gym instructor at the Academy flashed across his mind. He nodded, Bob nodded back. They both opened the door, aimed their guns, and screamed as if this was the end of the world: *"Okay, motherfuckers, you're under arrest, if you move we'll kill ya, get down on the floor with your hands up, don't move, we're cops."* Dave thought he might actually go crazy because these guys were going to turn around with machine guns and it was going to be the bloodiest shootout in the history of the world.

The three men were on their stomachs on the floor. Dave glanced at his partner again and wondered, what next? Simultaneously they bent down to search for guns. Dave was still so frightened that he grabbed Carlos's hair and pulled his head back and screamed into his face. Act mean, he thought; don't give them any chances. He was astonished to find no guns, not even a pistol; but each man was carrying a knife. Okay, three knives—now they're clean.

But wait a minute. Where was the dope? The ten bags of heroin? The five bags of grass? Dave started to feel dizzy.

"Search 'em again," he said.

Bob bent down and frisked the three men. Then he stood up, his face blank.

"Where's the stuff?" Dave shouted.

Angel and Carlos and Jimmy were silent.

"Where is it?"

No response. He motioned for Bob to keep them covered. Then he looked around the floor and went outside and checked the ground and the inside of the car. They could have thrown the drugs out the window while he was driving. He walked back into the foyer and looked at Bob and shook his head.

We're gonna look like assholes, he thought.

They handcuffed the three prisoners behind their backs and made them stand up in the entranceway.

Dave pulled out a set of keys and opened the door to his father's place. The apartment was empty.

"Let's bring 'em inside," he said.

He was going to find out what happened to those drugs if it took him all night. They led their captives into the bedroom.

"All right," he said, "I'm taking Carlos with me. Bob, you stay in here and watch these two."

He led Carlos out of the bedroom, closing the door behind him. They went through the living room and into the kitchen. Dave pointed his gun at the drug pusher's forehead and ordered in a low voice, "Scream like a motherfucker."

"What?"

"You heard me."

Carlos started to scream. Dave let him carry on for a minute and then gestured for him to stop. He handcuffed him to a radiator in the kitchen.

"Make a sound and I'll come back here and blow your head off."

He went back to the bedroom and grabbed Angel's arm. "You're next. Let's go."

They got out to the living room when Angel broke. "Don't hurt me," he pleaded. "Don't hit me, man! I'll tell you where it is!"

"Where?"

"Behind the door in the hall! Under the radiator!"

Dave brought him out to the hall and reached under the radiator. Ten bags of heroin.

"Where's the grass?"

"I don't know. I swear I don't!"

He led Angel back into the apartment and opened the bedroom door again. Bob was still holding his gun on Jimmy, who was trembling. "What'd you do to Carlos?" Jimmy said. "You kill him, man?"

"Hey, Bob, ask this guy where the grass is. I'll be outside with Angel."

Dave took Angel out to the living room and waited. A minute later, Bob opened the bedroom door. He was holding the envelopes with the marijuana.

"Where'd he have it?"

"In his underwear."

Jimmy was still worried about Carlos. "You kill my friend, man?"

"Listen," Bob said, "he never touched him."

Dave nodded and went to the kitchen and brought out Carlos. He was amazed that Bob had known the truth all along.

"Hey," Jimmy said. "He didn't hit you or nothing?"

"Nah," Carlos said.

Jimmy turned to Angel. "You told him where the shit is?"

"Yeah," Angel said. "He's got the shit."

The three of them started cursing each other in Spanish. Dave and Bob led them from the apartment and out of the building.

A woman's frantic voice filled the night air: *"What's going on down there?"* She was shouting from a top-floor window.

"Everything's okay," Dave called to her. "Stay inside!"

"I've already called the police!"

"Hey, Bob—you hear that? She called the cops!"

3

A feeling of pride and accomplishment came over Bob Hantz as they stood with their three prisoners, waiting for the radio car to pull up in front of them.

They had gone into the world of the junkies and had come out the other end with a major arrest; now they were confronting the world of the Police Department, starting the second part of the ordeal before they could savor the victory of the first.

When two officers got out of the squad car, Bob told them, "We're police. We've arrested these guys for drugs."

He noticed that the two cops were staring curiously at the Texaco uniforms and that they seemed a bit wary, so he took out his police shield and flashed it at them. The prisoners were led into the rear seat of the radio car.

"Follow us back to the precinct," one of the officers said.

Behind the wheel of his Rambler, Dave switched on the headlights and trailed the radio car.

"We did it," Bob said.

"Yeah."

Dave stopped behind the radio car outside the station house of the Sixtieth Precinct in Coney Island. The two officers brought the prisoners—and the drugs—into the building.

"Let's go," Dave said.

They got out of the car and walked into the station house. The officers stood to one side with Angel and Carlos and Jimmy. The sergeant behind the desk, puffing on a cigar, stared at them as they approached.

"Who are you?" he asked.

"Probationary patrolmen," Bob said.

"What did you say?"

"This is Probationary Patrolman Greenberg, and I'm Probationary Patrolman Hantz."

The desk sergeant puffed his cigar and looked up at them as if he thought someone was playing a joke.

"Where do you work out of?"

"Safety Unit B," Bob said.

"Where is that?"

"Forty-seventh Street, midtown Manhattan."

"Safety precinct?"

"Yeah."

The sergeant gazed up at them again in silence. He glanced over at the three prisoners, then back.

"What do you kids got?"

"Well," Bob said, "we got those guys for trying to sell us some drugs."

"Marijuana?"

"Yeah, five envelopes of grass."

"That's it?"

"No. Also ten bags of heroin."

The sergeant's eyes widened. He scratched the side of his head.

"You're from a *safety* precinct?"

"Right."

"In Manhattan?"

"Right."

"You direct traffic?"

"Right."

"Still on probation?"

"Right."

"You're off duty?"

"Right."

"And you just busted three guys, here in Coney Island, for narcotics?"

"Right."

The sergeant rubbed his eyes. "Go on upstairs. See the detectives."

The two officers brought the prisoners upstairs, Dave and Bob following behind. Seven detectives were in the office. The senior man walked over.

"Who are you and what d'ya got?"

Bob started explaining—safety, traffic, Manhattan, probation, off duty, marijuana, heroin. As he was talking, the two officers slipped out the door. Three detectives grabbed their coats and left. When Bob was finished, only he and Dave and the senior detective—plus the prisoners, handcuffed at the far end of the room—remained.

"Sit down," said the senior detective.

"What for?"

"Sit down!"

They remained standing.

"Never mind," the detective said. "Just give me the real story."

Bob thought for a moment. "What do you mean?"

"You know what I mean, kid!"

"Did we do something wrong?"

"That's what *you* are gonna tell *me.*"

"I don't know what you're talking about."

"All right, kid, let me give you the picture. You and your friend, here, you got your guns and shields from the Academy, and you're looking to make some extra cash. So you drive down to the hot spots, and you find some guys selling junk. And you tell 'em, 'Listen, we're cops—but we ain't gonna hurt you or nothing. All you gotta do is give us a little bread. How about fifty bucks?' But they don't have the money and you've got a big crowd around, watching the whole thing, so now there's trouble. You started something you couldn't finish. So it comes down to where you couldn't shake 'em down and you'll have to lock 'em up. In other words, for all anyone knows you're a couple of young cops who are crooks."

Bob looked at Dave, then at the detective. "Is that what *you* think?"

"It don't matter what *I* think, kid."

"What matters, then?"

"Just tell me what you were doing out in the street in those monkey suits in the first place!"

They sat in a corner of the office, trying to figure out their situation. The senior detective had gone to interrogate the prisoners.

"When this guy gets back to us," Dave said, "we'd better be ready with a story."

The truth was bad enough: they had gone out to make an arrest against the rules. But even if they admitted it, their motives would not be believed. Why would two cops want to make an arrest on their own time?

They agreed to say they had been visiting some friends in Coney Island; that they had stopped at Nathan's on Surf Avenue for some food at the sidewalk counter; that they had overheard Angel talking about how he had just bought some drugs; and that they had started up a conversation with him about wanting to buy drugs for themselves. From there, they could tell how Angel had led them to Carlos and so on, exactly the way it had happened.

The senior detective finished with the prisoners and the other detectives gradually drifted back into the office. Dave and Bob stuck to their phony story, but nobody really listened. The detectives reluctantly dropped the issue and started trying to pick apart the arrest itself. All of them felt that Dave and Bob had to have done something wrong; it would never hold up in court. But the night wore on and they could not destroy the case. Their motives were unclear. Were they jealous that two young rookies still on probation had been able to make an undercover narcotics arrest of this size?

Whatever the reason, they had no desire to teach or train or help; they were more concerned with blocking and putting down the arrest. Dave and Bob struggled through the paperwork, through the endless questions and misleading advice, until they had done everything correctly. It was legitimate. It was also five thirty in the morning.

They had to be in Brooklyn Criminal Court two and a half hours later, at eight o'clock. They drove home to get their uniforms and grab some breakfast, and then they went back to the Sixtieth Precinct to pick up the prisoners. In the station house, Dave picked up a phone and called Safety Unit B in Manhattan. The desk officer answered.

"This is Greenberg. I'm in Coney Island. We made an off-duty arrest here last night, and we gotta go to court this morning."

"Who's this again?"

"Dave Greenberg."

"Probationary?"

"Yeah."

"What d'ya mean, *'we'* made an arrest?"

"Me and Bob Hantz."

"He's on probation too? Right?"

"Right."

"Wait a minute, fella, *hold* it. Lemme put the sergeant on the phone. Tell *him* what you just said."

Dave waited until the sergeant came on the line.

"Hello!"

"This is Greenberg, I'm over in the Sixtieth Precinct, Coney Island. Me and Hantz made an arrest. We're going to court."

"Going to court? Wait a minute. Hold on."

Dave waited. Suddenly a lieutenant's voice barked into his ear.

"Who's this?"

"Greenberg and Hantz," said Dave, and he repeated the details.

"The two of you made an arrest?"

"Yeah."

"What were you doing together?"

"Visiting friends."

"What kind of arrest did you make?"

"Drug sales."

"Drug sales!"

"Yeah."

"Hey, who am I talking to?"

"Greenberg, sir. Me and Hantz, we—"

"Wait a minute! Just wait!"

Dave held the phone away from his ear. He looked at Bob and shrugged. The traffic officers in Safety Unit B apparently were not accustomed to their men doing off-duty, undercover narcotics work.

Now he heard the lieutenant's voice at the other end, shouting to another officer. "Someone call the captain!" There was a long pause. "Hey, Captain! We got two of our guys on the phone, here. They made a drug arrest!"

"Where?" came the captain's voice.

"Out in Coney Island someplace!"

"Get the desk officer there on the phone."

"Greenberg?" said the lieutenant.

"Yeah, I'm here."

"Put the desk officer there on the line. The captain wants to speak to him."

"Fine," Dave said. He held the phone out to the desk officer nearby. "Captain at the safety precinct wants to talk to you."

The desk officer took the phone. "Hello?" he said. "Yes, Captain, right. . . . Well, I don't know, sir. It seems that two of your probationary patrolmen came in here last night and, uh, made three arrests for drug sales, and— What's that? . . . Yes, all the paperwork is done, and I don't know what to do with them. I mean, that's about all I can tell you from here. . . . Okay, sir. Goodbye."

Now the desk officer looked up, relieved that he had curtailed his own involvement in this affair.

"Greenberg?" he said. "Hantz? When you get back to your safety precinct after court, be sure you go directly to your captain's office."

At Brooklyn Criminal Court they spent all day going from one line to another, feeling their way through the procedures, drawing numbers and waiting, only to be rotated backward by senior officers.

"Well, we're learning," Bob said at one point. "We're getting pushed around, but let 'em push. Our turn'll come."

The processing and arraignment of their prisoners lasted more than seven hours. It was five o'clock in the evening by the time they drove into Manhattan.

Dave and Bob walked into the safety unit headquarters to tell the captain what they had done, only to find that he had left for the day.

In the morning, they were off to Manhattan again. "We're in trouble," Dave said. "I just know they'll try to turn it around on us."

"They *already* tried to do that," Bob said.

Upstairs, Captain Leo Safron was waiting for them behind his desk. "What happened?"

Dave told him the story, making it appear more accidental than planned. He finished and waited for a response. Captain Safron thought for a while, a blank expression on his face. Then he shrugged.

"Fine," he said. "Go back to work."

Dave and Bob stood there waiting for more.

"That's all," the captain said.

They turned and walked out of his office, saying nothing to each other until they got downstairs to the first floor of the building.

"How d'ya like that?" Bob said at last.

"Well," Dave replied, "if that didn't faze him, baby, the *next* one will."

On his next day off, Dave Greenberg went back to Coney Island and drove around his old neighborhood. He went over the route of the arrest he and Bob had made, starting on Surf Avenue outside Astroland in the amusement park, where they had met Angel; down Seventeenth Street and left on Mermaid Avenue, past the rows of three-story buildings with shops and stores on either side; up to Twenty-fifth Street to the corner that had seemed so menacing because of the huge crowd at night; back onto Surf Avenue past the high-rise housing projects; right on Thirty-fifth Street, through a world of tenements, dirty storefronts, and littered pavements.

Dave parked the car on a side street. Strolling casually among crowds of blacks and Puerto Ricans along Mermaid Avenue, he wondered if the word had been passed that he was a cop.

Strange, he thought, how what he was doing right now, as a grown man of twenty-four, was so similar to what he had done as a kid. Then he had been the white, Jewish guy who set out to prove that he wasn't afraid of anything. He had earned the respect of the black and Puerto Rican kids, not only because he was unafraid to fight but because he would never rat on them, not for anything.

Seven or eight years had passed since then; the neighborhood had changed and he was a cop. The drug scene had taken over, bringing with it a new kind of violence, with new language and values and certainly new faces.

When he left the Navy at age twenty-one and married Irene, also from Brooklyn, they had moved to Sheepshead Bay. With financial help from his in-laws, Dave took over a gas station on Flatbush Avenue, turning it from nothing into a profitable business. That enterprise behind him, he went into the construction end of steelwork and again did well. To some people, walking eighty stories above the ground on a slab of iron was too dangerous, but Dave felt it was too easy, not enough of a challenge. So he became a cop, settling for far less money in return for the promise of a useful life—and more excitement.

Now he saw the familiar figure of a black guy he had known years ago, standing on the corner ahead. Dave shuffled up to him and said, "Hey, Tyrone?"

"Yeah?"

"Dave Greenberg. How're you doin', man?"

"All right." Tyrone Small looked down at Dave with a wary expression.

"Whatcha been up to?" Dave asked.

"Nuthin' much. Just got out of the can."

"Yeah? What for?"

"Stickup."

"Armed robbery?"

"Yep."

"How much time you do?"

"Three."

"Three years?"

"Yeah, man."

"You shootin' shit?" Dave asked.

"Yeah, but I need bread."

Dave made an instant decision. "Same here," he said. "I'm all messed up with it, man. Been trying to kick, but I can't. No bread around anywhere."

"How bad you want it?"

"Very bad. You got something in mind?"

"Well," Tyrone said, "I know some guys that are planning to do something soon."

"Like what?"

"Gonna pull a job on a jewelry store. We got it all planned."

"Yeah? Hey, count me in."

"You want in?"

"Yeah," Dave said.

"In the first place, man, you gotta have your own gun."

"Shit, I got a gun. In fact, I got a good friend of mine who's a real hit man. He's a button man for the mob. And he drives for 'em, too."

"Yeah? We could use a guy like that."

"I'll bring him along, if you want."

Tyrone hesitated. "Well, listen, come up to our pad and we'll rap."

"Right," Dave said.

He followed him into a nearby brick tenement building and up the wooden stairs to the third floor at the top. Tyrone knocked on a door. Okay, Dave thought. Here we go again.

He spent the day with Tyrone and two other black guys, sitting on the damp floor of a room, drinking wine and smoking. Gradually, they unfolded their elaborate plan to hold up a jewelry store in Manhattan. They brought out diagrams of the exact route to get there and back by car, and more diagrams of the store itself, a large one on Fifth Avenue.

The scheme was fascinating, especially because it was real. Dave studied it carefully, asked a few questions, and made some suggestions. They agreed with him on some points, but argued him down on others. In the end, Dave figured they had a very good chance of pulling it off.

"How much you think we'll get?" he asked.

"Two-fifty."

"How much?"

"Two hundred and fifty grand, my man."

"Whoo!"

When he was ready to leave, he said he'd be back in a few days, adding that he was getting so strung out that he had to go dig up some bread and find his connection.

"Listen," one of the black guys said, "we ain't doin' no shit at the moment, but next time we see you, we'll turn you on, man. You bring the money and *we'll* take care of your habit."

"Great."

He left the building and went back to his car. Christ, he had stumbled into one helluva deal.

But once again he remembered that he was only a traffic patrolman on probation, and that everything he was doing flew in the face of department rules. Friends and relatives who had heard about their arrest at the Sea Gate were saying that they had been just lucky to avoid repercussions. They should be careful, obey orders, have patience. Crawl into a hole and wait until the system says we're ready? The hell with that. He and Bob had survived their own backgrounds only by being exceptions to the rule—so what was the difference now?

"Bob?" he said on the phone. "I got something going."
"Yeah?"
"Met a guy named Tyrone Small in Coney Island. He and his friends are willing to get me some junk—probably want to set me up with a big habit and make lots of money off me. But they're also planning a stickup! Now, I figure we could do either of two things. We could nail 'em on the drugs when they bring the stuff, or we could go along with the stickup and nail 'em on that. We can decide as we go along."
"You think they know you're a cop?"
"Nah."
"You sure?"
Dave was anything but certain, but he replied, "Of course I'm sure."
"What if they check you out between now and then?"
"Well, we'll be able to tell by their expressions."
"Sounds risky, Dave."
"But think of the opportunity!"
"Yeah, I know."
"If we don't go ahead, we'll be sorry."
"So let's go ahead," Bob replied.
They hung up. Dave sat back in his apartment. He would discuss it further with Bob in the morning, on their way in to the safety precinct. Then he would find Tyrone Small again and set up a meeting.

It was set for three days later, on Friday night, in Coney Island. Meanwhile, word came from the district attorney that the case against Angel and Carlos and Jimmy was perfect. The defense lawyer thought it was so tight that he had advised his clients to take a plea! Already we're winning, Dave thought.

The annoying part was that they had been required to play down the arrest itself. Captain Safron had pegged them as just two young guys who had been in the wrong place at the wrong time, and he probably figured they had gotten out of it just by luck. No praise and no condemnation, only silence and the simple directive to go back to work. Well, Dave thought, that's just what we're doing—our *own* work, that is.

On Friday, they directed traffic during the morning and afternoon, then changed into some old clothes and drove back to Coney Island. They were supposed to meet Tyrone Small and his friends at eight o'clock. It was still early, and Dave wanted to show Bob the meeting place. From the car window, he pointed to the building.

"One of the guys has a room in there, on the ground floor," Dave said. "It's down the end of the hallway, right in the back. When I went to see Tyrone to set this up, he brought me in there. Dirty as shit! And it was night, man, and dark! I got the feeling that if I walked down that hallway and didn't come back, nobody'd ever miss me."

They sped off to a bar about fifteen blocks away and went in for some drinks to settle their nerves. This time, Bob had strapped both their guns against his stomach inside his pants. And they had left their handcuffs and police shields at home.

"The whole thing could be a setup," Bob said. "For all we know, these guys are just looking to get us alone someplace and take our money. And if they do get the drop on us, we sure as hell don't want them to find out we're cops. If they haven't figured that out already."

Just before eight o'clock, they drove back to the place and parked in front of a synagogue down at the end of the block. Dave had told Tyrone that he would meet him outside the nearly abandoned building.

"I'll go first," he said. "Give me about fifteen minutes, and then wander in. It'll look more natural that way."

Bob slid behind the wheel of the car and watched Dave walk up the block. It was growing dark, and he could see the lights of the amusement area several blocks away. His first job had been in that park, when he was fifteen. Bob had been forced to lie about his age to get hired, during the summer, to work at the "high striker," where people would come up and swing the mallet and try to ring the bell.

Now Bob saw two black guys come out of the building and join Dave on the sidewalk. He watched carefully; he didn't want to lose sight of his partner.

Suddenly there was a face at the window of his car—a cop on patrol in front of the synagogue. "You can't park here," he told Bob.

"I'm not parked—I'm idling."

"You can't stay here, though."

"Hey," Bob said, trying to keep an eye on Dave at the same time, "I'm a police officer, and I'm involved in something."

"Oh! Sorry!"

The cop backed off, but kept watching him. Maybe it's best to move the damn car, Bob thought. He drive off, straight ahead. He made one turn, then another, onto Mermaid Avenue. Just up ahead he would get to the same street again and hopefully be able to see Dave from that side of the block. But a police car came out of nowhere alongside him.

"Stop!" yelled the driver.

Bob pulled to the curb. He jumped out and slammed the door and went around the radio car to the passenger side. "Ah, shit," he said. "Now what the hell do *you* guys want?"

The cop on the passenger side was a sergeant. "What seems to be the problem?"

"Sergeant, don't they inform you of *anything* down here?"

"What do you mean? Who are you?"

"First of all," Bob said, "didn't anyone tell you that there's a narcotics investigation going on?"

"There is? No—no one told us."

"Well," Bob went on, "isn't it normal procedure that when there's a narcotics investigation, radio cars stay out of the area?"

"Yes, that's correct."

"Okay! Then what are you *doing* here? I'm the backup, and right now my man is running loose in the street, all because you decided to check me out!"

"I didn't know you were a cop," said the sergeant.

"Why are you checking me out?"

"The cop in front of the synagogue—he called us over and, uh, he wasn't sure if you were a cop. So we decided to go see."

"Well, do you see? Do you see I'm a cop?"

The sergeant hesitated. If he asks for my shield, Bob thought, it's all over. No shield on me, and two guns! And what about Dave?

"Yes," the sergeant said at last. "I see you're a cop."

"Fine! But you're still in the area!"

"We're leaving."

The radio car went off. Bob ran to the corner and looked down the street—just in time to see Dave and the two black guys heading into the building.

Dave stood inside the dimly lit flat at the far end of the hallway. Six men surrounded him.

"Hey, man!"

"What d'ya say, brother?"

"He's one of us, right?"

"Make yourself at home, my man."

"What's his name?"

"Dave's his name. He's *with* us, man!"

"Shit, yeah!"

"Slap me five, brother!"

He tried to keep his whole body relaxed. Are they goofing on me? Do they know I'm a cop? Are they gonna rip me off? He had walked into this without much forethought. When Bobby showed up, what were they supposed to do with six guys?

They sat around the shabby living room, and Dave figured he would concentrate on getting himself deeper and deeper into their mood. Reefers were passed around, and they all relaxed. Then Bob came to the door. Tyrone let him in.

"Hey, man," Dave said. "Glad you could make it." Just how glad, they'll never know, he thought. Now they were in this together. Bob was introduced around the room and he took a seat on the couch along the wall opposite Dave.

"Let's go over this hit," said Tyrone Small.

All heads turned toward the man named Otis, who was sitting

alone at the table near the center of the room. Otis, apparently the leader, opened a folder and spread out the diagrams in front of him. Everybody gathered around the table.

Otis looked up at Dave. "You've seen these, man?"

"Right. Tyrone showed me."

"What d'ya think?"

"Looks good to me," Dave said. "Why don't you fill Bob in—he's more experienced than me in pulling jobs."

Bob was playing it very cool, Dave noticed. His face showed hardly any expression; his manner was that of an experienced thief, skeptical of working with amateurs, even though these guys were probably professionals. Shit, Tyrone Small had done three years for armed robbery! And Otis—who knows what *he's* been involved in! Dave had a sinking feeling that he and Bob had gone into something way over their heads, and it was getting deeper all the time.

Otis explained the plan. They would drive two cars into Manhattan tomorrow night. The jewelry store would be closed, but the owners and employees would be inside, taking inventory. According to schedule, the floor waxers would show up in a truck. The plan was to intercept the truck about a block away from the store, tie up the men, and leave them in the back of the truck. Then they would drive up to the place and go in posing as the floor waxers. Once inside, they would calmly take out their guns and begin the holdup.

"Hey, Bob," said Dave. "What do you think?"

Bob paused, folding his arms and giving the impression that he was giving it careful thought. "Not bad," he said. "I'd like to see the alarm system, though."

Otis was already answering this question, evidently to maintain his own authority. There seemed to be no question in anyone's mind that Bob was a professional holdup man.

Dave could imagine himself and Bob going along with the stickup—to the point where they were right inside the store. He wondered if these guys could succeed. Then he wondered whether he and Bob could pull off the arrest, and it seemed too risky. How could they draw their guns against six guys who were also armed? In any shootout, they'd wind up dead. And besides, what were the laws involved? How far were they allowed to go as cops? Were they allowed to play along that far? Or would they, too, wind up charged with armed robbery? This was much too big a deal for two rookies just out of the Academy and on probation. Shit, what are we doing here?

Everybody wandered back to his seat. Otis pulled out his gun at the table, leaned on his elbows and toyed with it, pretending to examine it but obviously sending a message. "Where are *your* guns?" he said without looking up.

"I left mine at home," Dave said.

"Yeah," Bob said. "I don't carry a gun unless I'm doing a job."

"Well," Otis replied, still pretending to examine his weapon, "you won't need your guns on this job. We got ours, and that's enough."

"We can go get them," Dave said. "There's plenty of time before tomorrow night."

"No," Otis said. "We all stay right here in this room, until we go pull the job. No need for anybody to leave."

Dave decided it was best not to argue. He looked across the room at Bob. I've gotten him into this. He relied on me. That first arrest must have gone to my head.

"Listen," Dave said, "I'm gettin' uptight, man. I'd appreciate it if you'd get me some stuff. I lost my connection, man, and I just gotta cop some shit before we do this job. I'll be too strung out, man."

"You got any bread?" Otis asked.

"Yeah, I got bread."

"Okay, we'll get you some shit. Hold on, man. Tyrone, go get us some shit. We'll get this guy off on some real good stuff."

"Great," Dave said.

Tyrone Small left the flat. Dave leaned his back against the wall, wondering how Bob would ever get to the guns beneath his clothing. Otis still had his gun out, and now one of the guys in the corner was displaying another gun. Maybe they're planning to rob us after all.

Less than five minutes later, Tyrone came back with dozens of glassine envelopes containing heroin. One of the other guys brought out some works. Dave watched Tyrone cook up some dope and shoot it; then another guy, named Lyman; and then Otis. He watched them carefully to see how they did it. My turn is coming, he thought.

"Both you guys can get off," Otis said.

Bob shook his head. "I'm not into the shit."

Everyone looked at Dave, who had asked for the drugs in the first place. He saw them all waiting for him to make a move.

"I'll take a little snort," he said.

"Hey, man!" Tyrone shot back. "I went out there to get this shit just for you! Come on, man! Get yourself off!"

"All right," Dave said. "I will. Thanks."

He got to his feet, aware that every move he made was being observed. He glanced at Bob, who was in no position to help him. No chance to bust them, no choice but to shoot up with heroin? His fingers trembled when he took one of the bottle caps and filled it halfway with water from the dropper. He poured in some of the white powder and lit a match, holding the flame under the cap. He leaned over, stalling, and used a second match, then a third. He grabbed a tiny ball of cotton and put it into the cap. Then he noticed Bob get up from the couch.

"I gotta take a leak," Bob said, leaving the room.

Dave continued to stall. He was squatting on the floor and he glanced up and saw Otis staring at him. He heard the toilet flushing in the bathroom. If Bob comes back with both our guns drawn, we'll wind up in a battle with these guys, and we'll lose. Better to shoot up the dope and see what happens.

He took the eyedropper and squirted out the rest of the water. The objective, he figured, was to suck the heroin solution from the cotton into the dropper and then inject it with the spike. He set down the cap and the dropper and picked up a strip of rubber tubing, fixing it tightly around his upper arm. He felt a nudge at his shoulder. Bob? The nudge came again, so he reached behind himself and felt Bob hand him a piece of soaking-wet cotton.

Bending over in the semidarkness, he carefully replaced one ball of cotton with the other. Bob was already back on the couch. Dave squeezed the cotton so the water came to the surface, making it look as if the heroin was still in there. He drew up the liquid into the dropper. Then he took the spike and hit the vein in his arm, drawing blood, and injected himself with the water.

He crawled to one side of the room and sat once again with his back to the wall, nodding, pretending to be enjoying the warm rush of heroin through his system. Otis was still toying with his gun. So was the other guy in the corner.

Half an hour went by. Everybody settled down, relaxing. The guns were put away. Dave was wondering where to go from here. The sooner we do something, the better. No way to get involved in the stickup, no way. Bust 'em for the drugs—somehow.

"Let's go over the plans again," he said.

"Sure," Otis said.

They all stood up and made a circle around the table, where Otis remained seated. Bob said he was going back to the bathroom first.

"What's this arrow here?" Dave asked, drawing their attention to the diagrams on the table.

Otis started explaining. From the corner of his eye, Dave saw Bob coming into the room again, so he took a step backward and now saw that Bob had both guns. Now or never. Bob's hand moved quickly and one gun came through the air. Dave caught it just as Bob yelled, *"Okay, motherfuckers, get your hands up, and you—Otis!—stand up and drop your gun and you, too, over there, and nobody move or I'll blow your fucking heads off!"*

They all obeyed, the two guns dropping to the floor. "You taking us off, man?" someone said.

"Nah," Dave said. "He ain't taking you off. He's the man." They turned and saw that Dave, too, had a gun pointed at them.

"Shit!" another guy said.

"Everybody against that wall over there," Dave ordered, realizing that he and Bob had gained the upper hand but having no idea of what to do next. He kicked the guns away and started pushing the six men toward the wall.

He shoved Otis, who tripped and fell. Dave bent down; then he saw Tyrone leaping at him and felt Tyrone crash onto him. He went to the floor, thinking, *Oh, no, they're all over us,* but Bob was grabbing Tyrone by the hair and yanking him off, and the guy named Lyman was diving toward the window, smashing head first into the pitch-black rear yard of the building. Now Dave was shouting and acting psycho and telling Bob to pick up the guns and the shit and the works and let's get them out of here before there's a crowd at the door.

They pushed the five remaining men out of the room and through the dark hallway toward the front of the building.

"Down on the ground, on your stomachs," Dave yelled as they

emerged from the building, and the five men lay down in a row on the sidewalk. He looked around for any sign of a radio car at either end of the block. It might be a long wait. He glanced at Bob, shaking his head. No words were needed. If they were going to be this terrific cop team, they would have to learn to avoid such chaotic, dangerous situations, and have more concern for each other.

"Good thing I found that cotton," Bob said.

"Damn right. How'd I get into that spot?"

"I don't know, Dave. I just don't know."

4

Bob saw a radio car turn onto the block and approach them. He felt suddenly weary, exhausted, drained. He wanted to get this whole night done with, behind him, so he could start all over again. If we were just lucky, that's not good enough; we have to be better than that.

"Hey, slow down, stop, we're cops, we made an arrest." Just look at the expression on this officer's face, peering out the car window at these five guys on the ground, Dave thought.

"Everything's under control!" Bob yelled. "We just need transport assistance!"

The guys in the radio car were not budging. They were calling for assistance. Bob heard sirens, heading in this direction. What'd they call, a 10-13? More sirens filled the air and came closer. The whole precinct must be on its way! This was embarrassing; on top of all their own mistakes, this was almost more than he could bear. We don't need a 10-13; everything's under control!

He watched numbly as the squad cars raced into the block from either side. Well, this is the limit. He wished he could disappear. He saw Dave shaking his head in disbelief. Then he looked at all the cops getting out of the cars—and he laughed.

He went through the necessary motions without enthusiasm, explaining to the officers that he and Dave were arresting only two of the five men, Tyrone and Otis, on felony-narcotics charges. Now that help had arrived, they let the three others go. At the Sixtieth Precinct station house, they went right past the desk officer and upstairs to the detective squad.

The senior detective was off duty on this night, but the man in charge was about to say something. Bob waited for him to come out with the same old routine about how he and Dave were probably crooked cops who'd been trying to shake down junkies.

"Good work," the detective said. "That sonuvabitch Otis, we've been trying to nail him for two years! And Tyrone—*that* dude, he just got out of the can! We knew we were gonna get *him* again soon. Very nice—you saved us the trouble."

Maybe we didn't do so badly after all, Bob thought. He and Dave offered a detailed description of Lyman, who had escaped through the window, and they left the station house with the odd feeling of having been successful despite their private misgivings.

The following morning they went to court for the arraignment. Once again they were pushed from one line to another. But by late afternoon, Dave was already talking about making another arrest.

"Fine," Bob said, "but let's eliminate some of that confusion we got into."

"We have to keep in motion," Dave said as they left the Brooklyn courthouse.

It occurred to Bob that life with Dave Greenberg was going to be full of action, probably on a constant basis. Dave had enough motivation for an entire detective squad. His single, overriding goal, in terms of the Police Department, was to become a detective. Bob shared that goal, but his approach was different. At one time he had seriously considered robbing banks for a living, mostly because it would involve meticulous planning and thought. In a real sense, detective work involved the same talents. Making the bureau was something he could strive for in earnest.

We'll both get there faster, he thought, if we stick together; but at the same time we'll have to combine our personalities in the right way. I should do most of the talking to the brass, not him. He comes on too strong for their taste. But let him come up with the ideas, and I'll refine them. The task is to make two people function as one, so the end result is that we're five times as effective. We can get it down to a science, an art.

A few nights later, off duty, Bob joined Dave and Irene for dinner in their Sheepshead Bay apartment. During the entire meal, he noticed that Dave could hardly sit still. Fine, Bob thought;

keep throwing out the challenges, because I'm going to catch them and work on them and keep coming right back with the support.

"When you consider everything," Dave was saying, "we actually did a good job. We got two more drug collars, real bad-assed dudes, and we also stopped them from pulling that stickup."

"Right," Bob said. "But we'd better stay clear of Coney Island. If we go back there again some night, they'll *know* we're cops."

"What the hell? We can go anywhere in the whole city!"

True, Bob thought. If we're going to be out of bounds to begin with, we really don't have any boundaries at all!

"I say we ought to try the East Village," Dave said, "where there's lots of drugs. I got a purple shirt and some love beads. We can pose as hippies and bluff our way right into that scene. Too bad we don't have long hair or beards."

"When'll we do it?" Bob asked.

"Well," Dave said, pushing away his dinner and standing up, "how about tonight?"

"Right now?"

"Why not?"

Bob smiled. "Why not?" he asked. "Let's go."

Irene shook her head as they got ready to leave. She and Dave had been married four years, but she had known well before the wedding what kind of a life it would be with him. Never a dull moment, for one thing. Dave had been on his own from such an early age that no one—neither a wife nor a police partner—would be able to stop him from doing what he wanted. If you joined forces with Dave, you didn't try to hold him down and you couldn't worry; you trusted him and tried to help.

"Nobody would believe you two guys," Irene said when they headed for the door.

"They will," Dave said. "They will."

Dave was content to drive around the East Village for at least an hour or two, because he and Bob knew so little about the area and even less about hippies. They parked near a crowded street corner and got out of the car and stood leaning against it, observing the goings-on. At about nine thirty, Dave saw a black man approaching them. Some sixth sense told him that this guy was a drug user. Not an addict, maybe, but surely someone who was part of that scene.

"Hey, man," he said. "Have you seen Freddy?"

The man hesitated, then shook his head.

"You know Freddy?" Dave persisted.

"Nah, I don't know any Freddy."

"Well, *wait* a minute, man. Maybe you can help us out."

The man seemed in no big hurry, but he was clearly startled by this unexpected confrontation in the street. "What's the matter?" he asked.

"Listen, man, we've been waiting for a guy named Freddy. We're supposed to make a big buy tonight."

"What are you buying, man?"

"Six hundred dollars' worth of shit," Dave said.

"Yeah?"

"Yeah, but it looks like our connection split on us. Can you help us out? We'll cut you in, man."

"I don't know nothing about you guys."

"Shit," Dave said, "you never heard of Freddy Keyes?"

"Nope."

"What's *your* name?"

"Harold."

"Hey, man. I'm Dave, and this is my friend Bobby. We're getting strung out, man. Can you help us or not?"

Harold thought it over. "Well," he said, "I can take you to a hash connection."

Bob spoke up. "That's fine. We could go for some hash."

"We gotta go around the corner," Harold said.

The three men walked up the block and around the corner, up a short flight of steps and into a brownstone apartment building. Nothing in the world like being involved, Dave thought.

Acid rock music blasted through the stuffy room. Several people sprawled around the floor were either half dressed or naked, and thoroughly stoned.

Harold came out of another room with a young black woman whose name, he said, was Dolores.

"We want some stuff," Dave told her. He reached into his pocket and pulled out a thick wad of bills; Bob did the same.

"There's about six hundred here. We want everything we can buy with it."

Dolores was impressed. She went to the pay phone in the hallway and had a brief conversation with someone.

"All right," she said to them. "You guys wait here. I'll be right back. Give me the money and I'll go make the buy for you."

"Wait a minute," Dave said. "We'll give you a ride over, baby, 'cause we'd like to speak to your man."

"You can't speak to my man."

"Hey, baby, we want to try the stuff and see how good it is! I mean, shit, if we're going to lay out all this bread, *we* want to deal with the guy."

"He won't deal with nobody 'cept me."

"Sure he will," Dave persisted. "Look, you'll get your cut, don't worry. But we ain't turning any money over to you, just so you can split on us."

The conversation went on for another twenty minutes before Dolores finally agreed to let them drive her to the connection. But she still flatly refused to promise that they could deal with him directly. In the car, Dave followed her directions through the unfamiliar streets of the East Village until she told him to pull over. Harold, who had come along to get his cut of the money, remained in the back seat when Dolores jumped out and disappeared around a corner.

When she returned, she was holding a tiny sample of what she said was hash, wrapped in a piece of aluminum foil. Dave had no idea if it was the real thing. She got into the back seat again and handed Bob the aluminum foil. Bob opened it and examined the contents. Dave saw that he knew equally little about hash. And now Dolores wanted the six hundred dollars so she could go back and get the full load.

"I tell you," Dave said, "we gotta deal with the guy ourselves."

"Yeah," Bob said. "How're we supposed to trust you with our bread?"

"Besides," Dave went on, "we might want to do a lot more business with this guy. And there'd be a percentage for you every time!"

"No way," Dolores insisted. "My man ain't dealing with nobody 'cept me."

Dave wondered if they should bust her right now. Maybe if they threatened to arrest her, she would lead them to the connection. No, that would be a very bad move. She'd probably never rat on the guy. And then, how could they arrest her for such a small quantity of drugs? Maybe it wasn't even hash!

"Well," Dave said at last, "if you won't take us to your man, the deal's off."

"Drive me back to my place, then."

"Fuck you," Dave said. "Get out of the car."

Dolores got out, cursed at them, slammed the door, and hurried away.

Dave Greenberg fumed over his own inexperience and ignorance. At least we didn't make a complete mess of things. But look at all the time we've wasted! He turned around to Harold in the back seat. We've gone this far, he thought; let's keep it going.

"Okay, Harold. Who else do you know?"

"Well, I got one other friend who carries some big weight. Hangs out in the park. Good connection. I think he's over there now."

"What park?"

"Over near Avenue B and Tenth."

"Fine," Dave said. "Which way do we go?"

Harold gave directions, and they arrived at the park a few minutes later.

"Only one of you better come with me," Harold said.

"I'll go," Dave replied.

Bob slumped down in the front seat and watched Dave and Harold walk into the park. He thought he was probably doomed, if that was the word, to this end of the partnership—the backup man, the guy who stays on the periphery of the action until he's needed. In some ways, his role was more demanding than Dave's; at least Dave was in motion. Dave knew what the hell was going on. It was almost tougher, Bob thought, to be waiting and wondering about him and trying somehow to read his mind from a distance. And if Dave got hurt, Bob would never forgive himself for not having been at the scene in time.

He hated violence, had shunned it whenever possible, although violence had been all around him when he was growing up. He had learned the necessity of meeting physical threats with quick responses; but he much preferred using sheer intelligence, method, cunning. Better never to be in a position requiring the gun, better to use no physical force at all; better to do it cleanly, professionally, striving for a kind of grace and perfection. No need for heroics; better to be totally capable and leave it at that. What was hard was the waiting and wondering, the second-guessing, while Dave was somewhere else, stirring up the ingredients and igniting them.

Nearly an hour later, Dave returned from the park alone. From the front seat of the car, Bob watched the figure of his friend approach in the darkness.

"What's up?" he said.

"Man," Dave replied, "this is a whole new scene to me. I really don't know where I'm at. Beatniks, hippies, guys wearing cowbells—"

"What's happening?"

"They'll be back in a few minutes. Harold brought me to his connection. I start rapping like mad, and then the connection goes and gets *his* connection. So we got three guys, altogether. They're bringing a big bundle of dope. I told them to meet me here at the car. When they get here and there's nobody else around, we'll identify ourselves, throw them in the car, and split. Okay?"

"Fine."

Bob got out of the car. A few moments later, Harold and two other men approached on the sidewalk. One of them displayed a bagful of drugs and started to ask for money. When Bob saw Dave reaching for his gun, he did likewise. They both screamed, *"Get up against the fucking car or we'll blow your heads off, we're cops, don't move!"* Then there was a flurry of movement; frisking and handcuffing and yelling and throwing them into the back seat and hopping into the front and Dave screeching off through the East Village, driving with one hand, his .38-caliber Smith & Wesson in the other, pointed over his shoulder at the guys behind him. Bob had turned all the way around and had his gun on them, too. The car peeled around dark corners and through narrow one-way blocks the wrong way, finally coming to an abrupt halt. Dave glanced at Bob.

"What's the matter?" Bob said.

"I got a question."

"What is it?"

"Where's the police station?"

"*You* don't know?"

"Nope."

"Neither do I!"

Dave screeched off again down the street, turned right, went up another block, turned left, then right again, frantically searching for the East Village police station.

"Slow down," Bob said. They pulled up next to a man on the corner. "Hey," Bob yelled out the window. "Where's the station house?"

"What?"

"Police station! Where is it?"

"Go straight three blocks, make a left turn, and go two more blocks." The car lurched forward again, the three men in the back seat looking as if they were more afraid of an accident than of going to jail.

Dave Greenberg was fully intent on getting to the Ninth Precinct station house, wherever the hell it was, before the prisoners could cause trouble. He swerved left according to the man's directions—and found himself speeding right toward a fire truck blocking the narrow street. He slammed on his brakes. The car bumped over several hoses in the road before coming to a stop.

The block had been closed off because of a fire. The scene was chaotic: trucks, hoses, ladders leaning upward toward a burning building, smoke billowing out, water pouring all over, firemen hurrying this way and that. The spray, raining down on everything, covered the car completely, making it impossible to see out at all.

"Where are we?" Dave wondered aloud.

"A car wash?" Bob suggested.

A fireman appeared in the window next to Bob, screaming, *"Get this car outa here."* Then he saw the guns.

"We're cops," Bob said. "We have three important prisoners in the back seat. We're in a hurry."

"Oh! Sorry! Uh, hey! *Hey! Move the hoses, men, move that truck, let this car through here, police coming through, let's go!"*

One of the trucks backed onto the sidewalk, allowing Dave

enough room to get by. The car bumped over the hoses and headed out of the spray toward the station house in the next block.

Dave and Bob ushered the three prisoners through the door of the Ninth Precinct station house. This time, Dave thought, nobody's going to push us around. We've got these guys cold, and we don't have to stand for anybody giving us a hard time because of their own hangups. Step aside; no more shit.

The desk officer looked up. "What's this?"

No more of this "probationary" stuff. No more "Safety Unit B" or "off duty" or any other crap. They had just bluffed their way through the Fire Department—why not the police? Why give them a chance to accuse us of playing games? Why volunteer information they can hang us with?

"Officers Greenberg and Hantz. Three prisoners. Possession and sale of narcotics. Felony charges."

"Where you from?"

"Hey, listen, we'll take care of it. Let's go, Bobby."

They brought the prisoners upstairs to the detectives' office. Saying nothing to the detectives in the room, they lodged the prisoners and got busy with the paperwork.

"Hey," Dave said, "let me use your desk here. I'll be through in a few minutes."

"Where do you guys work out of?" the senior detective said.

"You'll have to give us a break," Dave replied. "We got three guys here, felony narcotics, no weapons, and we're in a kind of a hurry."

"Can you tell us about the arrest?"

"Look," Dave said, "there isn't much we can give you right now. We have to clear it with our bosses. You understand, don't you?"

"Well, yeah. Sorry."

Five detectives watched with considerable curiosity as Officers Greenberg and Hantz went about their business as if they had been doing it for years.

One detective went to speak to the prisoners, but Dave stopped him. "Listen, Officer! You'll have to do us a favor! You won't be able to interrogate those men right now. They're in *our* custody, okay?"

"Right! Sure!"

On his reports, Dave had put down "S.U.B."—the initials of Safety Unit B—for his command. A detective picked up one of the sheets. "S.U.B.?" he said. "What's S.U.B.?"

"Hey," Dave yelled, retrieving the page, "I'll take that, if you don't mind!"

The whole procedure took no more than an hour. From their previous few arrests, they had known the exact charges to make—PL220-35c, Felony, Criminal Sale of Dangerous Drugs—and everyone in that precinct headquarters had backed off.

They were on their way out of the station house at twelve thirty in the morning with enough time for a full night's sleep before having to go to court.

"Safety Unit B?"

"Yeah, who's this?"

"Probationary Patrolman Greenberg. I'm over at the Ninth Precinct. Me and Hantz are here. We made an off-duty arrest last night, and—"

"*Another* one?"

"Yeah. We're going to court again."

"Wait a minute, Greenberg. Just *wait* a—"

"Listen, you got what I just told you?"

"Yeah, but—"

"Fine! Take care of it! We'll call you back later."

It was nine in the morning, and they were an hour late. When they arrived at Manhattan Criminal Court for the arraignment, there were new procedures, but the same interminable waiting.

"Someday we'll get rid of this bullshit," Dave said as they stood on line.

They got out of court at about three o'clock and decided they wouldn't go back to Safety Unit B until the next full day of work.

When they walked into their traffic command in Manhattan the following morning, the desk officer told them Captain Safron wanted to see them.

They went upstairs and changed into their uniforms, stood through roll call, then got ready to go out to their traffic posts. Dave had no intention of seeing the captain. As they headed for the front door downstairs, the desk officer said, "Didja see the captain?"

"Ah, shucks," Dave said. "We forgot."

"You *forgot?*"

"Yeah. Well, look—if it's important, he'll call us."

They were out the front door and on the pavement when they heard the lieutenant's loud voice behind them.

"Greenberg! Hantz! Get upstairs and see the captain!"

"Right," Dave said.

They went back inside and upstairs to Captain Leo Safron's office for their second confrontation with him.

"Okay," Safron said. "I guess I'm gonna have my hands full. I have a feeling that I'm gonna get to know you two guys."

Dave felt his muscles tensing; it was hard to tell which way Safron was leaning.

"You've been making all these arrests off duty," Safron said. "Now, tell me—are you guys intending to continue in this type of work?"

"Yeah, Captain," Dave said.

"Is there anything I can say to get you off this track?"

"No, Captain."

"Well, all right. Then listen to me," Safron said, taking off his spectacles and rubbing his eyes. "You're going out, making arrests, and you're doing it in every precinct but mine. How about doing it while you're working?"

Dave was stunned. Was it possible that this was not a reprimand, but a form of guidance? Is he trying not to hold us down, but protect us?

"If you can do it *off* duty," Safron went on, "you can also do it *on* duty. What do you say?"

"Well, Captain," Dave replied, "what about the repercussions? I mean, can we just go out on traffic duty and try to make arrests?"

Leo Safron stood up. "Look," he said, "you're working for *me!* And when I say you can go out and make arrests on traffic duty, go ahead and do it! That way, you won't be sticking your necks out so far. Otherwise, this off-duty stuff is gonna get you in hot water. So go out and make the arrests for *me,* okay?"

Dave Greenberg looked over at Bob, who was smiling.

"Think of it this way," Safron added. "If you do a good job here, at least *I* get some of the credit."

Now both Dave and Bob were openly grinning, completely relaxed. Dave decided to push his luck.

"Captain," he said. "How about assigning the two of us together?"

Safron sat down again. He considered the request a moment, then said, "Well, let's put it this way, boys. We have no posts that require two men, because we're a traffic precinct. And I can't put you on patrol, either." He paused. "But what I can do, I guess, is give you posts down the block from each other. In which case, there'd be nothing to prevent you from wandering toward the middle of the block. And then you'd be together, right?"

"Great idea," Dave said.

"That'll be all," Safron said.

A few days later, they were both assigned to corners on Thirty-fourth Street, just a block from each other. They would be able to walk there together from Safety Unit B on Forty-seventh Street. Dave decided it would be best to go along Eighth Avenue, since it had a high crime rate. The captain had done them a favor, and Dave was determined to return it as soon as possible.

As they were leaving the station house on their way to the new posts, Dave saw two cops in uniform speaking in low tones. When he heard "Greenberg and Hantz" mentioned, he stopped to listen.

"Traffic cops making drug collars," one was saying. "Two crazy guys, I guess. Gonna get themselves killed."

"Well," the other said, "I heard that they ain't *really* traffic cops. Ritchie Miller told me they work for the Commissioner's office."

"Where'd he hear that?"

"I dunno. Overheard some other guys, I think."

When the two officers realized that Dave was standing right there, they stopped talking. He caught up with Bob at the front door. Outside, he broke into a big grin and repeated what he had heard.

"We're already getting a reputation!" he said as they headed down the block.

He felt as if he'd been given a shot of new energy; not only was the captain expecting great things from them, but now there were all sorts of rumors flying around. Let them fly!

"Don't walk so fast," he said as they started down Eighth Avenue. He imagined that the entire street was filled with criminal activity—and he was going to find it. He wished a holdup man would come running out of a store in front of them. He hoped they would never make it to their posts.

Nearing Forty-second Street, he saw a glistening new Buick, bright blue, parked on the opposite side. He paused and looked at it closely. The lone guy inside it was about twenty-two, he judged. A white guy, well dressed, but somehow he didn't fit the car. Or the car didn't fit him. Dave had been in many stolen cars during his youth, and he always had had a certain feeling about those cars—the same feeling he was having right now. That car has to be stolen; I don't know why, but it is.

Going on sheer instinct, he headed across Eighth Avenue, with Bob right beside him. They circled and approached the car from behind. Dave moved to the left side and Bob went to the right.

"Hey," Dave said to the guy behind the wheel. "Let's see your license and registration."

The young man started to protest. He reached for his wallet, then rummaged in the glove compartment, talking rapidly and making excuses. Bob took out his gun and pointed it at the guy.

"Step out of the car," Bob said.

Dave was torn between his excitement over what was happening and his gratitude to Bob for trusting him so totally. Man, he thought, I'd better be right about this.

The young man's license showed his name to be Arthur Valentine, which didn't jibe with the registration. It was a New Jersey driver's license; the car was registered in New York State. A Long Island address. The more the young man tried to explain, the more confident Dave became that the car had been stolen.

"Stay with him, Bobby."

Dave went to a police call box to ask for a radio car from the Fourteenth Precinct. He was positive that the car was hot. And somehow, Bob knew what I was up to! He moved right with me, without a word between us, just as if we'd rehearsed it.

The radio car showed up almost as soon as he got off the phone. Dave explained to the officer that they were arresting Arthur Valentine for grand larceny auto. They put him into the squad car and said they would drive the blue Buick back to the station house themselves.

On the way to the Fourteenth Precinct headquarters on Thirty-fifth Street, he wanted to tell Bob how great he felt. But he said nothing, because there was still a chance that the car hadn't been stolen. Jesus, he thought, sometimes it seems as if Bobby believes in me more than I believe in myself!

They went into the station house and the radio-car patrolman walked up to them. "I put it over the air," he said. "And they say there's no report on that car. How do *you* know it was stolen?"

Dave glanced at Bob, who had not even flinched.

"Let's call the owner of the car," Bob said.

"Right," Dave said.

The car was registered to someone named Gerald Roth on Long Island. Bob got the number from information, then placed the call.

"Hello?" answered a woman.

"Mrs. Roth?"

"Yes?"

"Is your husband at home?"

"No, he's at work."

"Has your car been stolen?"

"No, of course not."

Bob cupped his hand over the phone. "Dave, she says her car's not stolen."

"Fine," Dave said. "Ask her where it is."

"Ma'am? Where *is* your car?"

"It's out in the driveway! Who is this, anyway?"

Bob turned to Dave again. "She says the car is out in her driveway."

"Ask her to take a look."

"Hello? Mrs. Roth? You there?"

"Yes, I'm here!"

"Will you look out the window and see if the car's in the driveway?"

"I just did! It's not in the driveway!"

"Hey, Dave—the car's not in the driveway."

Mrs. Roth's voice came over the phone. *"What happened to my car? It's been stolen! My car's been stolen!"*

Bob started to reply, but she hung up.

"She hung up, Dave."

"Call her back."

Bob placed the call again.

"Hello?" answered Mrs. Roth. "Who is this? My car has been stolen!"

"Listen," Bob said, "I forgot to tell you—this is the police. Why are you so upset?"

"I just looked, and my car's not there! It's completely gone!"

"Well, ma'am, it's been found. Did you report it stolen?"

"Of course not! I just realized it was missing!"

"Okay, then. We have your car. Please describe it to me, so we're sure."

"I can't."

"Why not?"

"Because I'm in shock, that's why!"

"What's your husband's number at work?"

She gave him the number and Bob finally reached the husband at his office. Mr. Roth described the blue Buick down to its last detail.

"Hey," a sergeant said. "Which one of you guys is making the arrest here?"

"Both of us," Dave said.

"No, no, that's impossible. You got one prisoner, so only one of you goes to court. Which one?"

"You go," Bob said. "After all, Dave, you saw the car in the first place."

"We *both* made the arrest," Dave insisted. "What the hell is this, anyway?" he roared at the sergeant. "You mean to say he's going back on traffic duty while I have to go to court alone?"

"That's right."

"Shit!"

Dave made up his mind that from now on he and Bob would always arrest more than one person at any given time.

5

The next morning at work, Captain Safron greeted Dave and Bob inside the safety unit headquarters and told them, with a big smile, that he was quite happy about their stolen-car arrest. "I sent a little note about you guys up to the division boss," he said. "Keep up the good work."

Minutes later they were strolling down Eighth Avenue toward their traffic posts on Thirty-fourth Street. Dave was thinking about his conversation with the three drug pushers in the East Village park several nights before. While Bob had been waiting in the car, Dave had spent about an hour talking with Harold and the connection and the connection's connection. It seemed like a chain with innumerable links that kept leading backward, or upward, to the prime source. If you were set on fighting the heroin trade, he thought, maybe the best idea was to follow the chain backward, link by link.

One of the connections in the park had mentioned that there was an apartment on the second floor of a building on State Street in Brooklyn, just off Atlantic Avenue, where they kept a large supply of heroin—at least three kilos, Dave remembered—for a number of pushers. That apartment, or whoever operated in it, was another link in the chain—a much more important link, no doubt.

We should go there, Dave thought as they walked along.

But he also felt indebted to the captain. Such guidance had been rare—in fact, it had been almost nonexistent—in their experience as cops up to that point. Dave felt torn between his desire to go make more drug arrests and his sense of obligation to Captain Safron.

They had strolled downtown and had turned onto Thirty-fourth Street, and now they found themselves walking past the Empire State Building. Suddenly a man carrying a woman's purse bolted out the door. Bob casually stuck his foot in the man's path, tripping him. He sailed forward and landed on the pavement, sprawled out and nearly unconscious.

"What d'ya think about that?" Bob said.

"Well," Dave replied, "it would seem to me that if he was running, somebody must be chasing him."

"Sounds logical."

About thirty seconds later an executive rushed out of the building.

"Oh!" the executive gasped. "Great! You caught him!"

"Yeah?" Dave said. "What'd we catch?"

"That guy on the ground—he just came into our office and stole my secretary's pocketbook!"

Another arrest for Captain Safron, Dave thought with a smile. He asked us to make collars while we're working, and that's what we've done. Now we can go out and do something on our own again.

After work they went out to a restaurant for dinner, and then drove to Brooklyn. Dave slowed down the car along State Street. When he came to the block in question, he immediately recognized the tan-brick, four-story apartment building that had been described to him. In there, in one of the apartments on the second floor, was a major drug supplier. He wondered why the city's narcotics squad hadn't raided the building—or why the F.B.I. wasn't on continual stakeout. It seemed unlikely that two probationary patrolmen would be the only ones who knew about the place or who cared enough to do something about it.

"The problem is," Bob was saying, "how do we find out which apartment it is?"

"I don't know," Dave said, "but just look at all these prostitutes!"

There were numerous women on both sides of the street, standing in doorways or against walls, soliciting customers. Dave pulled into a parking space so they could watch. Some of the women came around the corner from Atlantic Avenue with their customers. They were using two or three buildings in this block, including the tan-brick one.

"Let's get one of these whores to take us up there," Dave said. "We'll go proposition 'em."

They got out of the car and went to opposite sides of the street. Dave wandered along his side, slowing down in front of two women in a doorway.

One of them called to him. "Wanna have a good time, honey?"

"Yeah, sure," he said, walking right over to them. "How much you want?"

"Never mind, honey. I don't trust no clean-cut types like you."

Embarrassed, he wanted to reply, but causing a scene would not help. He moved on, aware that he and Bob were just too clean-shaven and young-looking for this environment.

"Hi," he said to one woman who seemed younger than the rest.

"Hi," she said, smiling. "Looking for a date?"

"Yeah, well, maybe. How much?"

"Can you afford twenty dollars?"

"Yeah."

"It's ten dollars for the room, also."

"Where's the room?"

"Right near where we are."

"I mean, which building?"

"Down there," she said, pointing to the wrong building.

"Maybe later," Dave said. "See ya."

He walked away, wondering how Bob was doing. He saw him talking to a girl across the street. If nothing else, they were having a little fun.

Just as Dave came to the tan-brick building in question, a tall black woman with a pocketbook slung over her shoulder was walking out the door to the sidewalk.

"Excuse me," Dave said. "Hey, wait a minute."

She stopped and turned toward him. "What is it?"

"Wanna make fifty bucks?"

"Whatcha got in mind?"

"You work up there in this building?"

"Once in a while."

"Want to go back up there? Fifty bucks?"

"Ten dollars for the room as well," she said.

Dave cursed under his breath.

"Okay," he said. "But let me get my friend." He looked across the street at Bob, who seemed to be having no luck. "Hey, Bob! Come over here!"

"What's this?" the prostitute said. "Who's he? What's goin' on?"

"Don't worry," Dave said. "This here is my friend. Bob? Come here, man." Bob approached; Dave turned back to the girl. "The thing is, my friend's gotta have somebody, too. I don't want to go up there alone."

"Well," she said, "I can take you both."

"No, no," Dave answered. "Can't you get someone else?"

"Well, all right. Wait here."

She went off down the sidewalk. It would be better to get two prostitutes—two possible sources of information.

When the woman returned with a friend, Dave and Bob followed them into the building, up the narrow staircase to the second floor. Dave counted four doors—which one led into the apartment with the kilos of heroin?—and then on up to the third floor. They went into separate rooms.

The tall black woman with Dave sat down on the edge of the bed and pulled her sweater over her head. Then she stood up and removed her skirt. "Get undressed," she said. "What are you waiting for?"

"Listen," he said, "maybe you can help me. I'm kind of strung out, and I'd like to buy some shit. You know anybody in this building who's doing stuff?"

"That ain't my trade," she replied, looking at him as if she found it hard to believe that he was an addict. "You want it straight or d'ya want me to blow you?"

"Straight," he said. "But listen, I'll pay good bread for some junk. You must know people in this building, and—"

"Are you gonna get undressed or not?"

"I will, I will," Dave said, thinking that he'd better get some information from this chick soon. He couldn't get undressed, because the gun was stuck under his belt beneath his shirt.

"Come on, then! I don't got all night!"

"Look, all I really want is some information. I'll pay you for it, don't worry."

"Hey, man," she said, glaring at him, "if you're a cop, boy, I'm either gonna kill you or kill myself. You a cop?"

"No, no. I just want some information. If—"

"If you don't get yourself undressed right now, I'm gonna holler for my man. And my man'll come up here and kill you!"

"Calm down," Dave said. "Let me just explain something." He decided to identify himself as a cop and then ask her to tell what she knew about any drug operations below on the second floor. If she refused to cooperate, he would threaten to lock her up for prostitution. "Now, listen to me. I'm a police officer and—"

"Ahhhhh! Ahhhh!"

"Hey, what are you yelling about? I didn't finish!"

"Help! Ahhhhh! Help! Rape! He's killing me! Not again, not again! I'm being busted! I can't take any more! The pain, the pain, help me, please! Ahhhh!"

Dave tried frantically to get her to stop, but the more he talked to her the louder she screamed. By now, everybody in the whole building had to have heard it. Hell, he thought, I'd better get out of here quick. Bobby must've heard the screams, too. Wonder what he's thinking and doing, with that chick in the other room.

In a panic, Dave opened the door and slipped into the hallway. Bob was coming out of his room at the same time.

"What's going on?" Bob said.

"She's screaming, that's all. I told her I was a cop, but—"

All of a sudden it sounded as if a stampede of cattle was coming up the stairs. Over the prostitute's screams, he heard men's voices and loud, hurried footsteps on the wooden stairs.

"Come on," he said.

They got down the first flight—but at the bottom of the next set of steps, glaring up at them, were several black men carrying guns and knives. Pimps for the girls, Dave thought; and they know something's wrong.

They started up the stairs. Dave froze. What to do? No way we can throw these guys off. We're outnumbered; they've got weapons out. We have the high ground, but that's not going to last long. Don't panic, don't bolt, don't say a word. Let 'em come.

The chief pimp came first, the others behind him. He reached the stairwell and pointed his gun at them. "What the hell is goin' on, man?"

Dave and Bob said nothing. The prostitute was still screaming. "Well?"

"Bad news," Bob said at last. "Girl's very sick up there, man. She's in labor. You better go up there and help her."

"What did you say, man?"

"It's the truth," Bob said. "She's having a baby."

Dave glanced at Bob. A prostitute having a baby! Plausible, but somehow ludicrous—so unexpected an explanation that the chief pimp went past them up the stairs, followed by the others. Dave and Bob stood aside to let them pass. Nine men—with four guns, three knives, and one chair leg.

When the last man had passed them, the two of them started down the stairs, calmly, moving quickly but not running. They heard a commotion up on the third floor and realized that the pimps were coming back down after them. "Holy shit, are we on borrowed time," Dave muttered, and they walked quickly to the car.

At least, he thought as he drove off, neither of us panicked. Neither one of us ran out and left the other one up there. We came in together, and we went out the same way.

"She shouldn't've screamed," Dave said, stopping for a light. He was still savoring the relief he had felt when they had escaped, but instinct turned his remaining fear into anger. He crashed his fist into the dashboard. "Who the fuck do they think they are?" It was the way he had reacted to fear all his life, refusing to be intimidated, building his nerve until he felt he was invincible. "I'm going back there!" he shouted.

He made one left turn, then another; then he went down the block and turned again, into the same part of State Street. He cruised along the parked cars until he came to the tan-brick building. The chief pimp was standing in the doorway.

"Watch this," Dave said, leaping from the car. "Come here, you!" he yelled at the pimp. The pimp came forward and Dave stepped toward him on the sidewalk and grabbed him by his shirt. "Listen, baby," he said, "if you're looking for trouble, we're the guys that'll give it to you! We came here looking for some information. You got some psycho chick working for you, and she ain't gonna do nothing but give you trouble, man. Lemme tell ya, you better be careful about who you have working for you!"

"Yeah?"

"Yeah! That girl's got some nerve, risking our lives like that! We could've had a shootout in there!"

"Hey, man," the pimp said. "Don't worry, man! You're right, baby, I'm sorry. I mean, I didn't know what was comin' down, you dig? But I'll take care of it, okay?"

"That's better!" Dave shouted. He turned and jumped back in the car. Driving off, he felt good in spite of the fact that their drug collar had blown up in their faces.

Although it was late at night, Bob asked to be dropped off at a girl friend's apartment in lower Manhattan. Dave drove him there and said, "Listen, the hell with what happened. We got into a bad scene, but we stood our ground and came out of it." They had three days off coming up, so Dave added, "Let's just relax, and when we get back to work we'll stick to making arrests *on* duty from now on. After all, we got the captain on our side."

Driving home, he imagined what would have happened if they'd been hurt, or if they'd been forced to shoot someone. How would they have explained their presence in that building? Good thing there's only the two of us, Dave thought; one more would be one too many.

He and Irene went to the beach a couple of times over the next three days, and he enjoyed telling friends about his and Bobby's exploits. Sometimes he skipped over sensitive details—like the time he had injected himself with water. A cop isn't supposed to inject himself with anything, he had found out. But after a while, he realized that few people really believed him anyway—they seemed to regard him either as a colorful storyteller or a careless freak. "What do you do those things for?" a friend asked. "How come you do it, if you're not getting paid any extra?"

"Just for the hell of it," Dave answered.

It was more than that, of course, but he found it simpler to give the impression that he was half crazy than to explain about how he was trying to "beat the system." He felt surrounded by people who would never understand, and who therefore would never really believe, his motives. To most of them he was just a wild man who would probably get himself killed before he reached thirty. Rather than argue, Dave agreed—and began to almost believe it himself.

On his third day off, he got a call from Safety Unit B and received orders to show up for the four-to-midnight shift. All probationary guys were going to be working straight four-to-twelves from now on. But he and Bob would still be assigned to posts within a block of each other.

As they were about to leave the station house for their posts that afternoon, Dave declared for everyone to hear, "Bob, we're not gonna direct any traffic—no more! I guarantee you, we'll never get to our posts!"

Another probationary patrolman, Kevin, accompanied them as they walked to Eighth Avenue and started downtown. We'll have to get rid of him as soon as something happens, Dave thought; it's enough to be responsible just for each other.

Two blocks later, Dave spotted a brand-new white Cadillac, occupied by four young men, three white and one black, parked across the street. No question about it—that Cadillac had been stolen.

He poked Bob in the ribs and nodded in the direction of the Cadillac. He's done it again, Bob thought. "Hey, Kevin," Bob said. "I'm gonna buy you a sandwich."

He took the startled young rookie by the arm and walked him back up the block to the coffee shop on the corner. Inside, Bob guided the young man to a booth.

"Have a seat," Bob said. "Waitress? Over here! This hard-working officer here would like a tuna fish sandwich on white toast, no lettuce, and a cup of coffee. Kevin, I'll be right back."

Leaving a perplexed Kevin in the coffee shop, he went to join Dave, who was already talking to the men inside the Cadillac. Bob walked to the opposite side of the car, calmly took out his gun, and ordered, "Everybody step out of the car. You're under arrest."

They called for radio-car transport for the prisoners and drove the Cadillac to the precinct house, where they checked it out and verified that it had been stolen. They both went to court that evening.

The next afternoon, three other traffic cops tagged along with them to see how they did it. Dave was annoyed by their presence and said so, but apparently the whole safety unit was talking about how Greenberg and Hantz could never get to their posts because of their grand larceny auto collars.

"What a sight," Dave said. "Five cops in uniform parading down Eighth Avenue! People'll think we're the riot squad!"

He was hungry, so he suggested they all go into a restaurant for some food. They sat around a table and ordered sandwiches. Dave suddenly jumped up from his chair and looked out the window.

"Excuse me," he said. "Come on, Bob."

The two of them hurried out of the restaurant. Dave walked up to the driver of a car that was parked just outside. The man admitted right away that he had stolen the car. Bob walked back into the restaurant and approached the other cops.

"Here's to pay our check," Bob told them, slapping several dollar bills onto the table. "We've just made an arrest, and we gotta take care of it. See you."

The three officers, who had been watching through the window, stared at him in amazement.

Reporting for work the following afternoon, Dave and Bob discovered that they had become minor celebrities. Even officers from other precincts had come over to see these two traffic cops who were making all the arrests.

"You guys are just lucky," a patrolman challenged them. "Lucky?" said Dave. "Fuck you!"

"Well, you're not trying to claim that it's *skill*, are you?"

"Damn right I am!" Dave roared. "I'll tell you something. If we wanted to, we could go out there and bring in two stolen cars—in one day!"

"Bullshit!"

A small crowd of officers had gathered around, enjoying the argument and watching to see if this Greenberg character would back down.

"Come on, Bob. Let's go prove something to these jerks."

They walked out of the building and went over to Eighth

Avenue and down three blocks. Crossing the next street, Dave saw a black Ford with three men in it. He approached the driver and told him to step outside with his license and registration. Bob kept watch on the other two men until Dave made sure the car was stolen. They called for a radio car and, when the officer arrived, Dave told him to wait there with the car and the three prisoners until he and Bob returned.

They walked four more blocks and Dave saw a shiny maroon convertible heading down Thirty-ninth Street at about thirty miles an hour. He flagged a taxi; he and Bob jumped in and ordered the cabbie to give chase. They came alongside the car and flashed their shields and yelled, "Pull over!" The driver and his companions admitted they had just stolen the convertible from a parking garage.

Dave and Bob drove the convertible, with the two men in it, back to where the first car was being detained. A second radio car was called for the additional prisoners. Dave got into the Ford and Bob took the convertible, and the whole parade—two radio cars, five prisoners, one stolen Ford, one stolen Cadillac—headed for the station house.

"Now, listen," Captain Safron was saying, "all you men are being taken off your regular traffic assignments for a special operation! You're all going into the garment area to give out summonses!"

Dave stood with the others in the safety unit headquarters, thinking that giving out summonses to trucks was about the last thing he wanted to do. On a new daytime schedule, he and Bob had continued to make all sorts of arrests over a period of weeks, including several more car-theft collars, again never once making it to their traffic posts. Yet they were still on probation, with no prospect of getting into anything really challenging.

Captain Safron was explaining that he wanted them to give out tickets to all trucks parked in the garment district for longer than three hours. The traffic situation was terrible, as it had been for years, mainly because of the huge trucks. The latest theory was that three hours should be ample time for them to load and unload and get out again.

"Okay," the captain said. "Now, let's get out there and see if we can't clean up that mess!"

Dave felt his depression growing.

"Greenberg! Hantz! I want to see you two in my office!"

What now? He and Bob waited until Safron had gone back upstairs; then they followed. When they entered his office, he greeted them with an enthusiastic wave.

"Come in, boys. Listen, I know that you guys wouldn't be very happy giving out summonses, so I've got a special job for you. We have another problem in the garment area besides traffic congestion—guys stealing things off trucks. Payrolls, clothing, boxes of stuff, everything. Now, you two are my men. Handle that."

"Right," Dave answered, grabbing Bob by the arm and hurrying downstairs again. An unexpected opportunity! It occurred to him that all he really needed, most of the time, was a little nudge from a superior. Well, Captain Safron seemed to supply the nudges just when they were needed most. "Let's go take a look at the place," he said.

He and Bob walked over to the garment area and wandered among the crowds, examining the massive trucks and watching all the bustling activity. A truck would pull up for delivery and the driver would leave it open while he and his helper brought packages into the building. No wonder thieves found it so easy to grab stuff! They could wait for the truckers to go inside and then hit the back of the truck and beat it. Looking at the situation from a criminal's point of view, Dave could see all sorts of possibilities.

"The trouble," Bob observed, "is that we're not gonna catch anybody while we're in these uniforms. They'll just wait till we leave, that's all."

"You're right," Dave said. "Let's go see the captain."

Safron looked surprised to see them back so soon. "What's the matter?" he said.

Dave spoke up. "Can we wear plainclothes?"

"No, no, no. You're on probation! I'd get *fired,*" said Captain Safron. Then he seemed to be catching on. "Of course," he said, lowering his voice, "what I don't see doesn't hurt."

"Okay," Dave said. "See ya."

He and Bob went downstairs and grabbed some shirts and jackets out of their lockers. They walked outside again and returned to the garment area, forgetting all about lunch. In one of the warehouses, Dave slipped out of his police jacket and put on a sports coat. Then they went to the stockroom supervisor and asked to borrow some equipment.

Minutes later, Dave Greenberg was pushing a rack of long overcoats through the streets of the garment district. Bob Hantz was riding on the center bar, hidden inside the coats. He was still in uniform, clutching his hat close to his chest, as he rolled and bumped along the rack.

This went on for more than an hour, with no success. "How're you doing in there?" Dave kept asking. Bob replied in the strongest possible language that he was hot and uncomfortable and ready to trade places.

Suddenly Dave saw a man grab a woman's pocketbook and start running right toward them. "Bob—purse snatch in progress! The guy's coming on the left. Now!"

Bob's arm shot out from the overcoats just in time to grab the man's shirt. The startled thief found himself pulled into the clothing rack, with Bob's arm around his neck. Dave took the pocketbook and began pushing the rack, with Bob and the thief still on it, toward the precinct house.

"We've got your purse!" he yelled to the woman as they passed her. "We're cops—meet us at the police station!"

The following morning they were back in the garment district, using a storage house as a place to change out of their uniforms. They made arrangements for one of the trucks to remain parked with its back door open. Then they brought a huge cardboard TV box out to the sidewalk. Dave climbed inside and Bob closed it up.

"Hey, fellas," Bob called to a pair of workers. "I'm a police officer. Would you lift this box into the truck, please?"

The two workers obeyed, hoisting the box, with Dave inside it, onto the back of the truck. Bob went around to the driver's seat in the cab and lay down on the floor.

Crouched inside the box, Dave punched a few holes in it with a key so he could see out and, if necessary, point his gun. He also punched a larger hole in the rear of the box so he could reach out and grab on to something. Then he waited.

Twenty minutes later, he saw two young men loitering by the rear of the truck, staring at him. Actually they were just staring at the box. One of them reached up and pushed it, testing its weight. Then they left.

Within five minutes they returned with two other young men. The four of them tried to pull the box off the truck. Dave stuck his hand through the rear opening and held on to a metal bar. They struggled and pulled, cursing, as he held on with all his strength. Can't let them get me off the truck, he thought. What would I do then?

Frustrated, two of the young men jumped into the truck to push the box from that level. Luckily there was no room for them to get behind the box and see Dave's arm.

Up in front, Bob felt the jolt when they leaped onto the truck. He slipped out of the cab and ran to the back. The two men on the pavement saw him and ran, but the other two were still inside. Before they could react, Bob slammed the rear door shut on them, locked it, and ran up front again and started driving off.

Dave remained absolutely still inside the box. With the rear door shut, it was too dark to see much through the holes. He felt the truck moving and knew that Bob was driving it to the station house.

"Hey, man," he heard. "You think they're gonna work us over?"

"I dunno, man. We're going to jail, that's for sure."

"Hey, it's dark in here."

Dave relaxed; and decided to have some fun. He moved back and forth, causing the box to rock from side to side.

"What's that?"

"The box! It's moving!"

Dave rolled and tipped the box one way, then another, moaning, "*Ooooooooooooooh.*"

"You hear that, man?"

"Yeah!"

"*Ooooooooooooooh.*"

"What is it?"

"The box! Inside the box! The TV is on!"

They both leaned closer to the box and put their ears up against it.

"Get away from there!" Dave shouted.

The two young men leaped backward and started pounding on the rear door of the truck to get out. All of a sudden the truck stopped.

Bob opened the door and grabbed the two captives before they could jump off. "All right," he told them, "take that box off the truck!" They obeyed, struggling with it. "Be careful!" Bob shouted. "Easy, now!" They set it down on the sidewalk. "Now—open it!"

Dave, unable to stop laughing, stuck his head out.

Dave Greenberg stood on a Broadway sidewalk, in uniform, watching the crowds of theatergoers. He was not looking for stolen cars or for criminal activity. He was trying to spot a pair of young women who would assist him and Bob in their efforts to cut through the red tape of the criminal justice system of the City of New York.

Phase one involved finding two females—not hookers, but reputable young ladies—who could help them eliminate the hardships that developed whenever they were too late for night court. If they made an arrest and it got to be past two in the morning, they would normally have to lodge the prisoners, drive for an hour back to Brooklyn, try to sleep a few hours, and then fight the traffic all the way into Manhattan for court again by eight o'clock. The physical and mental strain was heavy and, besides, if they could speed up the process, everybody would benefit—not only the court staff and the prisoners themselves, but also the public, because policemen were not much good if they had to be off the street. At any rate, if they did happen to miss night court, how much better it would be if they had somewhere to sleep right near the courthouse! Rather than rent an apartment, why not find a couple of women with a place close by?

They had decided to spend two or three nights, on duty, "apartment hunting," as Dave referred to it. In other words, looking for the right pair of young ladies. Bob's post was on Broadway, below Fiftieth Street, and Dave's corner was a few blocks farther uptown. They planned to compare notes at the end of their tour at midnight.

Around nine o'clock, as Dave was heading across Broadway toward the east side on Fifty-third Street, he spotted two blond girls stepping off the opposite curb.

"Excuse me," he said, gently taking their arms and leading them back to the sidewalk. "The sign over there says 'Don't Walk'—so I'm afraid I'll have to give you both summonses for jaywalking."

He took out his memo book and pretended to write out summonses for them. "Names, please?"

"Karen Weitz and Sheila Rennie, but *wait* a minute!"

"Where do you live?"

They gave their addresses, both downtown and near the Police Academy building. Dave turned on the charm, making it more and more obvious that he had stopped them only in order to chat. Smiling now, they relaxed and said that yes, they lived in separate apartments and worked as secretaries and were, at the moment, going to see a movie.

"Well, listen," Dave said, "I have a friend who's also a cop, a real dynamite guy, and maybe the four of us could get together afterward, you know? We're in the safety unit right over on Forty-seventh Street, and we get off at midnight. Why don't you meet us there at twelve thirty?"

Karen and Sheila were uncertain. They each had to be at work in the morning, and twelve thirty was awfully late to be going out with two men, one of whom they hadn't even met. But Dave said that he had a special reason for asking them to meet him and Bob right away and that it had to do with an "important assignment" they were on. Intrigued, and no doubt flattered as well, they promised to show up at Safety Unit B at half past midnight.

It turned out that Bob had also met two young women. When he and Dave got together in the station house, Bob said, "Okay! We're all set! I have it fixed so we can stay up in the East Seventies, but there's still a few manipulations to be done. Like the chicks don't even know my name yet. And we'll have to overcome their looks."

Dave broke in to announce that he, too, had been successful, but that the girls he'd met happened to live closer to the Manhattan courthouse. "They're kind of dumb," he added, "and I guess we'll have to overcome *their* looks, too. As far as location goes, though, we're in luck. So why don't we hold your two in reserve, in case my two don't work out?"

They changed out of their uniforms and went outside to wait for the girls.

Arrangements for living quarters near the courthouse were made over the next three days. For both Karen and Sheila, life suddenly became more exciting than it had been. Dave and Bob took them out to various bars and restaurants in the city, spinning yarns about their police work. Dave was especially good at describing the occupational hazards involved in his job, but he never admitted that he was just a rookie traffic cop who happened to be dedicated. "Well," Karen asked him at one point, "what were you doing on Broadway, in a uniform?" Dave replied that, of course, he was an undercover agent, working on a secret case.

"And," he added, "the best way to make observations is to stand there in a uniform, because nobody pays attention to you."

That, he said, was the "special reason" he had mentioned. Both he and Bob needed places to stay in Manhattan, so they could be close to their work. Karen lived around the corner and across the street from the Police Academy, and Sheila's apartment was just a few blocks farther away.

The only real trouble occurred when the two girls compared notes. Sheila reported that while Bob also wasn't owning up to being a mere traffic cop, he had implied an entirely different explanation. The next night, Dave walked into Karen's apartment and found her quite upset. He had to spend several hours convincing her that no, he wasn't a con artist, it was just that he and Bob had highly sensitive jobs that required them to be anonymous and, at times, ambiguous.

Since Sheila was under a great deal of pressure from home to find a husband, she was ready to believe almost anything. "Look," Bob told her, "Dave and I are involved in something. Now, we don't do this with too many people, so you'll have to swear you won't tell anybody."

"Okay, but can you give me any idea what it is?"

"No, I can't. No questions and we're fine. Start asking questions and we'll have to end it."

Dave, more outgoing in "revealing" his identity to Karen,

continued to drop hints that he was either a detective or a secret agent. One time he casually mentioned that the President's plane was flying in, so he couldn't spend the night.

Phase one was accomplished. Whenever they got done at two in the morning, Bob could go to Sheila's apartment and Dave to Karen's, and they would have six hours of rest. Now they could go on with their plan to speed up the procedures following their arrests.

On Broadway, at about ten o'clock at night, they came up with another stolen car with three prisoners. Dave put handcuffs on them and said, "I'll stay here. You go ahead and begin phase two."

Bob went down the block to a sidewalk phone booth and placed a call to the Fourteenth Precinct station house.

"Listen," Bob said when the desk officer answered, "this is Grumpernick of S.U.B."

"Who? Where?"

"Grumpernick! S.U.B.!"

"Yessir!"

"Look," Bob went on, "I'm at a high-level meeting right now!"

"High-level meeting?"

"Right. And I understand that two of my men have just made an arrest in your precinct, on their way to this meeting!"

"Oh!"

"It's imperative that these two men be at this meeting right now! Chief Inspector Breadchop is waiting for them!"

"I see, sir. Uh, where are your men right now?"

"Forty-third Street and Broadway," he said. "And I want them at this meeting on the double!"

"Yes, sir. Uh, where do I call for verification of this?"

"*Verification?* Of what? Are you questioning my authority?"

"No, no, sir. Uh, just a minute, sir."

Bob listened to the confusion at the other end of the line.

"Uh, Lieutenant?" the desk officer was saying. "I have something on the phone, here, from S.U.B."

"S.O.B.?"

"No—S.*U*.B."

"Well, who is he and what is he doing?"

"He's at a high-level meeting!"

"Where? Omaha Beach?"

"I don't know!"

"Well, do what he says! Give him whatever he wants!"

The desk officer came back on the line. "Sir?"

"Yeah," Bob said. "What's the trouble?"

"Uh, never mind, sir. It's all gonna be taken care of. We'll get your men in here and have 'em out as fast as we can."

"Good," Bob answered.

He hung up, smiling and shaking his head.

Siren blaring and red light flashing, a radio car came around the corner and stopped in front of Dave and Bob and the three men in handcuffs. The officers moved quickly to take the three prisoners. Dave got into the stolen car with Bob.

"Now," Dave said as he drove, "we'll find out what happens in phase three."

He parked in front of the Fourteenth Precinct headquarters and they both hopped from the car. At the door of the building, several officers, including the lieutenant and the captain, were waiting for them.

"Good evening," Bob said.

"You're wanted at a meeting," the lieutenant replied. "We have everything ready to get you through this, a.s.a.p."

Two officers were sitting at desks, ready to type out the details of the arrest. Dave and Bob made their separate statements quickly, the typists furiously trying to keep pace. The detectives, meanwhile, had the fingerprint cards all laid out for the prisoners. The desk officer said he was taking no more work until he could do the booking. Instead of calling a wagon to bring the prisoners down to court, they would have radio cars outside, waiting to do that job.

"Excuse me," said the lieutenant. "Where did you men say you work out of?"

"Safety Unit B," Dave answered. "We're traffic cops, still on probation."

"And you made an arrest?"

"Looks that way, doesn't it?"

The lieutenant nodded. "You *are* the two men who have the high-level meeting to get to, right?"

"That's what we're told," Dave said.

Now the lieutenant walked away, mumbling to himself. Dave and Bob finished dictating and went to sign some papers. The lieutenant came back.

"Excuse me again," he said. "Do you men work for Internal Affairs? Is that it?"

"Sorry," Dave shot back. "We can't answer that."

Now everything was finished, and they were ready to leave for the courthouse. Instead of three or four hours, it had all taken only thirty-five minutes. Record timing.

On their way out, Dave called to the desk officer. "Hey, we'd appreciate it if you'd notify the photo lab that we're on our way down there! Speed is essential!"

The desk officer nodded. The lieutenant, standing by the door to see them out, by now had determined, apparently, that they were more than just traffic cops on probation.

"Don't worry," he was saying. "We'll take care of it."

"Thanks," Dave said as they headed toward the door.

"Yes, *sir,*" the lieutenant replied.

"See ya."

"Yes, *sir,*" the lieutenant repeated.

Then he saluted.

Startled, Dave and Bob saluted him in return.

The lieutenant grinned.

They grinned, too.

He winked.

They winked back.

They got into one of the radio cars and rode in style to the courthouse, delighted with the way things were working. The bureaucratic machinery—normally a slow-motion movie—had been speeded up all of a sudden for their sake.

A man from the Bureau of Criminal Identification was waiting for them at the photo lab. The prisoners had already been taken in and photographed. In less than half an hour they were in the complaint room.

Dave walked up to an assistant district attorney and said, "I'm Greenberg. We've got something that has to be taken care of."

The A.D.A. was busy. "You have a number?"

"What?"

"Do you have a number? You have to get a number and wait your turn."

"Hey, Bob—come here! Do you wanna hear what this guy just said to me?"

"What'd he say?"

"He said do I have a *number!*"

"No kidding. He said that?"

Dave turned to the A.D.A. again. "What's *your* number?"

"I haven't got a number."

"Well, neither do we," Dave said.

"But you're supposed to!"

"Hey," Dave shot back. "Didn't anyone call you and say that we were coming here?"

"No."

"Fair enough. Do me a favor—call the Fourteenth Precinct."

The A.D.A. got on the telephone and spoke to the desk officer and then to the lieutenant who had saluted Dave and Bob. "Lieutenant, do you know anything about these two officers, Greenberg and Hantz? . . . Oh, I see . . . Okay, fine . . . Will do." He hung up the phone with an apologetic look on his face. "Sorry about the mixup," he said. "I'll take you guys right away."

The A.D.A. interrupted his work with another pair of officers to handle the paperwork for Dave and Bob. The dictating and typing took less than ten minutes. As they walked downstairs to the courtroom, Dave realized that he and Bob were in the night session for the first time. But there were still about twenty-five cases ahead of them. Suddenly they heard their names being called for the arraignment. Minutes later, they were on their way out of the building, finished for the night. On a chart, what they had accomplished would have looked like this:

BEFORE	NOW
Arrest: 10 P.M.	Arrest: 10 P.M.
Procedures at the precinct: 3½ hours	Procedures at the precinct: 35 minutes
Time: 1:30 A.M.	Time: 10:35 P.M.
Courthouse paperwork: 1½ hours	Courthouse paperwork: 25 minutes

Time: 3 A.M. (too late
  for night court)

Traveling home, sleeping,
  returning to court:
  5 hours

Court Procedures: up to
four hours

Time: 12 noon (the next day)

Total hours spent: 14

Time: 11 P.M.
Court procedures:
  30 minutes

Time: 11:30 P.M. (the same
  night as arrest)

Total hours spent: 1½

What had required from twelve to twenty-four hours on previous occasions had taken, this time, just an hour and a half.

The more Bob thought about it, the more he felt that he and Dave had demonstrated one of the major weaknesses in the police bureaucracy. People who worked at so many of those jobs were accustomed to doing only as much as they had to do. They were lazy, with no reason to work faster. They were going to get the same salaries, and get out at the same time, whether they moved slow or fast. So why work hard? Well, Bob thought, we proved that the process *can* be speeded up. People need motivation, that's all. And we provided it—by making them believe that we had the authority behind us.

Lining up for roll call the next afternoon, Dave realized that he and Bob were getting weird stares from the other cops. It seemed that someone from the Fourteenth Precinct had called up Safety Unit B to warn everyone that two traffic cops named Greenberg and Hantz were not really rookies at all but, in fact, a couple of "bosses" in disguise. As they were leaving in uniform to go outside, another probationary patrolman came up to them and said, "Uh, sirs?"

"Yeah?"

"Sir, I have a problem with my hours and, uh, I wonder if you can help me out."

"Put it in writing," Bob said. "We'll see what we can do."

They went off toward their posts, laughing and telling each other that they must have conned the whole world.

"But listen," Bob said, "I don't think we can pull that stunt in the Fourteenth Precinct again. We'd better try another precinct next time."

They decided to make the next collar in the Eighteenth Precinct, whose headquarters was on Fifty-fourth Street. Dave and Bob wandered slowly up Eighth Avenue, but found nothing to get involved in. They took their traffic posts for the next few hours and then met each other to continue surveillance. A short while later Dave's sixth sense landed them another stolen car. By now he had lost count of the number of arrests they had made—somewhere between thirty and forty individual prisoners.

This time there were two young men who had stolen a pale-blue Mustang. Bob held the prisoners while Dave went to call the Eighteenth Precinct. Without identifying himself over the phone, he informed the desk officer that "two bosses" had just made an arrest while on a "special investigation." He gave the location and hung up.

Within a few minutes, five radio cars responded to the scene. The sergeant in the lead car got out and greeted them—but he seemed confused. He looked at them, at their new uniforms and shields (Dave was wearing No. 27306 and Bob had No. 27318), which were only twelve digits apart. "Has anyone *else* made an arrest here?" he asked.

"I don't think so," Dave said.

"Well, are you two guys *covering* this arrest for someone else?"

"Nope."

"What are your names?"

"Probationary Patrolman Greenberg and Probationary Patrolman Hantz."

The sergeant said nothing more for a full minute. Then, like the lieutenant the night before, he apparently decided that they were two high-level bosses posing as rookies. "Well," he said, "we'll bring in the prisoners for you, sir."

"Hey," Dave replied. "Drop the 'sir' shit, for now."

"Yes, sir."

"Drop it," Dave said. "Relax, okay?"

He stared meaningfully into the sergeant's eyes, trying to convey the impression that yes, he and Bob were not really probationary cops but that they wanted to make sure no one else caught on.

"I got it," the sergeant said. "Got it!"

"Then let's go."

The procedures went swiftly once again, this time at the Eighteenth Precinct station house. The same assistant district attorney was on hand in the courthouse. When he saw them walk in with two more grand larceny auto arrests, any suspicion from the night before was wiped away. Now he, too, was positive that Dave and Bob were special cops, probably investigating a ring of automobile thieves. And if high brass was involved, then other cops had to be suspected as part of the ring. It followed that the Police Commissioner's men, and the district attorney's office, were conducting the investigation. The A.D.A. in the courthouse had to figure that Dave and Bob were agents of his own superiors.

"Is there anything special you'd like me to write?" he asked at one point.

"No," Dave said. "Go ahead—you did fine last night, so just do the same thing again."

"Fine, fine."

Then they went downstairs to the courtroom, where the arraignment took place as speedily as it had the night before. In all, the arrest procedures took an hour and twenty minutes. They had cut ten minutes off the time of the previous night.

As they were leaving the courthouse, an officer from the Eighteenth Precinct greeted them and announced that he had orders to escort them back to their command.

Dave gulped. Which command was this guy talking about? Internal Affairs? The Commissioner's office?

"Where'd you like to go?" the officer said.

"Where were you told to take us?"

"Well," the officer said, looking confused, "I was told by the lieutenant to take you to S.U.B." The officer paused; obviously he hadn't figured out yet what S.U.B. stood for. "Then the *sergeant* told me to take you to the traffic precinct up on Forty-seventh Street."

Dave and Bob tried not to laugh out loud.

"The lieutenant was right," Dave said. "Take us down to headquarters."

On the way, Bob figured that this turn of events could create problems for them. If the officer followed them inside, he might find out in a hurry that they weren't really bosses. For one thing, they'd have nowhere to go once they got inside the building.

"Okay," Bob said when they pulled up in front of the headquarters. "Thanks for the ride."

They got out and started up the concrete stairs toward the front door. Coming out of the building was either a deputy inspector or a full inspector. The officer in the car was still watching, and he would see them salute. Dave and Bob held back and waited for the security cop at the door to salute the inspector. Then they returned the salute, making it appear to the officer behind them in the car that the security cop had saluted them as a greeting. And when the inspector came out the door, it looked as if he, too, was saluting them. The officer in the car drove away, convinced he had just given a ride to some very important superiors.

They repeated their speed-up techniques in the Thirteenth and Seventeenth Precincts, and then they went back to the Fourteenth again. Eventually there was no need to call ahead to alert everyone; it was just assumed that Greenberg and Hantz were more than what they appeared to be. For as long as they were able to get away with it, the speed-up enabled them to complete their work each night and, therefore, to double the number of arrests per week. Instead of two or three, they could make at least five.

Then one afternoon, reporting for duty at Safety Unit B, they were told that Captain Safron wanted to see them. One look at his face told them there was trouble.

"Listen," the captain said, "something's fishy about you guys. I've been looking at the log, at the diary, and from what I can tell, you guys are making arrests and going through booking procedures and court procedures in record time. And, uh, I've been told that people are saluting you, and calling you 'sir' and, uh—is there anything you'd like to tell me?"

"No, Captain," Bob said. "We're just doing what you asked us to do."

"Well, I want to know how you're doing it."

Bob hesitated, glancing at Dave. "We're just doing the job as best we can."

"Okay, okay," Safron said. "Now I know how I should go

about this, but let me say that I've got a problem with the two of you. The trouble is, in spite of my suspicions about what's been going on, I feel you've been doing good work. So I'm not sure how I want to tell you the problem. I want you to understand it the right way."

Safron paused.

"Here goes," the captain went on. "I received a letter stating that you guys are overzealous."

"What?"

"Overzealous. Off the record, the F.B.I. informed us that you'd blown a top-level investigation. I looked into it myself, and it seems that the investigation you'd blown wasn't really blown. What really happened was that you disposed of something they'd been trying to do for six months. You guys took care of it in one night!"

He was referring to the narcotics arrests they had made in the East Village. Federal and state officials had been trying to catch the same men for a long time, hoping to get information from them that would lead to a much larger arrest. Dave and Bob had done the job for them, making it possible for the prisoners to have been interviewed in jail.

"In other words," Dave said, "we embarrassed the F.B.I."

Safron looked down at the blotter on his desk with a pained expression. Ignoring Dave's comment, he reminded them of the possible repercussions involved in making off-duty narcotics arrests. Superior officers might conclude that Dave and Bob were trying to shake down junkies for money. Maybe the pushers they had locked up were the ones who had refused to pay. No such accusations had been made, but anything was possible. If two young rookies were creating controversy or making waves or causing embarrassment, they could be gotten rid of quite easily. It didn't take anything but the slightest suspicion to get you thrown off the job when you were on probation.

"I'm telling you all this for your own good," the captain told them. "You guys are traffic cops. You're not supposed to be out headhunting while you're off duty. I want you to go back to directing traffic and issuing summonses."

"But—"

"Don't argue with me, boys. I know you're enthusiastic about doing a good job, but I'm giving it to you straight. Stop making waves. Just do what you're assigned to do. Have patience."

Captain Safron had looked up at them as he finished talking. Now he looked down again and coughed.

Dave and Bob stood there a few moments in silence and then they left.

7

Out on the sidewalk, they turned to look at each other.

"Overzealous," Bob said.

"Shit!"

There was nothing more to say. Dave hadn't cried for fifteen years, but right now he could feel his eyes burning and filling up with water. Rather than being reprimanded or told to stop trying, he thought, we should have been encouraged. Even if we *had* screwed up a little—which we didn't—someone should have tried to help us! If we already have the incentive, why not give us the means to use it?

Well, they were making waves. And the captain was right—they could be gotten rid of very easily. It wasn't his fault, though. It was too much to expect Safron to stand up to the system and try to fight it for their sake. He was another spoke in the wheel; when the wheel turned, he went with it. The message was clear: Go back to directing traffic and stop being an individual.

Rather than go home, Dave called Irene and said he was staying in Manhattan for the next few nights. He gave her an excuse instead of going into the whole story. For the moment he wanted to forget everything.

He and Bob decided to use up some of the overtime they had accumulated. They went back to Karen and Sheila, spending two nights in the separate apartments. During the third day, when the girls were on the phone with each other, Dave asked to speak to Bob.

"Where are you at?" he asked.

"Ready to go to work," Bob said.

"Same here. Listen, they only kicked us once. But there's two of us, and if we kick back, you know, they're gonna fall harder than we did."

"No question about it."

"See you this afternoon," Dave told him, handing the phone to Karen and heading for the shower. He would probably see her a few more times, but that was all.

He and Bob met at a bar in Manhattan that day and talked for more than nine hours, rebuilding their resolve to keep doing what they felt was right—to keep "playing it to a bust."

When they finally showed up at the traffic command after five days, they went up to the captain's office. Safron seemed to be expecting them.

"Okay, Leo," Dave said. "Here's where we are, like it or not. We don't want to jeopardize your career or anything. We respect you—not as much as we did before—but we still respect you to an extent. But we're telling you, right now, to get out of our way."

Safron had been a cop in supervisory positions for more than twenty years, and he had been successful in dealing with all sorts of men. He had seen attitudes like this before—not as intense, perhaps, but similar.

"Somehow or other," he replied, "I had a feeling that you two would react this way. So I've already made plans. You're going to see the inspector in charge of the First Safety District at nine o'clock tomorrow morning. Don't do anything rash, fellas. In fact, don't do *anything* until then."

The next morning they went to the office of Inspector Thomas Heffernan, who appeared delighted to see them. Heffernan spent most of the morning recounting stories he had heard about their activities—with narcotics, making off-duty arrests; in the garment district; on traffic duty, nabbing people in stolen cars. He even hinted that he was aware of the bluffing they had done at the precincts and in the Manhattan courthouse. He said he respected them for their ingenuity and enthusiasm.

"Listen, fellas," he went on, "what do you want from me? How about plainclothes?"

Dave leaned forward, incredulous. "Do you think it's *possible* to put us in plainclothes? I mean, we're still on probation. We're still inside the Academy, so to speak."

The inspector smiled. "You know something, I'm glad you said that. You know, you're right. Listen, plainclothes isn't good enough for you guys. I'm gonna have you made detectives."

Dave and Bob were speechless.

"Don't do anything," Heffernan continued. "I'm setting up an appointment for you with a very close friend of mine who's in charge of the Bureau of Special Services."

It sounded too good to be true. The Bureau of Special Services, otherwise known as Bossy, was an elite group within the Police Department. Its men acted as bodyguards for high officials and dignitaries and did investigations of labor groups and political organizations of all kinds. Bossy agents infiltrated such groups as the Black Panthers and the Students for a Democratic Society to monitor their activities. Maybe even organized crime is involved, Dave thought. If we've ever had an opportunity, this is it!

They agreed not to do anything until their interview with Bossy, and for the next two days both Dave and Bob could hardly contain their excitement. Then, sure enough, a call came from the office of Inspector Knapp, head of Bossy.

"The inspector would like to see you two very much," an officer said. "He wants to interview you both."

An appointment was made for ten days later. They went out to their posts and directed traffic, doing just what they were supposed to do, passing the time.

When they showed up for the interview, Dave got his first clue that something was wrong. He and Bob would not be questioned together, as partners, but separately, one after the other. Dave went in first. Inspector Knapp greeted him and, after a few pleasantries, came to the point: "If you were assigned here, would you work alone?"

"Without Hantz?"

"Yes. Would that be all right with you?"

"No, sir."

"Well, what if you *can't* work together? I mean, what if you're assigned to Bossy and your partner doesn't make it? How would you feel about that?"

Dave was noncommittal. What was the point? Was his friendship with Bob being tested? Why do they want to split us up? Have we become too powerful in some way? Does the Department want to get us apart to reduce that power?

He left the interview uncertain of everything. While Bob went in, he talked to some people in the outer office who told him not to worry, that they would probably be made undercover agents by the end of the week.

When Bob came out, he was shaking his head. He had been subjected to the same line of questioning. Would he jump at the chance for a promotion at the expense of his sidekick? Well, Dave thought, we squelched that idea fast enough.

But maybe there was even more to the test. Maybe their determination to stay together only confirmed the worst suspicions—that they had teamed up as cops to shake down junkies. How could you fight those suspicions? On the other hand, hadn't they been told they were becoming detectives within a week? There weren't any clear answers.

They wound up telling everyone at the traffic command that they were being promoted. The news caused a bit of confusion, because so many of the men thought they already were high up in rank. Others were cynical, feeling that Dave and Bob probably had contracts set up, or hooks in, for their advancement.

Friday came and went without a word from the inspector. They let another day go by, then another, and then Dave decided to call up the Bossy office.

"We were expecting to hear from someone," he said on the phone.

"Greenberg and Hantz? Oh, yes. Well, something came up, and it'll be a while, I think, until—"

"Is it all right if we come back and speak to the inspector?"

"Well, the inspector's busy and I don't know, uh, so why don't you call back tomorrow?"

The next day they called back and were told to wait another day. They did so and the reply was, "How about calling back Friday?"

On Friday they were put through to the inspector himself, who explained that there were too many men in Bossy at the moment. "We're cutting down in numbers," he went on. "But we'll get in touch with you. Don't call me again. I'll be back to you."

That was the end of it. Dave slammed down the phone.

Their worst mistake, Dave figured, was that he and Bob had agreed to hold back and do nothing. They had been conned or misled or tested or bullshitted, and they had fallen for it. They had gone for more than three weeks without making an arrest of any sort. The mistake was to have depended upon anyone else but themselves.

Well, he thought, we'll have our revenge. He vowed that as soon as they got together again, they would make an arrest of some kind and do it all by themselves, do it absolutely right, and just see if anybody could pull it apart. The hell with them all, he thought. We've wasted enough time, and if they want to suppress us they'll have to do it on *our* terms, not theirs.

Dave went home that night with his mind made up that he and Bob would virtually make war against the forces holding them down. When he stepped outside his building the following morning, he saw a new Mustang parked across the street. The young white man at the wheel looked nervous. Dave walked over and flashed his shield. "Let me see your license and registration."

The young man had neither. It was a friend's car, he said. Dave's sixth sense told him otherwise, but there was no way to check out the car right now. No police radio and, besides, Dave was alone. So he wrote down the young man's name, Robert Calvano, and his address—a house in an upper-income neighborhood of Brooklyn, the Sixty-ninth Precinct—and let him go.

He and Bob got together that afternoon and ran a check on the Mustang through police records. The car had been reported stolen.

"Let's go get him tonight," Dave said.

"It's risky," Bob said.

"I know."

To begin with, a search warrant was probably necessary; neither Dave nor Bob knew for sure. And weren't they supposed to turn this arrest over to the detective squad? Was that a law, or was it just a tradition? Then, too, they had agreed to stop making off-duty arrests. But what had they gotten in return?

"Well," Dave said, "we've already created waves, just going out of our way to do a job! Well, if waves are gonna be made by what we do, and if we're *right* in what we're doing, then everyone else better learn how to swim!"

They went to Safety Unit B and directed traffic from four to midnight. Afterward, they rode back to Brooklyn in Dave's car. At two in the morning, off duty, they pulled up in front of the house where Robert Calvano lived. The Mustang was in the driveway.

They knocked on the door. A young woman finally answered. She opened the door halfway. "Yes?"

Bob spoke up. "Is Robert home?"

"Yes—but he's asleep."

"We're police officers. We have to see him."

"Oh! Well, I'll get him."

They stepped inside and waited. Robert Calvano, who was no older than seventeen, came down the stairs in his pajamas.

"You're under arrest," Dave said. "For stealing a car."

"Get dressed," Bob said.

They followed him to make sure he tried nothing foolish. The mother and father were not at home. Both Dave and Bob were probably more nervous about the whole ordeal than the young man; they knew that what they were doing was entirely unorthodox, even if basically correct. They were relieved to get Robert Calvano out of that house.

Dave took the prisoner in his car, and Bob followed in the Mustang. They got to the Sixty-ninth Precinct house, fully prepared to handle this arrest with cooperation from no one. Dave was determined to bring Calvano to court, with or without his being booked.

Officers in the station house immediately started in with their questions:

"Why didn't you arrest him when you first saw him?"

"Fuck you," Dave said.

"How did you know the car was stolen?"

"Fuck you."

"Why did you stop him to begin with?"

"Fuck you."

"How come you didn't get the detectives to go in there and get him, if you had this information?"

"Fuck you!" Dave roared.

He and Bob went through the proper procedures for the arrest without once answering a question unless it was absolutely necessary for what they were doing. At one point a detective told them they had erred completely. Not that the arrest was invalid; it was just unusual for two off-duty patrolmen to have done such a thing.

"*So what?*" Dave told him. "We're not buying your side, man! You've been a cop *longer* than me, so you're telling me what to do? You got a higher rank than me, and *for that reason only* you know more than anyone else? Give us constructive criticism, man! *Then* we might listen! But don't come on with this thing about the way it's *been* done. Don't tell us something just for the sake of tradition, Charlie! Forget it!"

As he was talking, he noticed that a few of the younger officers on hand were nodding in agreement. But for the most part, Dave and Bob left the station house with a score of new enemies.

The word was out that Greenberg and Hantz had gone back to being themselves—although considerable debate still existed as to just exactly what that was. Dave's resentment hadn't lessened, however; he was simply determined to keep pushing, with Bob, until someone had the nerve to either throw them off the job or give them the go-ahead to accomplish the work they were capable of doing.

In the mailbox at Safety Unit B they found a message to call Inspector Heffernan of the First Safety District for an appointment. He wanted to see them again.

"Well," Dave said, "it's too bad about the inspector. It's time to take some more holidays that we have coming to us. If Heffernan really wants to see us so badly, why didn't he leave a message telling us to report to his office right away? What is this nonsense about *calling* for an appointment? Set up something for *ten days from now?* and do *nothing* again, between now and then? Bullshit!"

Moreover, it wouldn't be long before they would have to go back to the Academy for additional classes before graduation and assignments to precincts as full-fledged patrolmen. All their efforts to learn, to gain experience, to become good at the job, had come to nothing. They had been accused of being "overzealous" and, instead of encouragement, they had received warnings about suspicions that they were crooks. They had been tempted with promotions at the price of being split up. They had been told to stop initiating arrests, to just go along and in effect be swallowed up in a system that not only encouraged mediocrity but almost demanded it.

Later that afternoon, through a female acquaintance in the personnel office of the Academy, Dave found out that he and Bob were being assigned to different precincts, the Sixty-third and the Sixty-ninth. So they were being split up after all.

The next day there was another message from Inspector Heffernan's office. This time it said to go see him as soon as possible. They went right over, and Heffernan greeted them expansively.

"I'd like to do something for you guys," he said. "But first I should tell you that you're in line for citations."

They were eligible for about fifteen citations apiece, the inspector said. They had made between forty and fifty arrests altogether, and it was time they received the proper recognition. As Dave listened, it dawned on him that maybe Heffernan was giving him and Bob the means to avoid repercussions. How can the Department give us citations and then dismiss us for the same work?

"The second thing," Heffernan was saying, "is that I'd just like to do what I can for you both. Is there anything you'd like?"

"Well," Dave said, "we want to work together, in the same precinct."

"Uh-huh."

"But listen," Dave continued, "we only want you to try to arrange it if you don't think it's beyond your authority."

Now, Dave thought, we're even with him saying he could make us detectives without really being able to do it. Unless you can do it this time, baby, keep your mouth shut and we'll work it out by ourselves.

"Fair enough," the inspector said. "The only way I can arrange for you to be together is if we put you in a high-crime area. The Twenty-fourth Precinct, for example. Or the two-five, the two-seven, the seven-seven, the seven-nine . . ."

Heffernan went through the numbers of all the precincts in high-crime areas, and Dave picked out the one he could remember most easily. "How about the seven-seven?"

The inspector paused. "Do you two know where that is?"

"Of course," Dave said.

"Sure," Bob agreed, although neither of them had any idea where the Seventy-seventh Precinct was, nor did they care.

"Well," Heffernan said, "I'm not certain exactly where you'll be going, but I do guarantee that you can be together. And it'll be high-crime, that's for sure."

They were in a coffee shop near the corner of Forty-second Street and Eighth Avenue, taking a short break from their traffic posts. "We got a helluva lot to learn about everything," Dave was saying. "Drugs, blacks, slums—everything. If we're gonna work in a high-crime area, and if that means strictly black slums, I want to know what it's like to *be* black, to *be* a junkie, to *be* down and out."

Bob nodded. "Not just look into someone's eyes and see what's there, but look out of that person's eyes."

"Right, man. I don't want to become one of the best cops in just certain circumstances. I want to be able to go *anywhere* in this city and do a professional job. I don't want to be considered the guy that's white in a black neighborhood and not knowing what he's doing. Or have anyone say, 'That guy shouldn't be here, he doesn't know what's coming down.' You know?"

As they sat there talking, Dave realized that it had to be one of the oddest conversations between any two traffic cops in Manhattan or anywhere. It pleased him to think that not only were they perhaps exceptional in terms of potential, but that their determination was uncommonly strong. He knew that Bob shared his own drive to involve himself totally in whatever he set out to do. That same commitment was also the foundation for their friendship—all or nothing, no compromises—and for their relationship with the Police Department.

Bob was making a point, but suddenly Dave's attention was drawn toward a black face staring at him. The face, which reminded him of some of the prostitutes he had seen in Times Square and other sections, belonged to the waitress who had served them. She was heavily made up, wearing a wig, and she was thin, but well packed in the right places. She must have one of the biggest asses in the entire world, Dave thought; an ass that's had more action than a hundred others put together; an ass belonging to a chick who comes from some hell I've never seen.

He was staring back at her. Bob had stopped talking. Dave searched the woman's eyes to get some understanding of the feeling that she was pouring back at him. Hatred? Bitterness? He had never really tried to get inside a black person's head in this way, no doubt because he had never wanted to until now. This was different than it had been with his black friends in Coney Island; this was a kind of leap out of himself, and although it unnerved him, he went with it because it was exactly what he and Bob wanted.

This chick is seeing a white man and a cop, he thought, and all I'm seeing is black. He motioned for her to come over to their table.

"What are you staring at?" he said.

"You the one that's staring."

"Maybe I like what I see," he said. "I was just telling him that if I'm gonna work in a black neighborhood, I ought to know what's coming down, right? And he said the same thing."

"Yeah?"

"Yeah."

He kept the conversation going, flirting with her and, at the same time, getting across the message that he was different from other cops. He told her that he was going to be transferred soon to Harlem or someplace like that, and he said he realized how much there was to learn. He didn't want to go around cracking heads or shooting people, and he wished there was someone who could give him a crash course in the best way for a cop to behave and react in the ghetto.

She seemed to believe him. She was either flattered or intrigued or both. He was telling her something she probably never had heard from a white man, especially a cop in uniform. He said he was off duty tomorrow. What time did she get out of work?

"Early shift," she said. "I'm done at three."

He had no idea where this would lead, but the only way to learn anything was to start something rolling and go with it.

Dave was off duty when he went back to the coffee shop the next day. He knew she would be surprised to see him, and she was.

When she saw him come through the door and take a seat at the counter, she smiled and said she'd be with him in a few minutes. Then she disappeared into a back room.

Now, he thought, I'm going to become part of her world, if I can, and live in that world until I can say I've been there and back.

She appeared again wearing slacks and a short red jacket, a pocketbook hanging from her shoulder. He followed her outside and walked her down the block to where he had parked his car. He said he would drive around for a while so they could talk. As she told him about herself, he thought that here was a nice person, intelligent in terms of common sense; but she was from an environment that was far worse than anything he had experienced in Coney Island. At one point he explained that he and Bob would probably wind up spending a lot of their time in black slums, hopefully in narcotics work. By the time he got through explaining his problem, with considerable emotion, she had moved next to him and had put her head on his shoulder as he drove.

"Listen, baby," she said, "when I get through with you, you gonna be the blackest white cop in this country! And if you got any intelligence, and if your partner got any smarts, then when you get through tellin' him what I tell you, you'll be the *two* blackest white cops in the country."

As they rode around and talked, he asked her to repeat herself a lot, because of the ghetto language she slipped into so often. She would rephrase her sentences in order to make Dave understand. At the same time he felt himself moving closer to her way of talking, so she would comprehend him as well.

He could not openly admit that education was his sole reason for spending time with her. It seemed that she hoped his main reason was romantic. So he combined both aspects, becoming emotionally involved with her while trying to learn from her at the same time.

Her name was Mildred. She was a strip-tease dancer, currently unemployed and therefore working as a waitress. She lived on 114th Street, near Amsterdam Avenue, in Harlem.

"Let's get off the street," he said.

"How 'bout a motel?"

"Nah, why not your pad?"

"I don't want you comin' to my place."

"Why not?"

"'Cause a motel is better."

"Hey, baby, you're too good for that motel scene. If I'm digging you, I wanna see where you live, where you hang out."

"You won't like my pad."

"Why not?"

"Bad scene, baby."

"Hey, listen, if *you* can live there, what makes you think *I* won't like it?"

"*'Cause I hate it, man!*"

"Wait a minute. You're living there, right? Whether you like the place or not, that's where you're at, right?"

"Yeah."

"Okay, then. That's where I wanna go. Anything that's good enough for you is good enough for me. If you can handle it, so can I."

She studied his face for a full minute, then said, "You win, baby. I appreciate what you're saying. But you asked for it. I told you so."

"I know," Dave said, heading uptown toward Harlem and wondering just how bad a place it could be.

Much worse than he had thought. He pulled up to 114th Street and into the block. This had to be the dirtiest, most horrible slum area he had seen in his life. The street and the sidewalk and the stoops and the old brownstones themselves looked as if they had been the scene of a battle. The stench from the loose, overflowing garbage and litter filled the air. Too many people crowded into one neighborhood, a kind of frustration suspended. And all the faces—children, young people, men, and women—were black. As a white man, he was alone.

Standing outside Mildred's building were maybe twenty sullen dudes who seemed about to shift their positions and block the way to the door. One was cleaning his nails with a huge push-button blade; another was using a knife to pick his teeth. Mildred sensed Dave's involuntary shudder as they approached the group. She took him by the hand and said, "Nobody fucks with you when you're with me."

The authority in her voice surprised him. He followed her up the filthy stairs of the brownstone flophouse, a building intended for only three or four moderate-sized families that now contained thirty large families. Behind each door was an apartment. One bathroom per floor. By this time, Dave had become accustomed to the smell of the place—resigned to it, was more accurate.

Mildred lived at the top, on the fourth level, in one room near the front. As they entered her room, it occurred to Dave that it wasn't really clean, but neat. Clothing hung on nails all over the walls, because there were no closets.

"How come those dudes down there are afraid of you?" he asked.

She told him about two of her brothers in jail on homicide charges and another one behind bars for armed robbery. The first two brothers were serving life sentences, the other was doing forty years. "And I got a lot of friends," she went on—not just ordinary friends, but men who paid a hundred dollars to go to bed with her and who bought her expensive gifts on occasion.

"Sit down," she told him, and he slowly lowered himself to the edge of the bed. "I wanna show you what I do best," she explained, taking off her clothes. "I made good money at stripping, very good. Baltimore, Chicago, here in New York—but people don't care 'bout strippers no more."

She put on her costume, a three-piece outfit—one piece for each breast and a bottom. Dave leaned back against the wall, seated on the bed, wondering if she was going to shut the door of the room. People were walking back and forth, but she didn't seem to care. She turned on a small radio and waited for the right song and then she started her show for him. The people outside the room were not bothering to look inside.

He watched her, smiling. He was in a room on the top floor of a noisy, crowded, dirty building in Harlem, a lone white man watching a near-naked black woman wiggle and bump for his enjoyment. When the song ended, he said her dancing was fine and she came to him and the door was still open but he took his cue from her that here, in this world, privacy was extinct. He was a rookie cop beginning a course of instruction that no Police Academy could ever give him.

It was dark outside when he woke up, but he saw by his watch on the floor that the time was only ten past eight. Mildred had taken off her wig and her eyelashes and he saw that she was not as attractive as she had seemed.

"Can I take a shower?" he said.

"Huh?"

He felt ridiculous for having asked. "I guess there ain't any showers," he said.

"Yeah, there is. Come with me."

She got up, stark naked, and without putting on any clothes she went out the door. He followed her past some men in the hallway and downstairs to the third floor and into another apartment. They walked through a roomful of people and went into another room where a man and woman were writhing together in bed. The woman looked up at Dave briefly but the man kept right on with his part of the activities, so she joined in again and that was that. Mildred went to a dresser, opened a drawer, and took out a towel and a bar of soap. Dave followed her back upstairs and down the hall to the bathroom, which had hardly any floor.

You had to be a tightrope walker to get around the bathroom without falling through the holes in the floor. When he stepped into the bathtub, it shook and rocked from side to side. He balanced himself carefully before turning on the water. There was no shower curtain, but the water worked okay.

Later he got dressed and they went out to a crowded bar nearby, where Dave was again the only white man. Aware of the stares that were coming his way, he tried not to show his apprehension.

A tall, powerfully built man with a mustache walked over to Mildred, said hello to her, and then turned toward Dave. "What you doin' here, man?"

Before Dave could react, Mildred said, "Listen, nigger, beat it before I cut your heart out!"

The man looked at her with surprise, then turned away and left them alone. They talked for several hours, and every time someone stopped by, she introduced Dave the same way: "Meet my nigger."

Eventually he passed a certain point—it was hard to recall exactly when or how—and he found that he had gone beyond his own color and onto a new level of awareness of himself and of the people around him. He was beginning to look at everything, including the world of which he was normally a part, from another point of view.

Mildred turned to him. "How're you doing?"

"Good. Real good."

She smiled. "There's a long way to go, baby. But if you stick around, I'll make sure you're the blackest white man on the planet."

He laughed and they talked a while longer and then they got up and left the bar and walked through the Harlem streets back to her place in the early morning.

Bob Hantz got a phone call from Dave, who said he'd be spending all his available time up in Harlem. "I'm putting everything into this," Dave said. "Let's take off our vacation time, and the days coming to us—and I'll see you in a week or two."

"Are you going home at all?"

"When I can—but I'm spending as much time with this chick as possible. When I get back we'll sit down and I'll rap the whole thing out to you."

"Be careful, man."

"Don't worry. I'm already a nigger."

When Bob got off the phone, he felt drained. He tried to put everything into focus. His life had been altered irrevocably by his friendship with Dave Greenberg, who became absolutely obsessed with whatever he was going. Together they had made dozens of collars while still on probation; it had been constant working and thinking and learning. Now that it all had stopped, for the time being anyway, he had to fill the void with something.

He spent his time socializing in bars and at parties and with a girl named Sonny, who worked as a fashion model. But all he could think of was the fact that Dave was alone, where the odds were totally against him in any kind of trouble. He could be hurt or killed, Bob thought, and I'm not there to help. Maybe I couldn't do anything even if I was there, but at least I'd be sharing it with him.

It was also painful for Bob to know that Dave was still learning while he was not. At one point he met a black woman named Brenda, and he thought he could learn something from her, but it turned out that she was more interested in being white.

Three weeks went by. He had accomplished nothing. He was angry and worried and frustrated, and he saw in the mirror that his eyes were sunken and his whole face had become drawn and pale. Then Dave called and said he was finished and on his way home to Sheepshead Bay in Brooklyn.

"Meet me there tomorrow," Dave said.

Bob agreed, thankful that his friend was all right. But there was a great deal of catching up to be done. He hoped the gap between them hadn't become insurmountable.

He looked into Dave's eyes and as he listened, tried to absorb the feelings that were being expressed.

"I tell you," Dave was saying, "me and this chick went through an intensive, three-week cram course. She didn't know the relationship was gonna come to an abrupt ending like it did. We were really involved, man. And she kept introducing me as her 'nigger' to all these other black people. 'Meet my nigger,' she'd say. I learned you don't have to be black to be a nigger. And a motherfucker? Nothing unusual there, man. You and I would probably kill somebody for calling us motherfuckers—but that ain't the way it's gonna be, because everybody calls everybody else a motherfucker, and it's just a figure of speech.

"And shacking up? Man, there's shacking up like I never *knew* about. In that kind of a neighborhood, nobody looks down on it. Marriage is zero! A woman takes pride in how many men she's had kids with—no down trip as far as how many kids she has by how many men, providing she knows *who* the men are and *where* they are. It's okay if she can say, 'This is my son, and that's his father,' and 'This is my daughter, and that's her father over there,' and so on. As long as the fathers come around once in a while, fine. They have their own life, their own language—something that unless you really know about, man, you're in a lot of trouble when you become involved in it . . ."

Bob kept listening, not arguing or debating but just taking it all in, trying to relive Dave's own experience.

"If you're white," Dave went on, "it don't matter if you're a good guy or a bad guy, because they'll call you 'whitey' just as a figure of speech. So I got rid of the idea that a black man is calling me 'whitey' because he's mad at me. Just the fact that you're white makes you a whitey. No big deal.

"I spent almost twenty-four hours a day with this chick. Just the place itself—to see a cockroach crawling into the bed I was sleeping in. But through her, I learned not to wince. There was a time when I lay down with my clothes on, and there was a rat chewing on the toes of my shoes. And I almost went through the ceiling. But she told me, man, 'If you're goin' black, go *black*, baby.' See, rats were just a common occurrence. And the chick just kept showing me, step by step. She just became my mother, you could say . . ."

For Bob, the most important goal was to be capable of operating effectively, as a cop, in any situation, anywhere. That meant having everything in his mind before walking into a situation, being in control of himself, and knowing what **the** people in the street were going to do before they even made a move. And so he began to ask questions. Hour after hour, he explored Dave's emotions, picturing himself right there, in Harlem, going through the same situation and learning the same things. They talked all night and into the next day.

"She tried to tell me about 'heart' or 'soul' or whatever," Dave went on. "She said I wouldn't know the meaning of 'heart' while I was with her, but that I'd find out soon enough. I never did totally understand what she was referring to."

It occurred to them both that they might be lacking the most important knowledge of all.

The following afternoon, Dave's phone rang at home and he knew, before even picking it up, that it was Mildred. He had left Harlem unable to tell her the truth—that he'd been using her all the time. He had no intention of going back, and he had begun to feel guilty and upset about what he had done to her. When he picked up the phone and heard Mildred's voice, he was ready for her to start crying and cursing him out. He was fully prepared to apologize and take whatever she wanted to throw at him.

Her tone of voice surprised him. "I know it's over," she said calmly.

"What makes you think that?"

"Well," she answered quietly, "you got everything you can get from me. I knew you'd be leaving all along."

I'm not as good a con man as I figured I was, Dave thought.

"I'm sorry," he said.

"Whatchoo sorry 'bout? You paid me two ways, man—by your company, your friendship, and by the fact that I *know* you're gonna deal with my people with your new attitude and outlook. And I *know* that your partner is gonna do the same. And that gives me all the pleasure I need, man."

Dave was stunned. "Yeah?"

"Sure! Hell, you know what I saw when I looked at you two whiteys? Two ambitious-as-hell guys that most likely were gonna be two maniacs out there with my people! Out there with black folks—causin' riots, killin' black people, bustin' black heads, spillin' black blood! And I *know* you ain't gonna be that way, now. I *know* it, baby. I turned you 'round! And you know what?"

"What's that?"

"I'm *sure,* now, that if any of my people gets hurt because of you and Bob, it'll be because they deserved it, and no other reason! I *know* you guys won't be goin' into a neighborhood just to whip people into place. Anybody gets in your way, you won't beat on 'em—you'll make 'em see the light. You ain't gonna be pigs! And it's 'cause of *me* that you'll have that attitude, so I'm glad of what we did. One black girl who ain't never gonna get outa this hell has done something for her people, and that's me, and I feel good about it."

"So do I," Dave said. "So do I."

"Take care, brother."

"Yeah . . ."

She had hung up. He sat down at the kitchen table and put his head in his hands.

He went to see Bob that night. Told him what Mildred had said. Leaned over his weak drink at the bar and confessed that it wasn't until today that he realized what a beautiful woman she had been. He wanted to tell her in person, to make it up to her somehow.

"Come on, man," Bob suggested, "let's go up there and see her. We'll get something together, okay? Because you're impossible right now."

"Thanks," Dave said. They left the tavern and drove up to Harlem. When they got to 114th Street and Amsterdam Avenue, people were running all over the streets. Dave pulled up next to a squad car and identified himself as a cop. "What's happening?" he asked. The officer said there had been a near-riot just twenty minutes ago. A white cop had shot a sixteen-year-old black kid in this neighborhood, and people had gone wild. The cops had locked up seven or eight of them, and things had cooled off some—but the place was explosive.

"You'd better leave the area if you're not on duty," the officer said.

Dave ignored the advice. He turned in at Mildred's block and parked near her building. Suddenly there were dozens of black faces around the car. Maybe thirty, forty people, yelling at them, pounding on the car, shaking it, rocking it from side to side. Dave and Bob sat tight, waiting for the right moment to make a move.

Suddenly Bob reached across Dave and out the driver's window and grabbed a young man by the hair and pulled his head all the way into the car onto Dave's lap. The young man's feet were off the ground and he was halfway inside the car. Dave put his arm around the young man's neck, took the knife that Bob handed him, and yelled, *"Your brother dies, unless you back off!"*

The crowd backed away from the car. Now, Dave thought, we've got a hostage.

But there was still one young man on the trunk of the car. Bob got out and walked to the back of the car, reached out his hand, and with two fingers grabbed the young man's T-shirt and yanked him off the trunk. The young man fell to the ground, but Bob made no move to kick him or do any more than what was necessary. He reached down and grabbed the young man by the crotch and pulled him along the street, away from the car.

Dave managed to ease his door open while keeping his hold on the hostage. He slipped outside and removed the young man from the window, keeping the knife at his throat. He and Bob with their single captive were immediately surrounded.

"Now," Dave said. "Gentlemen? We're here on a mission of mercy. We have no ideas of any violence whatsoever!"

The spokesman for the group stepped forward, scowling. "What're you selling, man?"

"Hey," Bob said. "Tell me one thing! What *is* all this? *Why,* man?" he asked, looking around at the mob. "What's the *reason* for all this? *Why?*"

The spokesman looked at his friends and they, in turn, looked at each other. No one spoke up.

"We got nothing to sell," Bob went on. "We got nobody to hurt. You're just coming down the wrong way, brother! There's no *reason* for all this nonsense, man! I mean, why? You should find out where we *are,* before you decide where to put us. You know what I mean?"

The spokesman nodded slowly. Here were two whiteys—he had no idea that Dave and Bob were cops—who were not necessarily out to do a number on them. Two white men who were not afraid, who knew how to handle themselves.

"Okay," the leader said. "Want a drink?"

"Sure," Bob replied, taking a can of beer.

"Now cut the brother loose, and do your thing."

"Well, listen," Dave replied, still holding the knife on the young man, "we've become very *attached* to the brother here. What we're doing now is *socializing,* man—and since we're so *attached* to him, we'd like him to socialize *with* us. And we'd consider it a *personal snub,* man, if he wouldn't."

The spokesman relented. "Go ahead."

"We'll be back," Dave told him.

He and Bob took the hostage into the building and climbed up to the fourth floor. The door to Mildred's room was open, as it always had been. Her clothes were gone from the nails on the walls, and she was gone. There was a note on the bed. Dave picked it up and began reading it, first to himself and then aloud to Bob. Scribbled over both sides of the paper, it covered much of the same ground as their telephone conversation.

Reading it for the third time, he began to get the full message. He sat down on the edge of the bed, amazed that Mildred had been so sure he would return to see her once more. "I know you're coming back here," she had written, "but I know that you were with me not because of love, but your job. And the only way to make it easy for us is for me to leave before you get here. If you are ever in Maryland, check the strip joints."

Dave read that part again and gave it to Bob, who had let go of the hostage. The young man had made no move to leave. Dave could not leave either. He thought how clearly she had seen his intentions. Bob handed him the letter and he stuffed it in his pocket.

He shook his head slowly. "We just found out what it means to have heart, man."

They walked downstairs and outside, but still they could not bring themselves to leave. The young men who earlier had surrounded their car were still there; this time, Dave and Bob sat down on the front stoop with them. They drank wine and beer and laughed and got drunk and kept on past midnight, into the early morning hours.

Dave Greenberg sat inside a classroom in the Police Academy building again, Bob Hantz beside him, and now he was even more certain that the only way to learn was out on the street. They had come back after less than eight months with between forty and fifty arrests, and with recommendations for thirteen citations apiece. As far as they knew, not a single other recruit out of more than eight hundred had done anything to receive even one citation.

But that wasn't the point; the point was that experience on the job was the best teacher of all, provided you could devise ways to get around or through the web of rules and regulations and procedures and traditions that conspired to drain you of any motivation you might have had when you started.

"I don't think the Academy relates at all to what's really happening," Dave said one evening after class. "I think it's a myth! It's a waste of time! If they taught you what was really happening, they would circumvent the fact that you had to go out in the street and *disprove* what they had told you and then learn all *over* again, by yourself. If they gave you the truth in the beginning, you'd save about six months of wear and tear and probably stop a lot of incidents that occur on the street in the first six months that a guy is a cop because he doesn't know how to handle himself."

He and Bob had judged themselves. After every action they had taken, they had sat down and gone over it, moment by moment, to see how they might have done better. They had gone out of their way to gain experience and, at the same time, they had acted as their own severest critics. The only criticism they could not stand was the kind that grew out of jealousy or resentment or tradition or fear or bureaucracy or any other force unrelated to what they had done.

What made Dave angry at the Academy was not just that he and Bob had disproved a lot of the instruction, but that they were so eager to learn more. Having had a strong taste of the street, it was almost unbearable to spend these last two weeks away from the places where they had learned so much.

Near the end of the two weeks there was a ceremony at which awards were given out. The trophies—off-duty pistols—were for various achievements including the "outstanding arrest" made by a student. For some reason, neither Dave nor Bob had been told to apply for any of the awards. Whether it had been deliberate or just convenient not to tell them about signing up for the trophies was a matter of conjecture.

Then came the day when assignments were given. The instructor read off a list of last names and precincts, in alphabetical order. Each rookie was being sent to a different command, until the names of Greenberg and Hantz came up, one after the other: "Greenberg, the seven-seven; Hantz, the seven-seven."

"Sounds like a PT boat," Dave joked. "Maybe they're putting us out to sea."

He remembered their picking the Seventy-seventh Precinct at random from the list Inspector Heffernan had recited. They were assigned to the same place. They were going to work in a high-crime area and, they soon found out, it was a mostly black slum section of Bedford-Stuyvesant in Brooklyn.

As a farewell gesture to the Academy, Dave and Bob decided to raid the clerical office that night and steal their records. In the two-week period they had received thirty demerits for poor conduct, and it was a much better idea to show up at their new command with a spotless past. The building was open at night, but only a skeleton crew happened to be on hand when they entered. A trainee was in the clerical office, so they created a commotion out in the hall.

The trainee ran out to see what the trouble was. Bob detained him while Dave slipped into the office through another door. He found the cabinet where the gigs were kept and went through the files until he came to his and Bob's records. He took out the stacks of demerit cards and looked through them, one by one. They were all minor infractions of the rules, such as smoking in the hallway. Some had just their names and no specific charge. Dave did find two cards out of thirty that he felt had been deserved. So he left those two cards in his file, congratulating himself on his honesty.

A few minutes later, Dave Greenberg and Bob Hantz left the Academy behind them.

BOOK 2

The station house seemed to blend in with all the other dingy buildings and tenements of the area; a shabby, run-down little fortress, a miserable-looking outpost in the heart of Bedford-Stuyvesant, it seemed to have been neglected entirely by New York City's huge Police Department. It occurred to Dave that quite possibly nobody would ever learn about whatever work he and Bob accomplished here; no matter what they did, it might very well go unnoticed by the outside world.

But we're together, he thought, and that's what matters most. They walked through the front door and stood there for a moment trying to get adjusted to the inside of the place. To their left was the captain's office; on the right was the main desk; the back room was straight ahead; upstairs was the detectives' squad room. That was about the extent of it.

They approached the officer at the desk. "Excuse me," Bob said. "We're Greenberg and Hantz. We're sorry about being late, but—"

"Greenberg and Hantz? Rookies? You got today and tomorrow off."

"Off work? We don't start until the day after tomorrow?"

"What, are you deaf? Listen, see if you can find a locker. There *ain't* any lockers, but if you can find one, take it."

They went into the back room. Several officers were lounging around, but no one looked up when they entered.

"Rookies?" one cop yelled from the corner. "Why do they send us these kids? Why don't you guys go back to the Bronx or wherever you came from?"

They ignored the insult. Word about what they had done in Manhattan must have reached someone in the Seventy-seventh Precinct, undoubtedly the captain. Surely their traffic command had sent word. Right now, the captain was probably waiting for them, anticipating their arrival, dying to meet these two marvelous cops who, while on probation, had made all sorts of arrests involving drugs and stolen cars, resulting in thirteen citations apiece.

"Let's go see the captain," Dave said.

It was crucial that their new boss understand that the two of them had to work together, as partners. Their teamwork had enabled them to take initiative in the first place; it had given them the means to cut through the bureaucracy of arrest procedures at precincts and in the courthouse. They would explain how they both wanted to become detectives as soon as possible, so they could get on with their war on drugs.

Bob knocked lightly on the door to the captain's office. "Yeah?" came a voice.

"Captain?" Dave said. "May we speak to you for a minute?"

"Huh?"

They swung the door open. Captain Irving Levitan was seated behind the desk, a beleaguered expression on his face.

"We'd like a word with you," Bob said.

"You want to speak to me?"

"Yes, sir."

"All right, then. Come in."

They stepped inside. Levitan looked up at them, waiting. "What is it?"

Dave smiled at him. "Uh, we're Greenberg and Hantz."

There was a long silence. "So?"

"Yeah, we're, uh, Greenberg and Hantz. We came from Manhattan, uh, from the traffic command in midtown, Safety Unit B, and, uh, we've made about forty felony arrests as probationary patrolmen. Uh, thirteen citations each. And, well, first of all, we wanted to stop in, being it was supposed to be our first day here."

Levitan squinted at them. Another strained silence.

"So, Captain, we've done a lot of things together," Dave

continued, "and it's worked out pretty well, if you've seen our record. We did it as partners. And I know that guys have hooks in all the time, but we're just coming in here on our own, see, and we're *not* asking you for anything like a radio car or a sector or any big special deal. We're just sort of trying to continue along, as we've been doing, so we can build from there. Right, Bob?"

"Right. No hooks, nothing like that."

Levitan broke in. "Get to the point."

"The point is, uh, that we feel we were sent here together so we can keep working as a team. Not with any special favors, but on foot posts or whatever, we don't care, as long as—"

"Wait a second," the captain said. *"Hold* it." He looked from Dave to Bob, then back at Dave. He leaned back in his chair, reached up his left hand, and turned on the regular AM radio. *"Now* you can talk," he said. "Far as I'm concerned, this whole station house is bugged. I *know* the phones are all tapped. But the bugging, that requires a little music in the background. Somebody once told me that if I play the radio, the guys trying to listen in won't be able to hear a thing that's being said. I don't know if it's true or not—probably just a joke. But I do it anyway, especially at moments like this." He turned the sound up a bit. "Now you can talk. Because I don't want *anybody* to hear what you're saying to me right now."

Dave hesitated. He went over it again: Greenberg and Hantz, fresh from triumph in Manhattan, thirteen citations, forty felony arrests, a desire to keep working together, on the basis of what they had done.

"Stop," Levitan said. "Please stop." He sprang up in the chair toward them, hands crashing on the desktop. "Look," he said quietly, "I don't care *who* you are, and I don't care what the hell you've done. Don't come in here and tell me what you've done in *Manhattan*. Because I'm not interested! Tell me what you can do in *this* precinct, and maybe I'll listen. But right now I wouldn't assign two rookies together, hooks or no hooks! If you want anything from me, you're gonna have to go out and *earn* it. And when I'm ready for you, *I'll* call *you* in here."

"But we—"

"Now get out of this office and stop wasting my time," said

Captain Levitan. "Out the door, boys. This conversation is over. Out."

They got out to the main floor of the station house again, the captain's words still echoing. With eight months of hard work behind them, they had come here only to be looked upon as a pair of inexperienced rookies who could not be allowed to continue as a team. Only to be told, in fact, to go home.

Few of the officers on hand would greet them with more than a grunt or a scowl. Wherever they looked, they saw the unhappy faces of men who seemed to hate this place and their jobs and maybe even each other. One young patrolman told them this was a "transition" precinct. It was a place to leave, not to get to. Most of the guys in this precinct had been sent from other places—"dumped" here as punishment for having messed up somewhere else.

"You know how guys used to be sent to Staten Island?" the patrolman said. "How they were sent way the hell out there because they fucked up? Well, *this* is the garbage dump now. Anybody who's been flopped out of plainclothes comes here, to the seven-seven. A guy gets knocked out of being a detective? He gets dumped right here. Even the bosses who screw up get tossed into this precinct."

They learned that Captain Levitan was probably being punished for some reason. Levitan had been in charge here for about three years—too long, in this precinct. He was fifty years old, a man with enough problems for anyone, trying to hold back the steadily rising crime rate in one of the most fertile breeding grounds for crime in the country. Delegations of poverty-stricken, welfare-supported blacks and other ethnic groups came to his office in a steady stream to complain about police protection and to demand or beg for more. Junkies, forced by their habits to rob and steal, multiplied the incidence of crime in this part of Bed-Stuy to the point where Levitan's one hundred and sixty cops were hard pressed even to slow down the rate of increase. Robberies, burglaries, muggings, stabbings, shootings—all were common occurrences.

In this volatile atmosphere, with the crew of controversial or "dumped" cops under his command, the captain dreamed of becoming a deputy inspector and leaving the Seventy-seventh Precinct far behind. He did not need more trouble. He did not need two rookies coming into his office and telling him that they were going to take on the whole world.

Dave wondered if he and Bob had been sent to the wrong place. But then he realized that the seven-seven was probably perfect after all. It offered a challenge. So what if Captain Levitan didn't want them to make waves? It was the same story everywhere they went. Well, he and Bob were dedicated to doing a job; they had come here for that reason. The captain was going to get the waves whether he liked them or not. The question was, how much more scheming and conniving would they have to do to get assigned together again?

In a young woman's apartment in lower Manhattan, Bob Hantz relaxed on the living-room floor and shut his eyes, listening to music from the stereo set. He thought about what he had seen of Bedford-Stuyvesant, of the Seventy-seventh Precinct, of Captain Levitan and the other men in the station house. All of it represented something new and unknown. Or maybe it was just too familiar—the regimentation of the Police Department, where nobody was willing to teach you anything except to obey like a trained dog, where you were no more than a cog in some huge quasi-military machine.

Maybe it would be too hard to maneuver this time. Maybe he and Dave would never be able to work as partners again. The system seemed to checkmate you, no matter what you did. If you went along with the program, you vegetated; if you tried to break out of the mold, you were likely to be suspended or tossed off the job altogether.

But then he thought of Dave Greenberg. Dave could never sit still for long. If he was ever quiet, it was because he was thinking, waiting, planning. Dave would say, "If we can't beat 'em, we join 'em. But while we join *them,* they join *us,* and we circumvent all the static."

There was a time to lie low, be humble, swallow your pride and ambition, and wait. Go along, figure out the rules of the game, the strengths and weaknesses of everybody who's playing, and then come up with a plan.

The best answer, usually, was to do something so well that nobody could criticize it. The way we've been able to make off-duty arrests, Bob thought. The only time they really came down on us was when we embarrassed the F.B.I.! Even then, they didn't have the guts to tell us to our faces. All they did was write a memo that we were "overzealous." We'll just have to make a career out of getting past whatever they throw at us to keep us down.

He wondered how they would do it this time. The captain had said to go out and "earn" their partnership. As if we've done *nothing* over the past ten months! Well, Bob thought, it's a sure bet that Dave'll have some sort of plan worked out. Bob's task would be to evaluate that plan, analyze it, refine it; and then, having no further objections, to "play it to a bust."

Right now it was time to relax and get ready.

Dave was alone, driving around Bedford-Stuyvesant in the early afternoon. He puffed on a cigarette and cruised slowly past a row of storefronts. Garbage and litter were strewn all over the sidewalk and in the street. He watched the people milling around—the junkies and the hustlers, people with nothing to do but get into trouble.

Then he sped up and headed for Sheepshead Bay. He and Bob had showed up for work again only to be given another two days off. Incredible, he thought, how every time I'm ready to get going, they tell us to get lost.

So they had today and tomorrow free. Restless, Dave had decided to go out and get involved in something, just as he had done during those first weeks at the Academy. The only way to make something happen was to start it moving yourself. It crossed his mind that it would be so much easier if he had gone into the other side of this work. As a "self-employed" criminal, he would have had no bureaucracy, no system, no bullshit to keep him down. A smart criminal could choose his own partner and make his own hours. He could do his job without the tangle of rules and regulations that saddled policemen. As a cop, Dave Greenberg knew he would have to fight just about the whole Police Department before he could get on with the important work.

He slowed down and glanced to his left, across the street. Three young white men were strolling past a row of parked cars. They seemed to be looking them over to see which one they should break into. He recognized everything—their mannerisms, the way they furtively checked the insides of the cars—from his own past. After a closer look, he realized they weren't kids; they were in their twenties, about his own age. And the guy in the dark-green sweater—was that Billy Metz?

"Billy? That you?"

The young man jerked his head up. He had taken a couple of tools from his hip pocket, having settled on one particular car; and he must have figured he'd been caught. It was Billy Metz, all right.

"Billy! It's me! Dave Greenberg!"

"Dave? Hey, man!"

He watched this face from the past walking toward him. Billy Metz had grown up in Coney Island. Dave remembered him from the days when the most important thing was how well you could take care of yourself on the street. Billy was one of the few white kids who had hung around Dave's weight-lifting gym. Dave had helped Billy many times. He had taken him in, protected him, given him encouragement. The kid had wanted to develop his muscles, learn how to box, have some confidence in himself. Dave had earned his friendship and respect.

He noticed how Billy had changed in the six or seven years since he'd last seen him. He looked as if he'd been a prisoner of war somewhere: thin and gaunt and pale. His eyes were sunken and dark and his whole body seemed shriveled. The kid was using dope.

"How are you, Billy?"

"Great, man! Great!"

Dave pulled the car to the curb and hopped out.

"What about you?" Billy asked.

"Well, I'm a cop."

Billy did a double take, then smiled. "You're a cop?"

"Yeah, well, I—"

"Holy shit! Davey's the Man! What d'ya know about that?"

Dave nodded, grinning, and reached in his pocket. "Listen," he said, handing Billy two ten-spots, "whatever you guys would've taken out of that car, I doubt seriously it's gonna bring you more than twenty. So take this and forget what you were doing."

"Hey, thanks, man. But you don't have to do that."

"Old times' sake," Dave replied. "What are you guys stealing for, anyway? I figured you'd outgrown that, Billy."

"Just messing around," Billy said, shoving the money into his pocket.

"Looks like more than that, to me."

"What do you mean?"

"Come on, Billy. You're using stuff, aren't you?"

"Huh?"

"You're a fucking junkie!" Dave said bitterly. "How bad? How much are you doing?"

Billy had begun to shake. Embarrassed, and suddenly dropping all pretense, he described how he had started on drugs about five years ago, and how his heroin habit had grown until now he could no longer keep up with it. The dope cost him about a hundred dollars a day, often more, and to avoid getting strung out he was always on the move, hustling or stealing and finding connections and copping and shooting and on and on in a continuous, murderous cycle. He shuddered.

"You cold?" Dave said. "You got a coat, or what?"

"Nah, I sold my coat. I'm just uptight, Dave. I gotta go cop soon. The twenty bucks won't go far, but I can use it."

Dave felt slightly nauseated. It was one thing to see a junkie nodding and swaying on a street corner, but meeting a friend from the past who had become an addict was different.

"Where do you get the stuff?" Dave asked.

"Around. Depends on what quality I can afford. Depends on a lot of things."

"Like where, though?"

"Anywhere," Billy said, and mentioned several street corners. He named one building that he said was probably the hottest spot in all of Brooklyn.

"Where's that again?" Dave asked. "What streets?"

"St. Mark's and New York Avenues," Billy repeated.

If Dave was not mistaken, that was within the Seventy-seventh Precinct. Was it possible Billy could lead him to one of the biggest drug peddlers in Brooklyn—before they even went on the job?

"Listen," Dave said. "Do me a favor, man. Give me a call later on. I live right over in Sheepshead Bay. Call me tonight, okay? We can get together and rap."

Billy was an out-and-out, strung-out junkie, a king of the junkies; and, Dave thought, anything I do with him is better than what he's doing to himself.

He got in touch with Bob and told him about his meeting Billy, adding that with a little help from him they might find a way to make an impression on Captain Levitan. "If we can put on a show to begin with," he said, "maybe the Old Man'll put us together." He told Bob to wait for his call later that night.

Billy came over at about nine o'clock, bringing a gift with him in a shopping bag.

"What's that?" Dave said.

"A tape deck for a stereo set."

"So?"

"That's for the twenty you gave me," Billy explained. "I'm a beat artist, man, but I don't beat my friends."

Dave shook his head. "Listen, man, later for that. You do what you have to do with that. And I don't even want to *know* where you got it. Don't even *tell* me it's stolen, 'cause I don't want to hear it."

He got Billy to sit down and relax and tell him more about his life as a junkie. Once again the building at St. Mark's and New York Avenues was mentioned. Dave became more and more excited.

"Billy, I'm gonna tell you something. Straight out, no jive—I've been a cop for about ten years."

"Ten years! You kidding?"

"Hell, no. I was undercover when you knew me way back there."

"Really?"

"Yeah, me and a guy named Bob Hantz. He was from Coney Island, too, but we didn't hang together then. Now we're partners. In the narcotics squad."

"Narcos!"

"Yeah, but relax. It's okay, man. We're friends, right?"

"Right. But that's a shock."

"We've been very busy over the years. Got a lot of informers working for us—and they get paid good money, too."

"Yeah?"

"Sure. From the city government, man. Listen, being as you're a good friend of mine, maybe we can get you on the payroll."

"Payroll?"

"Right. We could get you listed as a registered informer. For good money. Can't get any more truthful than that, Billy. The thing is, you'll have to turn us on to something, you know?"

"How come?"

"Well, after all, we'll have to show 'em that you're not conning us."

"Oh! Hey, man, I can turn you on to some heavy stuff!"

"That's great, Billy. Let me call my partner."

So far, so good. Dave called Bob and told him to come over as fast as he could. When he arrived, the three of them got down to specifics. Billy would help them try to arrest the dealer at 769 St. Mark's Avenue, a man named Earl King, who worked out of an apartment on the fourth floor of the building.

"It's a good thing you guys have ten years' experience," Billy said.

"How come?"

"The precinct and the narco squad and everybody and his mother have been trying to nail this one guy for about eight months!"

"No sweat," Dave said. "Me and Bob'll take this dude off in a day's work. You go on home, Billy, and I'll be in touch with you right after we make the collar. We'll get you put on the payroll, man."

Billy thanked him and left. Alone, Dave and Bob acknowledged to each other that they knew little or nothing about how to use an informer. But they had done some narcotics work on their own before; why not try it again?

That night, they drove out to Bed-Stuy and pulled up near 769 St. Mark's Avenue. On one side of the street stood a group of four large apartment buildings where some of the worst gun fights in Brooklyn had taken place. In summertime, according to Billy, kids threw garbage pails off the rooftops and snipers were always taking shots at people down below. Across the street was the building in question, loaded with junkies and people with weapons of all kinds.

More than two hundred people were milling around on the sidewalk when they pulled up in the car. Dave figured they could sneak into the building, get up to the fourth floor, and hide in the hallway near Apartment 4C. Somehow, they would catch Earl King in the act of selling dope.

As they left the car and started walking toward the building, the crowd began to disappear. Within half a minute the street was empty. It was as if everyone in Bed-Stuy knew they were there and that they were cops. He and Bob looked inside the door of the apartment building—nobody.

"Shit," Dave whispered. "What happened?"

"They made us," Bob said. "Before we even got out of the car."

"Well, we need some help. We know the guy's up there with all that dope. Let's go to the precinct tomorrow and tell the detectives."

The next day, still off duty, they showed up at the Seventy-seventh Precinct and gave the detectives all the information they had about Earl King. The detective in charge, a man named Foster, said it had taken him fourteen years to become a detective and who in hell were they to come in here and start giving orders?

"Look," Dave said, "we're cops just like you are, and we have this information, and we're gonna make this collar."

"Hey," Foster shot back, "*we* know about that guy, and *we're* gonna get him. We've been after Earl King for a long time."

"Well," Dave said, "if you don't go with us today, we're gonna get him ourselves."

Grumbling, the detective said that he and his partner, Boitel, would go along. In fact, he added, Dave and Bob could watch how it was done.

They rode out to St. Mark's Avenue in separate cars and pulled up near the building. Immediately the large crowd outside began to dissolve again; this time it took only fifteen seconds for the street to empty.

They followed the detectives into the building. The halls were deserted, as before. They began their ascent to the fourth floor.

Boitel was going up in the elevator, while Foster went with Dave and Bob up the stairs. On the way up Foster stumbled into a garbage can. The three of them turned and watched the can slam its way down a flight of stairs, the noise echoing throughout the building. Up on the fourth floor, meanwhile, Boitel stepped out of the elevator and let the door slam behind him. Another loud noise. Foster cursed, and his voice was even louder than the elevator.

"Sounds like the Army is here," Dave said as they reached the fourth floor. Boitel suddenly burst through a pair of fire doors. Instead of using just one of them to go through, he used both. Then he let the doors swing backward. More noise. As the doors swung back and forth, the entire hallway sounded like a wind tunnel. A lot of good it did to get help, thought Dave.

Now they were all on the stairway diagonally across the hall from the door in question. "Let's wait here," Foster said too loudly. At that moment a junkie came out of the elevator and walked right past them to Earl King's door. They had been seen. Dave figured that as soon as the door opened, Foster would storm the place. But everything happened too quickly and the junkie disappeared inside.

"Okay," Foster said. "There's somebody in there. And when the guy opens the door again, we'll make our move."

What makes Foster think anybody'll open the door again, Dave thought, if they know we're out here? And even if we do get in, by now they've probably thrown the dope down the toilet or out the window!

"We'll hide behind the wall down here," Foster said, indicating they should all go down a few steps and wait for the door to open again. Dave and Bob obeyed.

While they were hiding, people started walking up and down the stairs, right past them. Seeing the four white men crouched on the stairs, the passers-by began to whistle and hum "Dixie." That's a signal if I ever heard one, Dave thought. Within an hour, more than thirty-five men and women and youngsters, probably all junkies, had gone by.

Dave spoke to the detectives. "We'll see ya. Good luck. You guys can *have* the collars."

He and Bob left them on the stairs and walked down the hall toward the elevator. Bob glanced backward and whispered, "Hey, Dave—take a look at that."

Dave looked over his shoulder. Foster's belly was protruding from behind the wall.

Knowing that the detectives would never get inside Earl King's apartment, Dave and Bob decided to come up with a scheme of their own.

"We know the guy's in there," Bob said as they drove out of the area. "So there's got to be a way of getting to him."

Any arrest they made would have to be absolutely legitimate. After all, they were off duty and under a new command. They spent some time reading over the technical qualifications for drug arrests and then tried to devise a method to do what they wanted, within those laws.

"Why don't we get Billy to go over there and make the buy while we watch?" Dave suggested. "I don't know yet *how* we could watch him, but we can figure that part out later. We send him up there, and then hit the place on an observation-of-sale arrest. That way, we'll have Earl King for selling, Billy for buying, and the drugs as well."

He had no hesitation about deceiving Billy; there was a job to be done and if Billy had to get hurt, so be it.

"We'll get Billy to use his own money, so we won't get charged with trying to trap anyone. But where are we gonna be so we can watch the sale take place? Then how do we finally get into that apartment?"

Billy's heroin habit compelled him to go up to Earl King's apartment every day, sometimes twice a day, to buy the dope. What if he went up there one night with a big cardboard box of some kind? The box routine had worked once before—why not try it again? Billy could put the empty box in the hallway, right outside Earl King's door.

With Bob's help, the plan was laid out. Dave went to see Billy.

"It's gonna be very difficult for us to get this guy," Dave was saying, "unless you help us."

"Hey, man," Billy replied, "you know I'll do anything you want!"

Dave sketched in part of his plan. Billy would go to the building late that night or early in the morning. He would bring a large box, which he would place next to Earl King's door. After buying his drugs, he would leave the building and return to Dave's apartment.

At five thirty in the morning, Dave was awakened by loud knocking at his door. It was Billy and a junkie friend of his named Dennis.

"How'd it go?" Dave asked as they came in.

"Everything's all right—the box is there, baby! Me and Dennis went up there to cop, and we left a big refrigerator box next to the guy's door! We copped in the apartment and left it there in the hall."

"Fine," Dave said. "Hold on a minute, I'll make a call."

Bob's sleepy voice came on the line. "Yeah?"

"Hey, Bob! Step one is taken care of!"

"Huh? What are you talking about?"

"Step one completed, man! And I'm going through step two!"

"Okay," Bob answered, obviously still too sleepy to figure out what Dave was talking about. "Go through step two, and don't wake me up any more, will ya?"

"Bobby—the *box* is there."

"Box?"

"Yeah, the box! It's there!"

"Is it good?"

"Yeah, it's good!" Dave said.

"Well, enjoy yourself!"

There was a click at the other end of the line. Dave hung up the phone, glancing at Billy and Dennis. Okay, he thought, I'll call Bob again in a few hours, when he's awake.

Once more that day and again the following night, Billy went back to 769 St. Mark's Avenue, Apartment 4C, to buy his drugs. He reported each time that the box was still there in the hall.

Dave outlined the next steps of the plan: "Go up there at seven o'clock this morning. Knock on the door, but don't go inside. Make your buy right there in the doorway, okay? Then go downstairs and wait about twenty minutes. Come back up with Dennis. Knock on the door again, and this time go inside. When you come out, we'll be there to grab the guy. As soon as that door opens, we're gonna hit the thing. Got it? We'll be inside that box, watching what goes on. The only problem here, Billy, is that I gotta lock you up."

Billy choked. "Gotta lock me up?"

"Yeah, that's right."

"What for?"

"Possession of drugs," Dave said.

"Well, why don't I throw 'em away? I mean, why d'ya have to lock me up?"

"Because I wouldn't have any setup, if you threw it away. I *gotta* lock you up, Billy. Don't worry about it—I'll get you out. Besides, this way it'll make it look like you didn't inform on the guy, right? If you get locked up *with* Earl King, it'll look legit! And this is a way of showing that you're willing to work for us, so we can get you registered. Then we can get **you** *paid* for all this work."

Billy would have nothing to do with it. Dave argued with him, using every reason he could think of. He had no idea whether he could actually keep Billy out of jail, although he would make every effort to do so. If necessary, he would tell the district attorney and the judge what had happened, to get Billy out. How could they lock him up, Dave thought, if they knew the truth?

Three hours later, Billy relented.

When Dave and Bob arrived at St. Mark's and New York Avenues at four o'clock in the morning, the street was deserted. The junkies were indoors, sleeping. In a few hours, they would start feeling sick and begin another nightmarish day of hustling and stealing and copping and shooting up.

Dave and Bob got to the fourth floor of the building without being seen. They quietly turned the box upside down and put it over themselves. Then they waited, watching through a pair of small holes.

Five o'clock came and went, then six, then seven. A few minutes after seven, Bob heard the elevator door open and then he heard footsteps. Billy walked past the box and stood right in front of them, three feet away, knocking on Earl King's door.

The door opened a few inches and Billy extended some money that Dave had marked with his own initials in pencil. Earl King handed out a few glassine envelopes of heroin. Fine, Bob thought; we've seen the buy. Let's hope Billy remembers the next step.

Billy left quickly and headed down the stairs. The apartment door closed. Dave and Bob waited; now the minutes seemed to drag on much longer. Nearly half an hour later Billy came back up the stairs, his friend Dennis with him, and knocked on the door again.

Earl King opened it as far as the chain allowed. "Whatcha want?"

"Hey, man," Billy said in a low voice, "I got some heavy bread. I want a bundle."

Dave had given Billy some extra money for this transaction, which, if everything went all right, would not need to be made.

"I don't have a bundle bagged up yet. Come back later."

"No, man, I'll wait," Billy told him.

"Okay," said Earl King. "Come in."

The door opened a bit wider to let Billy and Dennis in. Silence. Carefully Dave and Bob lifted the box and crawled out. They positioned themselves on either side of the door. Then Bob realized that they had made a mistake. It would take much longer than a few minutes for Earl King to put the bundle together. Well, he thought, we'll have to sweat it out.

Twenty minutes went by. Then they heard someone coming up the stairs—a young addict who joined them in front of Earl King's door, waiting to buy his drugs. Before the junkie could knock, Dave grabbed him by the arm and pointed his gun at him. "You move and we blow your motherfucking head off," he said in a low voice.

Waiting in the silence, it occurred to Bob that nobody inside the building was going out. The only people moving around were those who had come into the building to buy their junk from various dealers.

He heard a voice behind the door. "Listen, man," Billy was saying, "let me go get some coffee. I'll be right back."

Billy fiddled with the locks—and then the door swung back, wide open. Dave and Bob crashed in, announcing themselves with guns pointed. Earl King was standing in the middle of the room holding some of the drugs in one hand. About a pound of heroin was on the table, where he was cutting it. The spoons, the money—everything was there.

Unbelievable, Bob thought. We've got this guy so wrapped up it's almost unreal!

While Bob held Earl King, Dave went through the motions of

searching Billy. He took the glassine envelopes out of his pockets. "You're under arrest," he said. Then he looked around for a phone. There was none. He motioned to Dennis. "You're clean. There's nothing I have on you, so go ahead and split." He took Dennis by the arm out to the hallway. The other junkie had left in a hurry. "Listen," Dave whispered to Dennis, "go call the police."

"Sure," Dennis said, running down the stairs.

Within minutes, they heard sirens; then a loud rumbling of cops coming into the building and upstairs. Whatever Dennis had said over the phone, the mere mention of this building had brought out every policeman available—two sergeants, a pair of detectives, some narco men, several patrolmen.

Dave and Bob watched as they poured into the apartment. The officers milled around, nervous, agitated, incredulous. Two off-duty cops in this pusher's living room, with a major arrest. Moreover, the cops were white men and—even more baffling—unknown to them.

"Who *are* you?" a detective asked.

"Greenberg and Hantz," Dave said. "We work in your precinct."

"You work where?"

"The seven-seven."

"You do? How come I never seen you two guys? When did you start working here?"

"Uh," Dave answered, "we started working here tomorrow."

When the entire procession of cars, including the two prisoners, rolled up to the front of the seven-seven precinct house, Captain Levitan was waiting for them at the door. In fact, he opened it to let them in.

Dave and Bob headed toward the lieutenant on the desk to tell him what kind of arrest they had. Suddenly Dave felt his arm being grabbed; it was the captain. "Into my office," Levitan said. "Both of you."

They marched into the office and the captain closed the door. Would he congratulate them for a job well done? He walked around his desk and turned the radio up high. "If you're wrong, I'll hang you," he said softly. "Get out."

10

They decided to keep their spirits up and win the captain's respect over a period of time. He would have to assign them together after a while. They had stepped out of his office and were still discussing it when they heard Lieutenant O'Shea, the desk officer, address one of the sergeants: "We got two cuties here, ain't we?"

"Yeah—two pricks. A coupla guys who're gonna break our balls."

Dave and Bob ignored the comments and went up to the squad room to process Billy and Earl King. The detectives collectively assumed the role of a defense attorney and tried to knock down the arrest. As far as they were concerned, there was no possible way for Dave and Bob to have done what they had accomplished, not legally. The detectives took it upon themselves to interrogate Earl King in an attempt to find a loophole. Dave and Bob heard talk of their being turned over to the Internal Affairs Department for investigation; one detective even suggested that they be arrested right then.

It took six hours for the two prisoners to be fingerprinted, something Dave and Bob had no experience doing for themselves. When they had finished, they went downstairs. Lieutenant O'Shea was still on the desk.

"This paperwork is no good," O'Shea told them. "You wrote it out wrong! Take it back upstairs and do it again."

At Brooklyn Criminal Court, they were bogged down in still more paperwork, but downstairs in the courtroom itself, there was a pleasant surprise. A young black woman named Cynthia, who worked as a court officer, recognized them from Manhattan. She had been transferred from that court to this one. She shifted their papers to the top of the pile, and they breezed through the arraignment.

But that bit of good luck could not offset another surprise: Billy had lied about his past. He had jumped bail on other cases in which he had been picked up, and several outstanding warrants had been issued for him. It was impossible for Dave to help him, at least right away. Billy would have to do some time for those past offenses.

The next afternoon they reported at four o'clock for their first actual day on the job. One look at the roll call told them that someone in the seven-seven precinct was getting revenge. Bob was assigned to the 124 desk as the clerical man, and Dave had switchboard duty. To be kept off the street was letdown enough; the irony was that Bob had no experience at typing, while Dave did.

They took their posts, and while Bob struggled with the typewriter, Dave created a mammoth crisis in police communications. Trying to dial numbers in Manhattan, he would wind up getting operators in Washington, D.C., and elsewhere around the country. People would call up the precinct asking to speak to a certain sergeant or lieutenant, and Dave would plug them into the Department of Public Works. After three days of confusion, it was a toss-up as to who had become more frustrated, the callers or Dave.

Lieutenant O'Shea, at the main desk, observed the proceedings with considerable satisfaction. It was he who had arranged for them to be kept inside.

Dave approached him during the third day. "Lieutenant," he said, "I'm not asking you to let us out on the street, but the arrangement here is backward. I should be typing, and Hantz should be on the phones. *I* can type, but he can't. Why don't you let me take the 124 desk, and let Bob have the switchboard? It would alleviate a lot of problems, sir."

Lieutenant O'Shea looked at him a moment. "No, no, no," he said.

"Why not? What does it matter if we change positions? The whole setup would be much more efficient."

"Listen," O'Shea replied, *"I'm* the boss in this situation, and I happen to know what I'm doing!"

O'Shea had been on the job thirty-five years. He had a respect for the system of rank and seniority, and their corresponding privileges, that bordered on reverence. In his mind, Greenberg and Hantz were two rookies who needed to be put in their places. He had seen their independent attitude on that first day, when they had come in with the off-duty narcotics arrests, and he had smelled trouble.

"Lieutenant," said Dave, "all I'm asking is—"

"Get back to that switchboard!"

The next day they were given the midnight-to-eight shift. Dave was assigned to "station-house security" and Bob got a foot post around the corner. Neither assignment was cause for rejoicing, but anything was better than the 124 desk and the switchboard.

Dave's job was simply to stand at the front door and guard the building. "I'm supposed to make sure nobody steals it," he joked.

Bob's task was to walk up and down the sidewalk, past a row of empty lots. "I have to call up every hour," he laughed, "and tell O'Shea that the lots are still there!"

It was depressing, knowing the next eight hours would be spent doing nothing worthwhile. But then Dave had an idea.

"Wait a minute," he said. "We're gonna be out in the street, right? So let's not knock it so fast, We oughta be able to do *something,* you know? Let's find out what we're *really* supposed to be doing."

They looked up the requirements for their posts in the police manual. According to the regulations, Dave was supposed to walk *around* the building. "I walk around the building and make sure they're not jacking it up and taking it away," he said. "So listen, Bob, this is it! The building extends halfway down the block, right? And your post extends halfway down the block! Your lots go right up to my building! The only thing separating the two of us is one lousy street! That shouldn't be too much of a problem. Now, how do we put this new information to good use?"

On inspection, they found two traffic lights. When the far light turned red, so did the one next to the station house. If a driver went through the first red light—committing a traffic violation—he would still have to stop at the second light. Every driver would stop at the second light, because the police station was right there.

"Okay, Bobby, you go down the block and hide in one of your empty lots. Give me a signal every time somebody passes a red light down there. When I see you waving, and the guy stops for the red light up here by the precinct, I'll nab him!"

"Nothing to lose by trying," Bob said.

Dave gave a passing thought to possible repercussions, but then he laughed. "Being an officer of the law, and knowing that a violation has been committed, it would be a crime if I didn't take any action. Right? I mean, can I help it if I'm so observant? Or that conscientious?"

"Absolutely not," Bob agreed, smiling. "It's your responsibility, man."

Just after midnight, they took up their positions. Within minutes, Dave saw Bob waving to him. A car had just passed the far intersection and had gone through a red light. The car rolled up and stopped at the second red light, and Dave walked into the street, yelling at the man behind the wheel to pull over.

"Let's see your license and registration," Dave said.

"I don't have any."

"You don't have a license or registration? Fine. *Hey, Bob!* Why don't you come up here and give this guy a summons?"

Bob walked up the block and wrote out summonses for three violations—running through a red light, having no license, and having no registration.

"Now," Dave said, "technically this guy is not permitted to drive the car. So let me go inside and get the proper orders."

He went into the station house and approached Lieutenant O'Shea, who was at the desk on the same shift. "Hi, Lieutenant!"

O'Shea scowled. "What are you doing?"

"Well, uh, Bob Hantz observed a traffic violation, and he pursued the driver to my post, where I assisted in stopping the car. And now, I'm taking proper police action, sir."

"Fine," O'Shea grumbled. He seemed to be wondering, How involved can they get in a summons? "Go ahead," he added.

Dave grabbed some property clerk voucher sheets. When an officer confiscated evidence—in this case, the car—he was supposed to fill out these forms. Then radio-car cops from the precinct would have to take the car to the police pound. When the violation was corrected, the owner could go to the pound and pick it up again.

Outside, Dave told the driver that his car was being impounded and that he would have to get home some other way. He filled out a voucher sheet while Bob parked the car in front of the station house. Then Bob walked back to his post by the empty lots, and Dave went inside the building. They had done everything according to regulations. He walked up to Lieutenant O'Shea and dropped the paperwork in front of him.

O'Shea glanced down at it. "What's this?"

"Well," Dave said, "I caught this guy with no license and registration. The registration had expired, sir. So I impounded the car."

"What?"

"I impounded the car."

"What do you mean, you impounded the car?"

"Well, what would you *like* me to do with the car, Lieutenant?"

"Give the guy a summons!"

"I *did* that, sir."

"Well, tell him to go get the license and registration!"

"I did that, too."

"Then what are you doing with the car?"

"Well," Dave said politely, "what was *he* gonna do with the car?"

"Tell him to take it home!"

"But Lieutenant, the man had no license and registration! The car was being operated illegally! Do you think, as a police officer, that I should permit a man to *violate the law?* Give him *permission* to do that?"

Lieutenant O'Shea was speechless. When he finally spoke, it was in a whisper. "What do you mean?"

"Well, sir, if I tell this man to drive the car, he'd be doing it illegally! Right? And he'd be subject to arrest! And then *I'd* be subject to *malfeasance,* for not taking action!"

Now O'Shea was purple. Here he sat, in charge of the desk, in a high-crime area in the heart of Bedford-Stuyvesant, and this rookie had impounded an automobile and was making it necessary for two radio-car men to be dispatched to take it to the pound.

Dave walked back outside, leaving O'Shea, still cursing, to do his end of the considerable paperwork involved.

Ten minutes later, Bob signaled again. Another car came by

and Dave stopped it. Bob ran up and said the driver had gone through the red light. And, it turned out, the car had not been inspected within the proper time period.

"Well," Dave said, "we've given O'Shea enough to keep himself busy for a while, so let's find another boss."

A sergeant was walking out the door, so Dave approached him. "Hey, Sarge! Uh, listen—we have a car out here and, uh, what do you think we ought to do?"

The sergeant was mildly annoyed. "Issue a summons! What else?"

"Well, the inspection has lapsed. What should we do with the car?"

"Jesus, kid," the sergeant snapped. "Put it over there!"

Dave shrugged as the sergeant got into a radio car and rode off. "Well, Bob, we've got to follow orders, right?"

"Right. I'll put this car behind the other one. You fill out the voucher."

This went on until about seven o'clock in the morning. There was an hour left of work, and they had left Lieutenant O'Shea alone since the first car. They had gone for "advice" to various other lieutenants and sergeants and even to deputy inspectors and bosses who wandered in from other precincts or districts.

Dave and Bob walked into the station house and placed a huge stack of papers on Lieutenant O'Shea's desk. "What is this?"

"That's all the vouchers for the cars outside," Dave answered innocently.

Lieutenant O'Shea looked down at the pile of vouchers, then back up at the two young men, finally back down again. He stood up slowly and without saying a word he went around his desk and walked to the door of the station house. He gazed outside and, at first glance, what he saw might have appeared to be a junkyard for automobiles. There were seventeen impounded cars lined up in various formations in front of the building. The cars were double- and triple- and quadruple-parked on the sidewalks and in the street. The early-morning traffic had been brought to a standstill. Seventeen cars. Lieutenant O'Shea just stared.

The whole station house was buzzing over what they had done to the lieutenant. It turned out that since not many officers in the precinct liked O'Shea much anyway, Dave and Bob became instant celebrities. O'Shea had been forced to do paperwork from eight in the morning—the time he had been scheduled to go home—until close to ten o'clock that night.

"I still can't believe it," the cops in the back room were saying. "How did you guys do it?"

O'Shea took a three-day leave of absence to recuperate. He had been a happy man until he had met up with Greenberg and Hantz. He had loved his job, especially the dignity and respect that went with it, but now he was furious at the two young rookies. He would either have them thrown off the job or make them so miserable that they would quit.

He left orders that whenever he was on duty as desk officer, he wanted Dave and Bob out of the building and out of his sight—which was exactly where they wanted to be.

"Step into my office, gentlemen!"

The captain looked up at them from behind his desk. Irving Levitan had decided to play his cards in favor of Greenberg and Hantz. As head of the precinct, he had to mediate disputes among his men—but he also had to make firm decisions and stand on them. His expression told Dave and Bob that he had done so in their behalf.

"You guys have done a few things, here, in the past few weeks," Levitan said. "You've caused trouble, but I think you've proved something, too."

Over the past two weeks, they had picked up several people on charges ranging from driving while intoxicated to possession of stolen property—not the most important collars in the world, but they had demonstrated a definite zeal for their work. They had also come up with two stolen cars.

"What can I do for you?" Captain Levitan asked.

"Assign us together," Dave said.

"Done!" Levitan exclaimed, but then he shook his head. "No, wait a minute. I can't put you together yet. But I tell you what I'll do. I'm gonna put you in radio cars. I mean, I can't put two rookies in *one* radio car, not together. That's out of the question. But I'll put you *both* in radio cars, in adjoining sectors! So that if there's a job, you guys can respond together! How's that?"

"Fine," Dave said. Just another step forward.

He was assigned to a radio car with a cop named Bert Williams. Williams was black, which was fine with Dave—but as far as he was concerned, Williams should never have been given a uniform or a badge or a gun.

Williams had a girl friend who lived in a room over a grocery store. He would park there, leaving his partner in the radio car while he went up to see her for two or three hours at a time. On this particular afternoon, he went up to get the girl friend and came back down with her. She got into the back seat, and Williams climbed behind the wheel.

"Listen," Williams said, "we're just going to drive her to the subway."

"Fine," Dave said.

When they got to the subway entrance, Williams jumped out of the car and said, "Let me walk her downstairs to the train. I'll be right back."

Dave waited in the radio car. Five minutes went by. Ten minutes. Half an hour. An hour. Two hours. Three hours. Finally Williams emerged from the subway.

"Where were you?" Dave said.

"I got on the train with her."

"What?"

"I rode up to Harlem with her. She was visiting relatives up there, so I—"

"You rode the train all the way up to Harlem and back?"

"Yeah. Look, I'm sorry."

Dave said nothing. It didn't bother him, except that he knew he was being paid to work, and Williams was stopping him.

By this time it was about 8 P.M., halfway through their tour. A call on the radio said that a woman's purse had been snatched. They responded to the scene, and she got into the back seat of the car. Williams continued driving around, hoping she could point out the man who had taken her purse.

Suddenly another radio call came over. This time, the dispatcher's tone was urgent: "Shots fired! 406 Kingsborough Walk!"

The address was only a block away. Dave waited for Williams to step on the gas. But he drove on calmly, as if he hadn't even heard the report.

A second call, even more insistent, came on: "Man shot! 406 Kingsborough Walk!"

Dave took a deep breath. "Hey, Williams—it's right around the corner! Let's get over there."

"Aw, nah."

"Hey! A man's been shot! Let's go!"

With the woman still in the back seat, Williams drove around the corner to the scene of the reported shooting—a housing project. He and Dave hopped out and ran inside the building, up the first flight of stairs. A young man was on his way down in a big hurry.

"Okay, Bert!" Dave yelled. "Grab this guy!"

He kept running up the next flights of stairs. The guy must have done something, if he's in such a hurry.

On the third floor, a man was sprawled out in the hallway. He had been shot. Dave leaned down, checked his wound, questioned him. The man gave a full description of his assailant. That's the guy we stopped on the stairs, Dave thought.

A woman also standing there in the hallway turned out to be the mother of the young man who had done the shooting. She told Dave where she actually lived—around the corner—and Dave made a mental note to check it out on the way back to the station house with the prisoner.

He went downstairs—but Williams was nowhere to be seen. The car was outside, with the woman still in the back seat. But where was Williams?

Dave glanced across the street and saw him standing on the sidewalk, eating a piece of fried chicken. Dave walked over to him. "Where's the guy I asked you to stop?"

Williams took a bite of chicken. "Hey, man, we have a job. We're on a job—this stolen purse! We gotta finish the paperwork on that first. I don't want to get involved in anything else."

Dave was very quiet. "Okay, motherfucker—let's go." He took Williams by the arm and marched him back across the street to the radio car. "The guy's around the corner," Dave said. "In another building. Let's go."

"No, no. We got this woman here. We gotta take care of this."

Dave's reply was sudden—and violent. He slammed Williams across the hood of the car and pounded on him with his fists. *"Fuck you,"* Dave shouted and broke loose, running around the corner. He came to the apartment house the kid's mother had mentioned. Someone outside said that the young man was hiding in the basement.

In the meantime, Bob had arrived at the scene of the shooting. The young man's mother told him what she had told Dave. Bob dashed outside and around the corner.

"Where's the cop?" Bob asked the small crowd that had gathered. "The cop! Where's the cop?"

"Down in the basement!"

Bob leaped down a flight of steps and crashed through the door. "Be careful!" he yelled. "I'm coming in!"

They found the young man curled up in a corner of the pitch-black cellar, shaking with fright. After Dave and Bob calmed him down, he took them up to his mother's apartment and gave them the gun he had fired.

The detectives arrived, all set to crack the case. Without knowing what had taken place, they tried to get a confession out of him and succeeded only in frightening him all over again. The detectives shouted at him to respond to their questions, but he wouldn't say a word.

At last Dave spoke up. "Listen, you guys, everything he said is already written down. Here's a signed statement. And here's the gun."

When Dave and Bob returned to the station house, they saw Williams in the back room, talking to a sergeant. Dave turned around to walk the other way. But Bob rushed over and shoved Williams backward, yelling at him, barely able to restrain himself from beating Williams' face to a pulp.

Dave went to the officer in charge of the roll call. "Never put us with that guy again, or we'll kill you," he told him. "Not for your system, not for your peace of mind, or any other reason you can think of, baby. We're not trying to get Williams in trouble, because the weight's gonna fall on him sooner or later. All we want to do is look out for each other!"

11

The captain's office was familiar by now. After the trouble with Williams the night before, Levitan had sent for Dave and Bob.

"I hope you guys aren't going to make me sorry," he sighed. "There's a radio car out there, number 2031, and whenever there isn't a regular man driving it, you two are. Provided, of course, there's no more activity like the seventeen cars—or anything like the incident with Williams last night."

It was unheard of—two rookies getting a radio car, even on a partial basis, after just weeks on the job. There were men in the precinct who had been cops for ten or twelve years without receiving their own car. The captain had really put his job on the line for them.

That night, number 2031 radio car was available. Dave and Bob were ready to go out and show the world what they could do, but it turned out that they had been assigned to a fixed post, the "taxi check" at the corner of Ralph Avenue and Fulton Street, from which they were not supposed to move all night, unless they saw a crime take place.

All the action was taking place around the corner, at Fulton Street and Utica Avenue, in front of a place called the Tip Top Lounge. The bar and its environs had a permanent population of hustlers, pimps, prostitutes, junkies, gamblers, and men with knives and guns—an urban version of a Wild West saloon.

The first night on the taxi check at Ralph Avenue, Bob and Dave went after a car that looked as if it had been stolen and arrested the driver. That was the end of the fixed post. On their next tour, the radio car was taken, so they got foot posts together on Fulton Street. Naturally, they went to the Tip Top Lounge.

Dave saw one man holding a gun, and he and Bob easily took him aside and made the arrest. On the same foot post the following night, they collared two men with guns inside the bar. And the night after that, again at the Tip Top Lounge, they rounded up still another gun.

They were on the midnight-to-eight shift the next time number 2031 radio car was given to them. Still they were assigned to the taxi check at Ralph and Fulton. They ate breakfast at a restaurant three doors down from the Tip Top Lounge, at Utica and Fulton, and returned to the taxi check at about three thirty in the morning. Dave saw a car go by and muttered, "Uh, uh, that looks bad. Looks stolen. Later for the taxi check. We got work to do." He pulled away from the fixed post and followed the car around Fulton Street. It came to a halt in front of the Tip Top. The driver got out and went into the bar.

Dave and Bob waited a short distance away in the radio car. A few minutes later the same man came out of the bar, but this time he jumped into a Cadillac and drove off. Dave followed him a few blocks and made him pull over. When they questioned him about the two different cars, the man was evasive, so they ordered him outside. As he opened the door, Bob noticed him slip a gun under the seat. It was a .22-caliber pistol, fully loaded. They also found a hypodermic needle concealed in the glove compartment. They placed the man under arrest, telling him they would try to help him with the District Attorney if he cooperated in any way.

The man, whose name was Calvin Tate, took the opportunity. "I know where you guys can get two more guns," he said.

"Where?"

"Back at the Tip Top Lounge. A friend of mine in there named Jesse Brown. Also a dude in the St. James Lounge."

"Name?"

"Frank Lomax. Owns this Cadillac. My own car is still in front of the Tip Top. Jesse's gun's in the glove compartment."

"Okay, let's go."

They handcuffed Tate and put him in the rear of the radio car. Dave drove back to the Tip Top bar, Bob following in the Cadillac. The problem was: how to get Jesse Brown outside? Bob parked the Cadillac and removed Jesse's gun from Calvin's car. Dave went into the tavern.

It was dark and crowded, so there was no way that he could be certain of getting Jesse Brown without a ploy of some kind. "Hey, listen!" he called out. "The car in front is illegally parked! Here's the keys! They were left inside the car! The owner is Calvin Tate! If anyone in here knows Tate, why doesn't he help him out and drive it away before I put a summons on it?"

"Calvin Tate?" came a voice. "All right, I'll move the car for him!"

The man came forward and Dave handed over the keys to Calvin's car. "What's your name?" Dave asked.

"Jesse."

"Okay, Jesse, just get in and move the car for your man."

"Sure," said Jesse, hopping behind the wheel.

"And now," Dave quickly added, "get right out of the car again, because you're under arrest."

Using the radio car's microphone, Bob called for assistance. When help arrived, Dave told the officers, "Watch these two cars. We'll be back."

They took the two prisoners, Calvin and Jesse, in the radio car and went off to the St. James Lounge to find Frank Lomax. The place turned out to be two miles away, in the Eighty-eighth Precinct.

When they pulled up in front of the St. James Lounge, Calvin identified a man on the sidewalk as Frank Lomax. Lomax saw the police car and headed back into the lounge. After handcuffing their two prisoners to the metal bar in the rear seat, Dave and Bob got out and walked into the lounge. Frank Lomax was standing in the back. They did not draw their guns or say a word, but simply walked up to Lomax, reached into his pants and took his gun, grabbed him by the arm, and marched him back outside.

The crowd on the sidewalk was not in a mood to be passive. About a hundred men surrounded the two cops and their prisoner, refusing to let Lomax be taken away. One look at their faces told Dave that he and Bob would have no chance of getting back into the radio car without a huge brawl, probably involving guns, in which they would lose their prisoner and probably wind up killed.

Suddenly he heard sirens. Someone must have called the police. Reinforcements arrived from all directions, and the crowd began to back off as the sidewalk swarmed with police.

A private car pulled up at the scene and a familiar figure got out.

"Hello, boys," said Irving Levitan. "I get word back in the seven-seven that Greenberg and Hantz are stuck in the eight-eight, with a ten-thirteen! What the hell did you guys do now?"

Dave began but it was all so confusing—two cars, three guns, one hypodermic needle, two nightclub bars, two different precincts, three prisoners, not to mention why they had left the taxi check in the first place—that after several minutes Levitan put up his hand. "Look, just bring 'em in. And come into my office when you get there."

"Okay," said Levitan. "Sit down. Smoke if you like," he said, reaching back to turn on the radio. "Now, tell me what happened. So if someone asks *me*, I can tell *them.*"

Bob went over the whole story—from the time they were on the taxi check at Ralph and Fulton to when they wound up two miles away in the Eighty-eighth Precinct with three prisoners and three guns.

"All right," Levitan said. "For some reason, that's what *I* would have told them. So far, I can see that you've left nothing open. All bases are covered."

Dave and Bob glanced at each other and smiled.

"Now, you've proved yourselves," Levitan went on. "You've done what I told you to do when you first walked in here two months ago. You were right—you *can* do a job if you're together. Now let me ask you—what do you want?"

"Just to be together," Dave said.

"Well, I'll give you that car, number 2031, on a permanent basis, and how about having your own sector?"

The captain quickly explained that he had been worried about the Tip Top Lounge at Utica and Fulton for a long time. He had never been able to understand why the taxi check had been over on Ralph Avenue instead of right there. Located at Utica and Fulton, by the bar, a radio car would frighten everyone away and also accomplish the taxi check. Despite Levitan's repeated requests, nothing had happened until Dave and Bob had started making arrests. The top brass had begun to listen, and the captain had got permission to change the taxi check from Ralph Avenue to Utica. The arrests tonight made Levitan ecstatic.

"From now on," Levitan said, "if I'm going outside, I'm leaving orders that if any incident concerns the two of you, I will be *personally notified.* At home, or elsewhere. What I'm doing now is very unorthodox, but I want you to know that I'm putting all my trust in you. As far as I'm concerned, when you guys are right I'll back you a hundred percent. But I'm not even gonna consider the fact that you're wrong. I haven't got much, but what I have I need. So I'm depending on you to keep everything as light as possible. You guys can do no wrong."

Dave and Bob shifted a bit uneasily in their seats.

"The wrong that you would do," Levitan continued, "is in disappointing me. And I *know* that you'd never want to do that. Even though I'm giving you basically what you deserve, I'm putting myself out on a limb. You've got your own car, and your own sector, and that's it."

They thanked him and got up to leave.

"One other thing," Levitan said. "I'm giving you a sector with nothing in it. Sector Edward."

"Nothing in the sector?" Bob said.

"Right. It's a small sector, full of empty lots, parking lots, garages. There's nothing there, but there is crime. I want you to prove that the crime is there, and I want you to apprehend the perpetrators committing the crimes."

From the time of an arrest to the moment Bob and Dave went before a judge, eight or nine hours usually elapsed. The list of what had to be done was long and dreary: precinct paperwork, fingerprints, photo lab, complaint room, courtroom. Waits and delays were inevitable—and infuriating.

Dave and Bob made an auxiliary career of coming up with new ways to get through the Brooklyn court system more quickly. They would drive into Manhattan with the fingerprints, eliminating the usual three- or four-hour wait for a messenger to go and come back. They would invent a suspense element to motivate the clerks: "This is a big case. A dozen murders involved!"

In the complaint room, the story would continue: "We've been working four days and nights in a row, and this is our day off. Sure hope we get some time to sleep." If the stenographer happened to be a young lady, one of them would make a pass at her. Anything to get the people in the bureaucracy over to their side.

On this particular morning, with the three gun collars, and after working all angles to get up to Brooklyn Criminal Court in the shortest possible time, Dave found a clerk to type up his complaint; but this clerk wrote out not what Dave and Bob told him, but his own concept of what had taken place. This statement would become a legal document they would have to sign and swear to in front of a judge.

Dave read over what the clerk had typed. "Listen, that's not anything like what I just finished telling you."

"Well," the clerk replied, "that's good enough."

"That's not good enough for me, because I won't sign it."

"Then go back to the end of the line and wait till it's your turn again."

"What's the problem?" Dave said.

The clerk stood up and muttered, "You guys always expect us to do things for our health. A couple of bucks, and things could be arranged."

"Listen, you're getting paid same as we're getting paid!" Dave shouted. "You want extra financial aid for typing up our complaint?"

"Well, we don't get paid as much as you do."

"I'm gonna ask you one more time to do this complaint and do it right! And if you ask me for any money again, I'm gonna arrest you for soliciting a bribe!"

"You can't do that," the clerk replied. "If you're not gonna give me the deuce, forget it."

Dave jumped over the counter, announcing that he was making an arrest, and began beating his fists on the court clerk's head. During the argument, Bob had gone to get a superior. When he returned, Dave was holding the clerk by the neck and trying to put handcuffs on him at the same time.

"Hold it," the supervisor was shouting. "Wait a minute! There's nothing we can do here—these clerks are civil service workers!"

Hearing the commotion, an assistant district attorney came over. They told him what had happened and he said, "You're within your rights to arrest him, but I wouldn't consider it malfeasance if you didn't."

In the end, they were talked out of arresting the court clerk.

"Sector Edward," Bob mumbled. "Really terrific, Dave."

"Yeah. Some sector, ain't it?"

They drove through the entire area within minutes, from Fulton Street to St. Marks Avenue and from Utica Avenue to Albany Avenue—two streets going one way and three streets going the other way. Six empty lots and more than two dozen parking lots. The only buildings were a Tastee Bread bakery, a structure occupied by the Sanitation Department, and the station house itself. Actually, the vacant lots and parking areas made it unnecessary to drive at all; they could see the entire sector from one corner.

Dave drove around and around, sinking into a mild depression. It was the four-to-twelve shift, their first night in Sector Edward, and each of them was carrying four or five dozen rounds of ammunition, enough for a full-scale riot. Empty lots ... the station house ... Tastee Bread ... sanitation trucks ... more empty lots. He and Bob kept listening to the car radio, hoping to hear "Edward" come over the air. Silence.

"Well," Dave said, "we can't go out of the sector, at least not yet."

Almost before he had finished that sentence, a call came. "Sector Edward, respond to ..."

They were already on their way, Dave speeding as if someone's life depended upon it. They jumped out of the car at the scene and discovered that the trouble in question involved a man with a headache. Since they had no idea what forms to fill out for aid cases, they had to call for another car to back them up. That done, they drove back to their own sector.

By the end of the tour at midnight they had taken care of a boy with a sick dog, a man who had run out of gas on Utica Avenue, and one minor car collision.

Depressing was not the word for it. Rather than go home, Dave and Bob went to a bar in Brighton Beach. They ordered drinks and stared down at the table in silence for twenty minutes.

"Look," Dave said at last. "There's nine blocks by twelve blocks in our whole precinct. I don't see what stops us from going other places, except for the fact that the captain might be watching..."

After only one night of confinement, Greenberg and Hantz decided to graduate from Sector Edward to the entire Seventy-seventh Precinct.

Over the next two weeks, what Captain Levitan started referring to as "the two-man army"—Greenberg and Hantz in car 2031—seemed to be everywhere at once, zooming through the streets in response to any call involving a gun, a burglary, a robbery. No matter what sector it happened to be in, they were always first to arrive at the scene. "I don't care if they call for some other company or some other nation," Dave said. "We're gonna be there."

They developed their own style of operating the radio car, according to their different personalities. The correct procedure was for one man to drive the first four hours, then for the second man to take over the wheel for the remaining half of the tour. But when Bob's turn came, he would always have an excuse: "My back's killing me," or, "I got a cinder in my eye," or, if it wasn't obvious the first time around that he simply didn't want to drive, "My left pinkie is deteriorating so fast that I won't be able to turn the steering wheel, Dave."

Moreover, Dave was the more impatient of the two. He couldn't bear to sit on the recorder's side and do nothing. They tried it once, Bob driving and Dave just sitting, and it was awful. Bob got bored and became too casual at the wheel. Dave smoked one cigarette after another, fidgeting and filling the car with smoke. Bob opened his window. Dave asked him to close it because of the cold. A few minutes later, Bob opened it again because of the smoke. Dave said please close it. Bob did so, and this time he took out a cigar and purposely created so much smoke that Dave wanted the window opened again.

"Slow down," Dave would say, "you're driving too fast."

"It's not fast *enough,* if you ask me."

After that experience, they dispensed with the regulations and Dave drove the car right through every tour. When Dave was at the wheel he became relaxed and alert; he would drive about five miles an hour, prowling, hunting, at times able to see something suspicious two blocks away.

"Listen," Dave would say, "how about that?"

"Yeah," Bob would reply. "Go."

They imagined a thin line down the center of the street. Dave watched everything on the left, and Bob was responsible for everything to the right of the invisible line. They would be able to call each other's attention to the left or right and respond immediately and with complete trust.

None of this would have worked, of course, if they hadn't had complete confidence in each other's desire to get involved. Even to stop and frisk a person on the street required a great deal of activity: filling out forms and making entries in the memo book. Stopping someone in a car meant that they both had to get out and check the driver's license and registration. If the car was stolen, that involved even more work.

With any other partner, either Dave or Bob would have been reluctant to get involved on the basis of mere suspicion; another partner might not want the extra work. But together, knowing that nothing either of them did was too much for the other, they felt free to take action at the slightest hint that it might result in a collar.

One night they arrested three young men riding in a stolen car—another grand larceny auto. All three were junkies. Where were they buying their stuff? No answer. Their names were Willie and Vernon and Oscar. Dave took special pains to show them that he was a cop who had to do a job but who was mainly concerned with drugs. He wanted help in getting to the pushers.

He told Willie, who had been driving the car, that he and Bob could talk to the judge about their case. Maybe get to the district attorney and secure a low bail for them. An early parole, too.

"In other words," Dave said, "it's to our advantage if you get back out on the street, if you stay out of jail while you're helping us. And if you give us enough help, man, it would be taken into consideration when the time comes for sentencing, right? You might not have to go to jail at all on this charge."

After Willie and his two friends were arraigned in court, Dave figured he would not see them again until the trial. Most junkies would talk to get cops off their backs, but would never seek out policemen on their own. But against all odds—perhaps because Dave had promised him no more than what was possible—Willie returned. Out on bail, he was waiting in front of the precinct house a few evenings later when Dave and Bob's tour ended.

"Listen," he said, "I got something for you."

"What's that?"

"I know a guy that's supplying the whole north side of Brooklyn!"

"What do you know about him?"

"He comes out of his house a certain time, gets into a Mustang and goes to Queens to pick up the stuff—two, three kilos—and brings it back. Cuts it up in his place."

"Take us there."

"Sure," said Willie.

They got in Dave's car and Willie directed them to the place where this pusher with the Mustang lived.

12

The pusher's name was Nathan Turner. "I'm not sure which building he's at," Willie told them, "but that's his car right there." He pointed to a light-blue Mustang parked halfway up the block.

Bob wrote down the license-plate number. Dave wondered how they were going to catch this Nathan Turner—not just see him, but catch him selling his dope. They dropped Willie off and went home.

Circling around the precinct on patrol the next day, they passed through the block in question every fifteen or twenty minutes, trying to spot someone getting into the Mustang. But from eight in the morning to four in the afternoon, no one touched it.

On their way to the station house the following morning, Dave and Bob drove through the block and discovered that the Mustang was now parked on the opposite side of the street. They kept up their periodic surveillance in the radio car, but there was still no movement.

"The guy *has* to be getting in and driving that car when we're not around," Dave exclaimed. "Maybe he's got us figured out already."

"Stay here a minute," Bob said. "Check those buildings."

They looked up at the row of buildings along one side of the block. It was clear that any further surveillance of the Mustang would have to be done from the rooftops. And that kind of work would have to be done off duty.

The following Thursday and Friday were their days off. At six o'clock on Thursday morning, Dave left his own car near the station house and they walked to where the Mustang was parked. This time it was more than two thirds into the block. Dave and Bob went into a building at the far end of the street and climbed the stairs to the roof. From there they could see that each building was connected down to the end. They could go all the way to the corner by rooftop and be perched right above the Mustang.

The first three rooftops were no problem. But the fourth, while still connected, was at least twenty-five feet below the third—much too long a drop to be jumped. They would kill themselves trying. Dave glanced at his watch: six thirty.

The question was, should they go down to the sidewalk, run past the lower building and climb the stairs of the next?

"We'd better stay up here," Bob said. "If we go back down, there's a good chance we'll be spotted." So far, they knew they had not been noticed by anyone.

They sneaked around the rooftop, trying to figure out a plan, when Dave came upon a clothesline. Bob glanced at him. "You *gotta* be kidding," he said as Dave walked to the edge of the roof. "Well, listen, Dave—I know you're a steelworker, I mean I know you're used to construction jobs, so you go first. Then if I fall, you'll be down there to catch me."

"What've we got to lose?" Dave said. "The only problem we have is getting back up the other side." The building on the other side was exactly the same height as the one they were on.

Bob cut down the clothesline with a knife and made a lasso.

"Now *you've* gotta be kidding," Dave said.

"Well, what else are we gonna do?"

But Dave was already checking out the lower rooftop. Instead of a doorway leading to an inner staircase, there was only a skylight.

"Well," he said, "this better work. I guarantee you that skylight's locked from the inside. So there's no way out, baby, if we can't get back up to the other roof."

Bob looped the rope over a small brick chimney and tied it securely. Dave dropped it over the edge and lowered himself down. Then Bob started down, but instead of doing it slowly he slid the whole way, burning his hands.

Now both down on the lower level, they **realized** that they needed the rope to get back up to the next roof. So Dave had to climb back up the wall to the roof they had just left, to loosen the rope from the chimney. After about seventeen attempts, he made one supreme effort and struggled his way back up, discovering that now *his* hands were burned.

"All this," he mumbled, "just to get back up to where we started from."

He untied the line from the chimney and this time he looped the rope around it, throwing the two ends down to Bob, who held them as Dave lowered himself down again. Then they let go of one end and pulled the rope from around the chimney.

Bob made another lasso and went to the opposite wall. He started throwing the loop upward to the next roof, but it would not go high enough; the rope was too light. While he kept trying, Dave went to the edge of the roof and broke off a brick.

"Okay," he said, "we'll tie this onto the lasso, and you'll be able to throw it up there easily."

They cut off a piece of the rope and tied the brick onto the loop. Bob stood at the wall and threw it upward toward the roof, but the rock slipped out and went flying over the edge and down to the street.

"Ah!" came a man's voice from down below. "Motherfucker!"

Dave and Bob went back to the task at hand. For another twenty minutes they threw the lasso upward; each time, it fell back down again. Then Bob twirled a huge loop around and around and let it sail. It missed the chimney, but somehow it curved to the left and landed around a jagged piece of brick wall at the corner of the roof on the street side.

Dave applauded. "You weren't aiming for *that*, were you?"

"Of course I was," Bob said. "Perfect aim!"

Dave took the rope. Now he realized how exhausted he'd become from his previous climbing to get the line back.

"Look," he said, "you go first this time."

"Fine," Bob answered, "but as long as I'm going first, why make me climb that high? Why don't you pick me up as high as you can, and then I'll pull myself up the rest of the way?"

Dave nodded. They each had twenty-five feet to climb. If I get him up on my shoulders, he thought, that's six feet plus six feet, or halfway there. Another thirteen feet shouldn't be too bad.

Bob climbed to Dave's shoulders, trying to get his feet lodged, wavering, kicking Dave's nose at one point. Then he grabbed the rope and started up the rest of the way. He inched himself up about seven feet, but he could hold on no longer.

"Watch out," he said. "I'm gonna fall!"

Dave quickly tried to loop the rope around Bob's foot and pull it tight so he'd be secure standing on the line, but the rope made three quick swings around Bob's neck instead.

"Keep going!" he shouted to Bob.

Driven by fright if nothing else, Bob caught his breath and pulled himself—and the bottom part of the rope—up the rest of the way. Now it was Dave's turn. He started climbing, but slid down again. Gripping the rope, he began once more. This time he kept going, all the way to where Bob could grab his hand. Just as Bob reached down, the piece of broken wall to which the rope was tied came loose. All the bricks came out, and Dave fell backward until Bob grabbed his wrist. Dave had swung around the corner of the building, and now he was dangling over the sidewalk instead of the lower roof, held only by Bob's strength.

"I can't hold you," Bob said.

"You fuckin' better."

"Hold onto *me*, Dave!"

"I'm trying. But *you* hold *me*, man!"

They were screaming back and forth at each other, Dave's feet kicking free. People had gathered on the sidewalk below him and were staring up at them both.

Finally Bob managed to pull him up to the roof. Dave's chest was scratched and his stomach was bruised in the process. Just then a radio car came into the block. Somebody had probably called the station to say that two criminals were crawling around on the roof.

One of the cops got out of the car and looked up. He recognized Dave and Bob and shouted, *"What are you guys doing?"*

"Just checking a few escape routes," Dave called back.

It was seven thirty in the morning. They lay down on the roof, figuring that whoever had seen them from the street would be gone after a while. At about ten o'clock, they brushed themselves off and proceeded over the remaining rooftops to the corner. Peeking through some openings in the ledge, they discovered that they had a perfect view of Nathan Turner's Mustang on the street below.

"Now," Dave said, "we wait."

The wait dragged on through the entire day and evening, until ten thirty at night. During those seventeen hours on the rooftops, looking down at the street, they were picking up an education beyond their wildest hopes. They saw the comings and goings of hundreds of junkies, sales on the street every few minutes, hour after hour. "Like a five-and-dime of drugs," Dave observed.

"I almost feel like running down there and just grabbing them all," Bob said.

"I know what you mean. But we came here to watch that car, so that's what we'd better do."

Meanwhile, they concentrated on the faces of the junkies. They observed who was selling dope to whom, which alleys or hallways they were going into and coming out of, the whole range of activity during the day and night. For each new face, they came up with a different nickname. It soon grew into a kind of game, a serious game to test each other's memory.

"Okay," Dave would begin. "There's a guy down on the corner who we named Alex about an hour ago. Without looking, tell me what he's wearing."

"Alex? Uh, Alex is wearing a brown hat."

"Right! Okay, next guy. Now I see, uh, the guy with the face like a pancake. What's his name?"

"Charlie? No, wait a minute. Charlie was the bald one. Uh, Mutzie? No, hold it! Chicken Nuts! The guy with the pancake face is Chicken Nuts!"

"Correct."

At first they had been afraid of someone glancing up and spotting them; oddly enough, they discovered, people on the street never really look up. So they relaxed and continued their watch until it was dark and they were cramped and tired and ready to leave.

Around ten thirty, they saw a man—Nathan Turner, no doubt —get into the blue Mustang. The problem was, they had been distracted by a sexy-looking girl on the corner just as he had walked out of his building, so they did not see which building he had come from.

"Goddamn it," Dave said under his breath. He could hardly bear the thought of going through the whole ordeal again.

Nathan Turner started up the motor and pulled out of his parking space. Suddenly he slammed on the brakes, threw the Mustang in reverse, and backed in again. He jumped out of the car, looked at his watch, and ran across the street into a building—in all likelihood the one he had just left.

"Jesus," Dave said, laughing, "he must've read our minds. Now at least we know where he lives."

A moment later, Turner came running out of the building again. He checked his watch for the second time and hopped back in the car, screeched out of his parking space, and disappeared around the corner.

"Looks like he's got a time schedule to meet," Bob said.

"Quarter of eleven," Dave said. "Let's check him again tomorrow night, same time."

They left by way of the stairs.

The next morning, still off duty, they decided to avoid the rooftops. This time they went to the headquarters of the Telephone Company and announced that they were detectives working for the narcotics squad. They got belts and other paraphernalia and returned to Nathan Turner's block in the early afternoon.

They went into a building halfway down the block, just past the one with the low rooftop, and knocked on a door. An elderly black man answered it.

"Telephone Company," Dave said. "What's wrong with your phone?"

"Nothing."

"Oh. I'm sorry. Must be another apartment."

They continued down the hallway, planning to work their way up as telephone repairmen. Then Dave saw the dumbwaiter. He climbed inside and Bob followed. They pulled themselves up, but it was slow going, since the dumbwaiter had not been used in years. At last they found themselves stuck between the two top floors.

"There must be a huge pile of garbage on top of this thing," Dave said. "Looks like this is as far up as we're going."

They lowered themselves to the second floor from the top and got out there, then climbed the stairs up to the roof. It was just past one in the afternoon, so when they got to the corner and looked down and saw the Mustang, they sprawled out and went to sleep.

In the evening, they took turns watching the car. Shortly after ten thirty, Nathan Turner came out of his building, looked at his watch, and drove off in the Mustang.

The next afternoon as they changed into their uniforms and went out on patrol in car 2031 on the four-to-twelve shift, they knew this was the night they would catch Nathan Turner.

"We're finally gonna get a chance to make a real collar," Dave said. "I hope so, anyway."

"Yeah, but how're we gonna do it legally?"

"Well, we know the guy'll be getting into that Mustang right after ten thirty tonight. We can't stop a car on a routine check and search it, but we *can* stop a car for a violation!"

"In other words," Bob said, "we'll have to *create* a violation."

"Right."

There was a stolen car, parked at Pacific Street and Schenectady Avenue, that they had been watching for a week or two, hoping to see someone get in it so they could make a GLA arrest. It had been stripped to its bare essentials, making it fairly worthless to its owner. Besides, there was no way of tracing the car to the owner anyway, because the plates and identification numbers had been removed.

But now they both realized how they could put this car to good use. Dave jumped the wires and got it started, and Bob got in and drove it back to the corner where the Mustang was parked. Nathan Turner would pull out of his parking space and make a left-hand turn onto a one-way street. He would be in a hurry, as usual, and if he got around the corner and discovered that the one-way street was blocked, he'd back up quickly into the intersection to head the other way down his own street. That little maneuver would constitute a traffic violation.

At around ten thirty, they positioned the stolen car across the one-way street around the corner. They got an ice pick and punctured all four tires; within moments the car sat on the metal rims. Dave took a few essential parts out of the motor.

"Nobody's moving this thing," he said.

They got into the radio car and parked on the other side of the intersection. At about twenty minutes to eleven the Mustang appeared. Nathan Turner made his left-hand turn, saw the stolen car blocking the road, backed into the intersection, swung around, and headed through his own street again.

Dave had intended to pull right up to him and stop him for the violation. But having been successful this far, he hated to bring it to an end. Why not see where he goes?

"Let's stick with it awhile," he said.

They followed the blue Mustang, thinking Turner might be going all the way into Queens. But after only three blocks he slowed down and came to a stop at the curb. Another man came out of a doorway and ran up to the car. Dave and Bob watched as the man took a silver gun from beneath his coat and handed it into the Mustang. At the same time, Nathan Turner passed a large plastic bag out the window to him.

The radio car lurched forward and very nearly flew toward the scene. Dave kept his eyes on the startled Nathan Turner, who was still holding the silver gun in his hand.

The man on the sidewalk, holding the plastic bag full of heroin, started running away down the sidewalk. Bob was already out of the moving radio car and sprinting after him. The man dropped the bag and Bob scooped it up on the run and caught up to him at the corner.

Meanwhile, Dave was standing at the driver's window of the Mustang, glaring down at Turner, who was trying to hide the gun. "What's wrong, Officer?" he was saying as Dave reached through the window and grabbed him by the throat, opening the door with his other hand at the same time. Then all of a sudden Dave released his grip on Turner's throat and in one smooth motion, flung the door wide open, pounced on the gun, and pulled the astonished Turner out of the car.

"How'd you know that gun was there?" Turner said as he picked himself up off the ground.

Dave was about to reply when Bob returned with the second man and the bag of heroin.

"What's this stuff in the bag?" Bob said, almost joking.

"Foot powder," Nathan Turner replied with a straight face.

"Is this yours?" Bob pressed him.

"Yeah, it's my *foot* powder!"

"What do you use it for?"

"My feet!"

Dave and Bob let Turner try to talk his way out of it while they handcuffed both their prisoners. Meanwhile a crowd had materialized out of the alleys and doorways and cellars—junkies who recognized that one of their main sources of dope had been collared.

Perhaps a third of the junkies surrounding them figured they could take the dope for themselves. Another third knew that if Nathan Turner was off the street they would lose their connection and be without their drugs altogether. And the rest, it seemed, were moving in and joining the mob merely because they hated police.

"Kill 'em!" someone shouted.

"Motherfucking pigs! You ain't taking none of our brothers!"

Bottles were smashed and a great roar went up from the crowd. The entire dark street was filled with movement.

"They're not giving these guys up," Dave muttered as he and Bob backed up against the radio car. He reached in and pulled the microphone out of the car, staring at the angry faces of the mob pressing in, and he shouted, "Ten-thirteen! Ten-thirteen! *Ten-thirteen!*"

"Where are you?" came the voice of the dispatcher. "Where are you?"

"Don't worry about that, just *get* here!"

Bob pointed his gun into the air and fired a shot, trying to keep the crowd back.

"Get help!" Dave screamed into the microphone.

"We can't *find* you! *Give your location!*"

Suddenly the mob was on him. He was pulled by the neck away from the car, still holding the microphone, ripping it out of the dashboard. Bob fired another warning shot; and this time the mob drew back. Then someone threw a bottle, and suddenly there was an onslaught of bricks, bottles, beer cans, and garbage. Bob was still holding the bag of heroin; Dave had the silver gun; and they both had the two prisoners. The mob had already been bold enough for one man to have grabbed Dave and pulled him. He had shaken himself free, but now the others were closing in again.

Radio cars poured into the block.

"Hey," Dave told two officers on the scene, "watch these two guys in the car a minute. Me and Hantz have something to do. It'll only take a few moments."

Without speaking, they walked toward the mob. Dave got to the chief agitator among the hecklers and let go with a smashing uppercut to the man's jaw, sending him onto the pavement. A short distance away, Bob had confronted another man who'd been inciting the crowd. "Is there anything else you have to say?" Bob was asking him.

"No, man, I think I said 'bout everything I had to, with all this pig around here."

"Okay," Bob said. "Nothing personal, but—" Bob let his fist finish the sentence.

When they got to the station house, Dave was still annoyed that the situation had gotten out of hand. Are those people gonna be out to get us next time? Do they think we slugged those two guys only because we knew that all those other cops would be backing us up?

"Hey, listen," Dave told the detectives in the squad room. "We'll be right back. We forgot something downstairs. Come on, Bob."

Leaving the precinct at this point was another violation of the regulations, but Dave figured there was some unfinished business. They got into the radio car and he drove back to the scene, cruising slowly, checking out the general mood on the street.

"Let's let these guys know we're here," Dave said, pulling up in front of the poolroom where most of the junkies hung out.

A man opened the door of the place and saw them and yelled, "There they are! There's them yellow motherfuckers! They're big shots with all their friends around!"

He ran back into the pool hall as Dave and Bob jumped from the radio car. They followed him inside, where about thirty men were congregating around the table.

"Here I am, folks!" Dave yelled to them. "And there's nobody with me! This time there's only thirty of you—no three hundred! Whatd'ya want to do?"

"Ah," one of them said. "You bad-ass fucks! You big shots with the guns, man!"

"All right," Dave said. "I'll be back."

He walked outside with Bob and gave him his gun. Then he went back in alone and Bob closed the door behind him. Well, he thought, Bob's gonna be standing right out there, and if he hears a big scuffle he'll come in shooting. He's out there with two guns.

"Hello again," Dave said to the group in the pool hall, and walked up to the man who had taunted him. "I have no—" he cut short his sentence and knocked the man to the floor—"gun now," he finished. "Okay, next? Let's go, folks!"

Nobody moved. Dave turned around and went to the door and knocked. Bob opened it and stepped inside, placing Dave's gun back in his holster.

"Everything all right?" Bob asked.

"Yeah, let's go."

Dave took the wheel of the patrol car and started back to the station house.

When they arrived, a crowd of people was outside. Junkies and their relatives—cousins, aunts, girl friends—were storming the door of the station, screaming about how Greenberg and Hantz had used excessive force in making the arrests. Word had already traveled about the poolroom incident, too, so there was added fury. Greenberg and Hantz were a pair of wild men, cops who'd gone crazy, roaming the precinct and beating up people on sight. Most of the crowd, however, consisted of drug addicts who simply wanted to get rid of the cops who had locked up their connection.

Dave and Bob pushed through the mob into the building. A delegation inside the station house was presenting a complaint. The lieutenant on the desk yelled, "You two guys better stay out of sight! They're out to kill ya!"

Ignoring him, Dave went to the window and scanned the crowd. He heard someone say, "I'll blow that motherfucker's head off." Dave glanced in the direction the voice came from and saw three men, one holding a gun.

"Bob," he said, and once again they went out the door of the station house. They pushed through the crowd and Dave walked up to the man with the gun. He took it away, grabbed him by the collar, and marched his prisoner back through the mob into the building.

It was four in the morning, long past night court, and arraignment procedures would begin at eight. The strain had built from one day to the next—seventeen hours of rooftop surveillance the first day, thirteen hours the second day, and now the preceding twelve hours. Neither Dave nor Bob had been able to sleep much.

When they showed up at Brooklyn Criminal Court, Dave felt as if he were sliding down the other side of a mountain. The court staff saw the condition both of them were in and helped to speed them along—so fast that the whole process took no longer than forty-five minutes, from typing the complaint to appearing before the judge. Turner and the two others were held on bail, but they were out on the street that same day, awaiting trial at a later date.

Driving back to the precinct, Dave and Bob realized they were scheduled to begin work again at four o'clock that afternoon. "No way we can put in another eight hours," Dave said. He couldn't bear the thought of getting into his uniform again. He could hardly keep his eyes open.

Without thinking he had driven into the very block where they had nearly been crushed by the mob the night before. He stopped for a light, rested his chin on the steering wheel, and watched three junkies on the street corner. As if in a dream, he saw a drug transaction take place.

Bob saw it, too. Dave backed his car to the roadside and they leaped out. As the junkies started to run, Dave tackled the one who had made the sale. Bob chased the buyer into an apartment building while the third addict disappeared around the corner.

Dave held on to his man, but Bob had gone and minutes went by with no sign of him. They were way off base—out of their sector, not in uniform, without the radio car, and what if Bob couldn't catch the guy with the envelope?

When he searched his prisoner, he found four or five dozen more envelopes of heroin. Fine, he thought, but we still need the other guy or maybe it'll be illegal search and seizure. Then he heard Bob's voice from the rooftop above them: "I got him!"

Dave looked up and saw his partner leaning over the edge of the building. "Do you have the stuff?"

"Yeah," Bob yelled down.

"Great!"

A crowd was forming again, with many of the same faces from the night before. Bob came out of the building with the junkie and he and Dave stood there with the prisoners as more than a hundred people gathered and slowly moved toward them from three sides. This time, the mob was quiet, waiting to see what Dave and Bob were going to do. In Bed-Stuy, they were accustomed to seeing white cops arrest their own people—usually with a fair amount of physical and verbal abuse—and at the moment they wanted to see just how much abuse these two prisoners would get.

Dave turned to one of the prisoners. "Okay, man. We got you right."

"You got me."

"So let's be cool. We'll take care of business and everything's fine."

"You got no problem with me, brother."

Dave was startled. It was the first time any of these people had called him "brother"—and he looked at the silent crowd and realized that there was a completely different attitude toward him and Bob, one of fear and, possibly, respect.

From the back of the crowd someone yelled, "Fuckin' whitey pigs! Don't let 'em take our brothers!"

"Forget it!" one of the prisoners yelled. "Don't do nothing! When I'm wrong, I'm wrong. When I'm right, then you can come ahead! But they got me! Fuckit—they got me good."

"You sure?"

"Yeah. They got me. I'll take my chances!"

The faces in the crowd were immobile. One man said to another, "C'mon, let's get away from here before we're in trouble."

Dave and Bob escorted their prisoners into the car and strolled around to the front doors. They had not removed their guns at any time, nor had they handed out any verbal or physical abuse. The crowd knew they were cops without a radio to call for help, yet everybody held back.

The eerie silence continued as Dave and Bob got into the front seat of the car and pulled away.

13

"Listen, man," said one of the prisoners in the back seat, "my people want to speak to you guys."

"Who're your people?"

"The people over on Rochester and Sterling, man. I heard they're looking to take care of you two cops. There's a lot of talk, I guess, and it seems it might be worth something to you. They'll do whatever you guys say, I think."

Dave was intrigued. Here was a man they had just arrested for selling dope on a street corner, and he was implying that his "people"—whoever was supplying him with the heroin he was pushing—wanted to make some sort of deal. Probably he and Bob already had made an impact. Maybe Nathan Turner was actually working for someone else—for some main suppliers—and maybe those people had decided to put out feelers to see if he and Bob would stop making narcotics arrests.

What made it even more intriguing was the fact that this man in the back seat had mentioned the area around Rochester Avenue and Sterling Place, the intersection Dave and Bob had watched so closely from the rooftop. The junkies on those sidewalks made hundreds of transactions every hour. Maybe there was a whole army of pushers working for the same supplier.

They took the next two days off, both of them sleeping thirty-six hours straight. At four o'clock the morning of their first tour back, Dave pulled car 2031 in front of the restaurant they frequented at Utica Avenue and Fulton Street. He had cruised slowly past Rochester and Sterling several times; there was no question that this was the hot spot. The idea was to catch the drug pushers legally so you could go to court and convict them, not just jump them in the street and find the drugs and lock them up and then have the case thrown out on the technicality of illegal search and seizure. Until eight that morning, they spent all their free moments trying to figure out how to do the job.

To begin with, observing a drug sale in the proper way was almost impossible if you were in uniform and in a radio car. It was especially difficult, at least in the seven-seven precinct, if your car was number 2031, because it was already known among the pushers and addicts that these two cops would not look the other way if they saw a sale take place.

One way to be rid of both the uniform and the car was to make the necessary observations off duty, as they had done before. But both Dave and Bob were still weary from their four-day marathon—two days off duty, making observations, and then another two full days of work. Their physical and mental resistance was much lower than it should have been.

"The best thing to do," Bob said, "is try the same surveillance *on* duty, and see if we can incorporate the observation and the arrest at the same time."

His idea was simple: abandon the radio car somewhere, while on duty, and change out of uniform into some other clothes. And then get back into uniform and back into the car when the job was done! It was against the department rules, but which was more important, an arrest or a rule?

On their next tour, again midnight to eight, they left the station house with some extra clothes in the car. They took off their hats and jackets and put on windbreakers. The only part of the uniform they kept on was the pants, which would be difficult for anybody to recognize at night.

They parked the radio car as far away from Rochester and Sterling as possible, then went to one end of a block and climbed the fire escape to the roof. From there they watched several pushers making repeated drug sales, remembering clothing and faces and whatever else they could see that would be useful.

After a few hours, they returned to the radio car the way they had come, changed back into uniform, and completed their tour of duty. The next night they brought police walkie-talkies. Bob remained in the radio car, in uniform. Dave changed into his windbreaker and climbed to the roof. Looking down, he saw a man make two drug sales within fifteen minutes. Now a third junkie approached this same pusher.

"Bob?" Dave said into his walkie-talkie. "One male wearing a long white coat is approaching our suspect."

Bob started the car up.

"Conversation taking place," Dave said.

The radio car began to move slowly toward the corner.

"Transaction made!" Dave reported.

Bob pulled the car up to the scene, jumped out, and grabbed the startled man who had just purchased the heroin. Better to get the one with the evidence. The pusher who made the sale had committed a felony, so you could go after him anywhere and at any time later, provided you had the drugs and the person to whom he had sold them.

While Bob grabbed the buyer, Dave watched to see what building the pusher would go into. But in this case, the pusher scrambled to hide beneath a parked car.

Bob handcuffed the prisoner and put him in the radio car. Then he spoke to Dave over the walkie-talkie: "Okay, where's the other guy?"

"Walk straight ahead fifteen feet." Bob obeyed. "Turn left," came the next instruction. Bob turned left. "Look under the car." Bob bent down and looked under the parked car. The pusher looked back at him with an expression of bewilderment.

"Out you go," Bob said.

From the rooftop, Dave could see that the new procedure had worked. Another crowd was forming, however, and his first impulse was to race down to the street and help out. But if he did, everyone would see him and probably figure out that he had been perched up on the roof. It would destroy their scheme in the future.

Calmly, Dave spoke into the walkie-talkie, which was linked to the police radio system. "Seven-seven, Edward here. This is a ten-eighty-five. Two units to Rochester and Sterling. Assist an arrest."

Dave watched from the roof as the two radio cars arrived before the crowd could become unruly. The other cops took both prisoners away in their cars. Bob got in his car and drove off. Dave ran back across the rooftops and down a fire escape and out to the corner, where Bob was waiting for him. He changed back into his uniform as they headed toward the station house.

Up in the squad room, the two prisoners were telling Dave and Bob the names of nearly a dozen heroin pushers within the confines of the precinct. The main areas of concentration were the Rochester-Sterling section and the corners of Albany Avenue and Bergen Street.

"I'm telling you everything," one of the prisoners said, "because I know one of them dudes gave me up."

"What makes you so sure?" Dave asked.

"Hey, man, how else would he know to pull up on us while I'm making a sale? Shit, he came out of nowhere on us. Somebody had us fingered."

"I see you're no fool," Bob said.

"Of course I ain't. Listen, who put the finger on me? How'd you know to pull up on me in the car like that?"

"No," Bob said. "You don't want to know who gave you up."

"Yeah, I do! Who was it, man?"

"You don't want to know," Bob repeated.

The pusher became more and more convinced that he had been the victim of a stoolie. By the time he was arraigned and out on bail, he had become a "friend" of Greenberg and Hantz, seeking revenge against the phantom enemies who had "fingered" him.

Meanwhile, Dave and Bob tried the roof routine several more times, alternating between who stayed in the car and who gave instructions from the roof. The pushers and their customers were so startled each time that they needed very little convincing to believe that they too had been double-crossed by someone. Dave and Bob treated these prisoners well, buying them coffee and cigarettes, encouraging them to talk, but always emphasizing that they never revealed the names of people who gave out information.

"Who gave me up?" a prisoner would ask.

"Listen, man," Dave would say. "We don't rat on people. If you gave us information, you wouldn't want us giving out your name, would you?"

"Shit, no!"

"Well, then you can't expect us to rat on the guy that put the finger on you, right?"

One night a call came into the precinct for Dave, from one of the prisoners out on bail: "Listen, my people are willing to set you guys up, providing you stay away from Rochester and Sterling."

"Set us up?"

"Pay you, man."

"Who're your people?"

The caller would not say, but it was clear that Dave and Bob were on to something. The main suppliers of the Rochester-Sterling area were hurting. Another night, coming out of the restaurant at Utica and Fulton, they met up with Willie again. Ever since Willie had set up the Nathan Turner arrest, he had been afraid of the possible repercussions. It was obvious that he felt it was best to keep Dave and Bob on his side, in case he needed protection.

"I think they're after me," Willie said.

"Who?"

"The Hayes brothers, man. I think they know I set you up. You better lay off, man, before they get *me.*"

"Hayes brothers?"

"Yeah, man. John Hayes and Frank Robinson. They're brothers. Also another guy named Joe somebody. He's their brother, too. They got a candy store on the corner of Rochester and Sterling. They're *it,* man. Kilos of stuff coming in and being cut up. Everybody out there is workin' for them, man. They got the word out that they're willing to pay you guys to lay off. I'd say you should get on their payroll, man."

"Listen," Dave said, "you send the word back to them that we're gonna bust their balls. Not only ain't we gonna lay off, we're gonna nail 'em and lock 'em up. You go tell 'em that."

Over the next few weeks, Dave and Bob continued to learn about drugs and about the junkies they were arresting. They took a couple of the prisoners to dinner before going into court. They would earn the defendant's friendship while pumping him for new leads. They made sure to slip a few dollars into the prisoner's pocket and to pledge their help if he wanted to kick his habit.

Whatever good they were able to do—and most of the time it wasn't much—they still found that more and more prisoners, once back on the street on bail, came to them as informants.

As they moved closer toward the Hayes brothers, the Police Department itself threatened to stop them. The Seventy-seventh Precinct detectives, embarrassed by the fact that Dave and Bob were making more narcotics arrests than the rest of the squad put together, retaliated by refusing to make fingerprints for them. Eventually Captain Levitan had another printing machine installed downstairs.

The sergeants, too, were trying to slow them down. Greenberg and Hantz weren't answering their radio calls; they weren't ringing in every hour, as required; they weren't staying in their sector at all; and the sergeants were yelling to the captain about it every day. Worse, they were disrespectful to the sergeants, refusing to salute them and making jokes and ignoring their orders.

The real cause of the sergeants' consternation, however, was that they, too, were being made to look bad. If Dave and Bob could make all these narcotics arrests in, say, Sector Charlie, then why couldn't other cops as well? The fact was that the kind of arrests Dave and Bob were making called for special, unorthodox behavior beyond what was required. Two exceptional cops who were bending and breaking rules to carry out their mission had begun to cause almost total insecurity on the part of nearly everyone else.

Lieutenant O'Shea, meanwhile, had begun writing up daily complaints about them and dropping his memos on the captain's desk. Other patrolmen, especially the old-timers, were content to try to discourage them. "You're wasting your time," they'd say, or, "No one's gonna appreciate what you're doing," or, "You're not doing anything but creating enemies, because you're making everyone else look bad."

Some of the black officers believed that since nearly all of the prisoners that Dave and Bob were bringing in were black, they were probably prejudiced. Then someone pointed out that the precinct population itself was almost totally black.

But the corruption rumor was still strongest. If Greenberg and Hantz are doing all this work, the theory went, it's got to be because they're making a lot of money in graft and bribes and contracts and everything else. And if they're arresting this many people who won't pay them off, imagine how many guys are paying and being let go! They must be making a fortune!

A torrent of complaints and allegations from prisoners and their relatives or friends began to flood the precinct. Charges of physical abuse and illegal procedure were filed with the Police Department's Civilian Complaint Review Board. Dave and Bob interpreted the complaints as attempts by drug pushers to have them transferred or suspended. But each accusation had to be dealt with and disproved; and so the complaints began to have an effect on Dave and Bob's motivation, their concentration, their will.

Through it all, Captain Levitan continued to extend his full backing and encouragement. He had been severely criticized for giving them their own radio car and sector. He had made a number of changes in the squads so that they could work together, and he took the brunt of the remarks from the other men under his command, most of whom had been at the precinct much longer than Dave and Bob. Levitan would tell the complainers, "When you can do the job that these guys are doing, and stand under fire the way they do, then I'll do the same for you."

One night as they were leaving the precinct house, a call came into the switchboard for Dave. He took the phone and recognized Willie's voice at the other end.

"Hey, man, I can't talk long. The people on Rochester and Sterling got a hit set up."

"What?"

"A hit, man! They got a contract on you two guys. I heard the talk, man."

"Who's got the contract, Willie?"

"The bosses!"

"You mean the Hayes brothers?"

Willie had hung up. Dave looked over at Bob, who had overheard one end of the conversation. They left the station house without saying anything to the officers on duty.

On the midnight-to-eight shift the following day, they showed up about an hour before roll call. At eleven fifteen, a call came in for Dave.

"Greenberg here."

"Hey," said an unfamiliar voice on the other end. "You guys are gonna get hit tomorrow."

The line went dead and Dave looked at the clock. Tomorrow? It was midnight in less than an hour. Did "tomorrow" mean right after midnight or the following night?

At eleven forty, another call came into the switchboard. "Greenberg, there's a call for you!"

Dave picked up a phone, but the officer at the switchboard shouted that two lines had calls for him. "Hey, Bob," Dave said, "grab the other."

One of the pushers they had arrested was on Dave's line. "You hear about the hit, brother?"

"You tell me," Dave said.

"A sixty-eight Buick, dark green. License number 9496-KR. New York plates. Three men. Two in the front, one man in the back. They got sawed-off shotguns. Waiting at the restaurant to hit you guys."

"Which restaurant?"

"Over at Utica and Fulton."

"Anything else I should know?"

"Well, I heard five o'clock this morning."

"Thanks," Dave said, hanging up the phone. The information sounded authentic. For one thing, he and Bobby ate their meals in that restaurant all the time. On the four-to-twelve shift, they would stop in for food at around ten thirty or eleven, if they weren't otherwise busy. And on the late tours, midnight to eight in the morning, they would often show up at the place at around five o'clock.

Bob was still on the phone, jotting down what was being said to him. "Restaurant ... Utica and Fulton ... 5 A.M. ... three guys ... shotguns ..."

Bob hung up. "Looks the same as what I got," Dave observed. "Give me what he said."

Bob went over his information. When he was through, Dave confirmed that it was exactly the same as what the other informant had just told him. There were three men out there, waiting to kill them.

When they left the station house for the midnight-to-eight tour, they saw a young black man waiting for them near their car. It was one of the junkies they had arrested for making a buy. He was out on bail. Dave remembered that he had offered to try to help him get into a narcotics program in lieu of going to jail. The young man, Robert, was shaking out of nervousness. For one thing, stoolies never showed up at police stations, because they didn't want other cops to see them and start chasing after them for information. For another, stoolies were afraid of being identified by cops who were on the take from pushers, because a corrupt cop would probably put the word out about who the stoolie was.

But Robert had decided that his information was more important than those other considerations. He told Dave and Bob word for word what they had just heard twice on the phone. Four different informants had come to Dave and Bob with the same story.

They got into the patrol car and drove a few blocks away, trying to decide what to do. At about one thirty in the morning, a call came over the radio to return to the station house.

"What the hell did we do wrong now?" Dave muttered.

When they walked inside, the switchboard operator said, "Don't go away. You got an emergency call—and it's being returned in five minutes. The guy said it's a matter of life and death. Might be just a crank, but you'd better wait here and take it when it comes."

Ten minutes later, the call came in. It was another addict, saying that the "main man" had hired three gunmen from out of state to come to New York and kill them. "They're gonna be sittin' on the southeast corner, at Utica and Fulton, and they're gonna take you when you get outa the car to go into the restaurant. They're gonna lay on the horn, man, to get your attention. And when you come walking up to their car, a sixty-eight Buick, they're gonna blow you away, man. They got pictures of you guys, and they got the number of your police car, and they got your shield numbers, even . . ."

Within the next hour, seven more calls came into the precinct. One anonymous tipster warned, "Not only be careful *what* you eat, but *where* you eat." Since the calls were all taken by the switchboard and the messages relayed secondhand to Dave and Bob, by now every cop in the station house knew that something was up, although they weren't sure just what.

"What we need now is a little independent research," Dave said. "The whole thing could be a setup, to get at our nerves."

They rode to Rochester Avenue and Sterling Place, cruising past the candy store–restaurant where the Hayes brothers apparently were located. It was now about two fifteen, and naturally the place was closed. Dave pulled up in front of the poolroom. There was a crowd on the sidewalk, watching curiously as Dave and Bob got out of the car.

Dave wanted to find two brothers named Steven and James, a pair of junkies who always seemed to know what was going on in the street. He asked among the crowd for them, and someone said they were inside in the pool hall.

They went in and approached Steven and James. Did they know anything about a hit that had been set up? They looked around at the others and stared back in silence.

"Okay," Dave said, grabbing Steven by the collar. "Come with us."

They marched him outside and put him in the radio car and drove back to the precinct. It was not an arrest, although no one else knew that. Inside the station house, Dave told an officer, "Listen, do me a favor and watch this guy. He's here for investigation."

Then he and Bob drove back to the poolroom. Bob got out and walked inside, grabbed James by the arm, and took him out to the car, shoving him into the back seat. Dave drove around the corner.

"Okay," Dave said. "Now listen, James. We're very interested in an occurrence that's supposed to happen in a few hours, at five o'clock this morning. What do you know about it?"

"Hey, man, you know I don't know nothing, man. I don't know nothing, baby."

"Listen, motherfucker, we got your brother. Your brother ain't about to come back unless you play square with us."

"What you mean you got my brother, man? What you doin' with him?"

"Eye for an eye, man. You don't give us what we want, and your brother ain't coming back."

James finally came out with the same information they had heard, with an additional detail that the three hired gunmen were from Maryland.

"Okay," Dave said. "Get out of the car. We'll go cut your brother loose."

When they got back to the station house, some of the cops in the back room were discussing what they had heard so far. Dave and Bob let Steven leave and then they confronted their colleagues.

"Hey," one said. "You better get the squad on this."

"Sounds hot," another said. "Better get some help on it."

Dave was thinking that he didn't want to involve the others. If the information was true—and he already believed it was—he didn't want anybody else getting hurt because of him and Bob. Also he was confident they could handle it by themselves. Left to their own devices, they could come up with a way of capturing the gunmen without even firing a shot.

"Listen," he said, stopping the discussion. "It's all bullshit! Honest, it's just a rumor that me and Bob started. We put it out in the street ourselves, and it just got out of hand! It's not true, so relax! Don't sweat it, guys. The whole thing is a phony."

Bob, he saw, knew exactly what he was saying. This was a personal matter. They would take care of it themselves.

14

For Bob Hantz, knowing the truth reduced the tension a great deal. You only feared what you didn't know or couldn't see. Now they knew what they were facing and he was almost glad to be going into action. Besides, to have such information and not act upon it would be wasteful. The whole ordeal could be looked upon as an opportunity.

They were in the radio car outside the station house, at about three in the morning. The gunmen would be expecting them in about two hours, waiting for them in a 1968 Buick on the southeast corner of Utica and Fulton with sawed-off shotguns.

"These must be just three dumb motherfuckers," Dave said, "because I can't imagine anybody who'd want to kill a cop, never mind two cops, and have so many other people know about it."

But such behavior was typical of the people in the area of Bed-Stuy. The men who hung around on the street corners and in the pool hall would brag about their crimes to each other. If they killed someone, a day later they would be in a bar telling everybody how they had done it. If they robbed a bank, the following day they were buying drinks for everyone in the bar and boasting that the money they were using came from the holdup.

"Either they're three dumb bunnies," Dave went on, "or they're very, very smart. Trying to work on us psychologically. Get us frustrated and scared, to the point where we're gonna be ineffective and as easy for them as they want us to be."

"Also," Bob said, "that thing about having a diversion, getting us over to their car so they can blow us away—that could be jive, you know—so we'll see the car and use a lot of caution and sneak up on it, and they could be laying for us on the roof and take us off that way."

They would have to decide first whether the gunmen would be in the car or not. If not, lots of other cops would have to get involved. They would have to cover rooftops, the streets, other cars, doorways.

"We have to decide on the likeliest theory," Dave said. "So let's put everything we have into thinking that they're gonna be in that car waiting for us."

The best information they had was that the gunmen would be on the southeast corner. The Tip Top Lounge was right across the street, on the southwest corner. There was a way of getting to one of the rooftops through Herkimer Street. Dave suggested that Bob go up on the roof, to the corner of Utica and Fulton, where he could see two or three blocks in all directions and make sure the car was there. Dave would go to the bus stop on Fulton Street about two blocks away. He would stop a bus, get inside, and have the driver take him right to the car, where he could jump out.

"You come down the stairs," Dave said. "That's a two-story building. You come down two stories, and I'll ride the bus two blocks. There won't be any traffic at this time of the morning, and there's no stoplight between the bus stop and the corner. When the bus starts to move, you start down the stairway. You should be coming out of the building at the same time that I'm getting out of the bus. And bango—we surprise 'em."

They went over this general plan several different ways, considering every factor. They would have no way of using the police radio unless they brought walkie-talkies. But if they went back into the station house to get them at this point, the other cops would know that something was up.

They decided to forget the walkie-talkies. It was time to begin, just the two of them.

They split up. Bob walked to Herkimer Street, through the courtyards between the buildings, and climbed up a rear fire escape to one of the rooftops. He crossed several roofs and came to the corner, from which he could watch the Buick parked below. All he could see was the top of the car. But it was there.

From where he squatted he could also see all the way up to the bus stop two blocks away. He would be able to go through the door on the roof and down the stairs. When he came out the front entrance of the building, he would be on the passenger side of the car.

Since the car was facing in the direction of the bus stop, the gunmen would see the bus coming. If Dave was standing inside the bus, near the front, would they see him? Would the driver let him off in the right place? Or would Dave suddenly be out in the street, alone, in full view of the gunmen? Probably, he thought, Dave will ride the rear bumper of the bus so he can jump off at the exact spot.

Bob waited on the roof. He told himself he wasn't nervous. If you're nervous, you make mistakes, and this was no time for an error of any kind. His gun was already in his right hand. He wanted to be at that car with the gun drawn. He had tied the gun to his wrist with a rawhide strap. If he had to hit the ground and draw the gun from his holster at the same time, he would be in trouble. The gun had to be in his hand. No matter how I get down there, no matter how I fall, I have to be holding this gun.

In the distance, he saw the bus.

Dave waited in the shadows of a building for the approaching bus. He planned to get inside and have the driver let him off right at the car. Then he remembered that these men had shotguns. If they opened fire, the bus driver would get hit, too. Dave decided he would have to be outside the bus at all times. In junior high school, he had taken many rides on the rear bumpers of buses; now the experience could be put to use.

When the bus came into the block, Dave stepped out of the shadows to make sure it stopped. It was almost empty. The door opened and Dave put his foot on the step.

"I'm commandeering the bus," he told the driver. "Will you please ask your passengers to leave." He was in uniform, so there was no need to go into a long explanation for the driver's sake.

The driver, although startled by the request, stood up immediately and turned to the three passengers in the bus. "Excuse me," he said. "The Police Department is requesting that this bus be emptied at this time."

When the three passengers had gone, Dave told the driver he

was going to get on the rear bumper. "You'll cross Utica Avenue, and on the corner there should be a green Buick. What I want you to do is pull up past it, so the back of your bus is even with the driver's seat of that car. Don't even come to a full stop. Just slow up, hesitate, and beat it out of there."

"Yes, sir."

Dave got out and started toward the rear of the bus. He wondered if Bob had been able to see all this from the roof. He wondered further if the Buick was really there. From where he was, it was impossible to see that far.

As he climbed onto the bumper, it occurred to him that his gun was still in the holster. That was the wrong place for it to be when he jumped off to face three men with shotguns. But if he grabbed the gun in his hand, it would be too difficult to hold onto the bus during the two-block ride. So he gripped the gun between his teeth.

The bus driver released the brake. This is it, Dave thought. All or nothing. No way for me to back out, because he knows I'm coming.

From the roof, Bob saw the bus start up again. He turned away from the ledge and went to the rooftop door and started down the inner stairs.

The bus shifted gears. Dave had the sensation that he was slipping off the back. He held on, the gun in his mouth. Suddenly the bus came to a stop and Dave realized that he was right next to the Buick. He jumped off and his teeth crunched against the gun, sending a shock through his jaw. He opened his mouth in pain and the gun fell out. He grabbed it in midair, wheeled around, and pointed it in the window at the driver. Bob's face appeared at the same time in the opposite window.

Inside the car were three black men, two in the front and one in back. The man on the passenger side of the front seat had a double-barreled sawed-off shotgun in his lap. The man in the rear seat was holding a pump shotgun.

"Whatcha doin', man?" Dave was shaking inside as he spoke, but he managed to make it seem a routine question.

"You got papers for those guns?" Bob asked.

The three men were silent.

"Motherfuckers," Dave said, forcing a wide grin, his feet planted apart and his gun aimed at them. *"Come out of that car! And you best maintain that white color in your faces! Because when it starts going back to black, that's when I start pulling the trigger!"*

They outnumber us three to two, Dave thought, and they have the big artillery. My gun looks like a water pistol next to theirs.

Cautiously the men emerged from the car. "Easy, now. Easy. Nice and easy," Dave said, looking at the shotguns.

Bob took both weapons and Dave lined up the three men alongside the Buick.

"What are you doing with these?" Bob asked.

"Cop-hunting, man."

"Doing *what?*" Dave could hardly believe what he had just heard.

"Cop-hunting."

"Who sent you cop-hunting?" Dave asked.

"Our boss."

"What'd you get?"

"Five hundred apiece."

"Five hundred apicce! You mean you were gonna kill two cops for five hundred dollars each? That's *all?*"

"Hey, man, they paid our carfare!"

"Carfare from where?"

"Baltimore."

"Baltimore! You mean to tell me they paid you only five hundred bucks to come all the way up from Baltimore to kill cops?"

The three men said nothing.

"Hey," Bob said, "which cops were you looking for?"

"Batman and Robin."

Batman and Robin? Dave thought.

One of the prisoners had a Polaroid photograph in his hand. As Dave was about to take it, he noticed that a crowd had begun to spill out of the Tip Top Lounge into Utica Avenue. He glanced at the picture, which showed a patrol car—number 2031—and the back of an officer getting into the driver's seat.

Suddenly a bottle crashed on the street nearby. The inter-section was filling up with people carrying chairs, bottles, cooking utensils. Bob faced the crowd as it drew closer and said, "Enough!"

Someone looking out a window in one of the buildings must have called the police. It seemed as if the entire precinct was arriving. Radio cars jammed the intersection. A sergeant saw the shotguns and the prisoners, and started giving orders to the other cops—one to handle any traffic, several to break up the crowd, others to watch the Tip Top Lounge. The sergeant then announced that the prisoners should be taken back to the station house.

"We've got to search them first," Dave said.

"You can't search these guys in the street!"

"What do you mean?" Dave shouted. "What if they got *more* guns?"

"You can't toss 'em in the street, Greenberg! Not with that crowd over there!"

"Bullshit!"

The sergeant said something to the effect that he would mention Dave's "disrespect" to the captain, and ordered them to stay away from the prisoners, who would be brought to the station house in two of the radio cars at the scene.

"Go into the precinct," the sergeant told them. "Meet me there."

"Where in hell *else* does he think we're gonna go?" Dave muttered under his breath.

When they got to the station house, the sergeant had already gone in. They checked the inside of his car, knowing that prisoners often leave drugs behind in radio cars. On the rear seat of the sergeant's car, they found ten bags of cocaine and a fully loaded and cocked revolver.

"If I'd had thirty seconds more," one of the prisoners was saying, "that sergeant would've been D.O.A."

It was nearly ten o'clock in the morning, and they were on the way to court with the three gunmen. There had been no way to charge them with possession of the revolver—or the cocaine—because nobody had seen them with it. The assassination attempt was also a charge that could not be proved. Somehow the Polaroid photograph of the radio car had disappeared. Dave suspected that one of the prisoners had swallowed it during the confusion with the crowd.

So the three men would be charged only with "possession of shotguns." Even though they had told Dave and Bob that they were "cop-hunting," the statement had been made before they were informed of their rights. Dave and Bob were happy enough just to have caught them. The only detail that really bothered them was that the gunmen had been paid so little money. Only five hundred dollars apiece for *our lives,* Dave thought.

On the way to court, the prisoners pleaded for mercy. "Hey, man," one was saying, "let's take care of business right here and now. We don't want to take this fall. We can work something out, ya know?"

First they're set to kill us, Dave thought, and now they want us to make a deal! They'd probably pay us off with the same money they got for the hit!

The prisoners abruptly quieted down, refusing to talk about anything aside from their offer to pay Dave and Bob in exchange for dropping the gun-possession charges and making it disorderly conduct instead.

"No deal," Dave said.

So they stopped talking altogether.

At the courthouse, they lodged the prisoners and went up to the complaint room where they waited to go before one of the assistant district attorneys. A small, gray-haired man in a tan suit approached them. "Greenberg and Hantz?"

"Yeah," Dave said.

"I'm Judge Rose."

"You're who?"

"I'm Judge Vinny Rose."

"Judge Rose? Fine. What can we do for you, Your Honor?"

"I want to speak to you before you type up a complaint."

"What complaint?"

"The one on the three defendants," Rose said, naming the men who had been caught with the shotguns.

"Fine," Dave answered.

"See me out in the hall."

As Rose left the complaint room, Dave turned to Bob. "What do you think that was all about?"

"Who knows?"

They went out in the hall to see him. "Hi," he said, smiling. "How are you?" He shook their hands. "I'm representing the defendants."

"I never heard of a judge representing defendants before," Dave said.

"I'm not a judge right now, but I *was* a judge. I carry my title, though. It's a lifelong title."

"Well, what can we do for you?"

"I'll tell you. For a certain consideration, I would advise that you have the complaint typed up as I tell you."

"What's the consideration?"

"Fifteen hundred dollars."

"Fifteen hundred dollars?"

"Yeah."

Dave was almost speechless. "Say that again? You're a judge?"

"Yeah. I'm not a judge right now. I *have* been. And I'll be back on the bench. But right now I'm on a leave of absence to represent the three defendants in your case."

"Who's paying the bill?" Bob asked.

"I am."

Dave said, "You mean to tell me that *you* are going to come up with fifteen hundred dollars for guys you represent?"

"I'm not at liberty to discuss it," said Judge Vinny Rose.

Dave stared at him. Could this whole discussion be real? He wondered why he and Bob hadn't already smashed this little man against the wall. Maybe it was sheer astonishment that held them back. A "judge" trying to bribe them? Maybe, Dave thought, this guy is involved with organized crime. Maybe we can make something of this. "What do we have to do?" he asked.

"Type the complaint up as I state, and before you go on the witness stand at the hearing, I'll tell you what to say. We'll get a reduction of the charges or have the case dismissed."

Now Dave really wanted to smash him. "Do you have any idea what we arrested them *for?*"

"Possession of sawed-off shotguns."

"Do you have any idea *why* they had those shotguns?"

"Tell me."

"They were paid," Dave said, "and what they told me, they were paid five hundred dollars apiece to kill us—my partner and me."

"Is that right?" said Rose. "Well, maybe we can get a little more money for you."

Ordinarily Dave would have lost all control of himself at this moment. But he glanced at Bob, whose face had turned deep red, and replied, "We'll take it under consideration."

"But I want you to put the complaint the way I want it."

"Well, forget about that," Dave said. "We'll put the complaint the way *we* want it. But we'll leave it open enough so we can say whatever we want on the witness stand."

"Did you inform them of their rights before they told you they had been hired to kill you?"

"No."

"Well, make sure you state that."

"Listen, we're not going to say anything that isn't true," Dave went on. "We *didn't* inform them of their rights beforehand because we had no idea they were going to admit that to us. Once we *did* inform them of their rights, they wouldn't make that same statement to us."

"So you'll take all this under consideration?"

"Yeah."

"Fine," Rose said, walking away. They watched him go down the hall and then they returned to the complaint room.

The complaint that was typed up stated that Dave and Bob had captured three men in possession of sawed-off shotguns. That was all. The word "possession" could have different meanings, depending on whether the men were actually holding the shotguns. Theoretically Dave and Bob could testify that they hadn't actually seen the guns in the defendants' hands. They could even testify that they had made an illegal search and seizure, which would result in dismissal of the case for lack of evidence. In other words, the complaint was accurate, but still brief enough to have left everything wide open.

Well, Dave thought, we've lost the assassination-attempt charges, but maybe we'll pick up an ex-judge for attempted bribery on the rebound! It was time to call Captain Levitan. Aside from needing his support and advice, this was also a way of showing him that they were good cops, capable of handling any situation—and that they were honest. This was their chance to eliminate all suspicion.

Bob placed the call. He explained to Levitan that no, this was *not* a theoretical question, but a matter of a real bribe offer from a judge who was temporarily off the bench and acting as the defendants' lawyer.

"Wow!" Levitan replied. "Fifteen hundred is a lot of money to throw a case!"

"Well, let me give you—"

"Wait," the captain interrupted. "Bob, we're on a Department phone! We're probably being tapped! So give me the details, but no names, okay? Not while we're on the phone!"

Bob went over it without using any names.

"Hey," the captain said, "I'm *very* happy, Bob, that you guys called me. *Very* happy. Listen, this eliminates a lot of doubts in my mind."

Bob wondered briefly why he and Dave had to prove anything in the first place. But no matter, he thought; if we need to display our honesty, that's what we'll do.

"Go straight to the District Attorney," Levitan said.

"Right," Bob said. "Will do."

He and Dave discussed it for a few minutes, weighing the consequences of working with a third party. It would be necessary, they realized, in order to have proof against Rose. They would have to go to the District Attorney.

The nearest D.A.'s office was up on the fifth floor of the court building. They went upstairs and asked for David Epstein, who was in charge.

"Epstein isn't in," said the man at the desk. "I'm Arthur Graham, next in charge. What's on your mind?"

"We've been offered a bribe by an attorney. What do we do about it?" Dave wanted to give him the facts without saying too much at this point.

Arthur Graham nearly leaped out of his chair. "You were offered a bribe? How much?"

"Fifteen hundred dollars."

"For what?"

"To have a complaint drawn up a certain way, and to testify according to the lawyer's specifications."

"Okay," Graham said. "Wait a minute, let me get on the phone." He called the Brooklyn D.A.'s office at the Municipal Building. When he hung up he said, "My boss says to find out the particulars."

Dave and Bob were somewhat wary of telling the whole story right here, but it seemed that Graham was in touch with the head man, Eugene Gold himself. So they filled him in about Vinny Rose and his offer.

"Well," Graham said when they had finished, "Vinny's not a judge now. He's a suspended judge. He was indicted in Queens, and they suspended him. We'll have to go to the Municipal Building, and what I'll do is tell the court officer not to have your case called for arraignment until we return."

Dave watched Graham write out a note: "Detain case until officers arrive." The message was sent into the courtroom by courier.

"Now," Graham said, "you're to go down and confirm the deal with Vinny—and then we'll go to Mr. Gold's office. I'll meet you by the front door of this building, and we'll go together."

Dave and Bob went downstairs and found Vinny Rose. "Okay, we got a deal," Dave said. "How much?"

"It's still fifteen hundred."

"Well, who's gonna give us the money?"

Rose looked down at his pocket. "I will," he said.

"Fine," Dave replied.

They left Rose and took a circuitous route to the front door of the courthouse. He must have gotten hold of that money since we first saw him, Dave thought. The connection must be right in this building.

As they walked over to the Municipal Building, Arthur Graham turned to Dave and Bob. "Do you guys really know what you're doing? I mean, it's not going to help you if you create waves."

Dave and Bob glanced at each other and kept walking in silence.

"Besides," Graham went on, "Vinny Rose isn't really such a

bad guy. You know, I went to school with him. He and I belong to the Masons together. I speak to him three or four times a week. He's a good man—takes care of a lot of people. It would really hurt me to see him get jammed up like this. Anyway, your own department is going to come down hard on you for creating a scandal. And the District Attorney's office isn't going to like this, either."

Graham paused, and they strolled a while longer without speaking.

"I'll bet you guys can probably find something to do with that money," Graham continued. "Anyhow, I don't personally think this is such a good idea. And if you ask me, I would play down the whole affair when we get to the boss's office."

It occurred to Dave, as they approached the Municipal Building, that no one had asked Graham's opinion.

On their way into the building, Dave was thinking that both Rose and Graham were in their mid-sixties at least—corrupt, maybe, but old and experienced. Bob and I are probably cutting our own throats. If the District Attorney and the Police Department are going to be so unhappy, maybe our own careers *are* coming to an abrupt end.

They followed Graham up to the D.A.'s office. "Wait here, fellas," he said. "I'll be right out." He went inside to speak to Elliott Golden, chief assistant to Eugene Gold, the Kings County District Attorney.

Dave and Bob waited nervously in the hall. "The whole thing stinks," Bob said.

"If that's what it's all about," Dave said, "I don't want to be any part of it. If it's that crooked, man, I don't *want* to be a cop."

"Same here."

"So let's put this thing right out in the open, where it belongs, and push it to a bust."

Suddenly they were called to go inside. Elliott Golden told them he was extremely interested in the affair. The D.A.'s office, he said, wanted to nail Vinny Rose on this bribery attempt at all costs. Dave and Bob were stunned but pleased by the complete reversal of what Arthur Graham had led them to believe.

They were taken to a conference room, where Eugene Gold

himself stopped in. "Let's get this guy," he said to Golden. Then he turned to Dave and Bob. "You fellas cooperate fully, and listen to whatever Mr. Golden has to say," he said as he left the room.

In the conversation that followed, Golden did most of the talking. He outlined the plan of action: Dave and Bob, after being wired with miniphones, would go back to the courthouse and conclude the deal with Vinny Rose. Members of the D.A.'s office would be nearly to watch the transaction, and they, not Dave and Bob, would make the arrest.

In the midst of this discussion, Arthur Graham stood up and said, "Well, I've got to go back to my office. I'm very busy and, uh, I'll see you later."

It took only a second for Dave to react. "You're making a mistake," he said to Golden. "I'm telling you right now: if you let this man out of this office, Rose is going to know everything we're doing!"

Graham was red-faced, flustered. Golden was curious but confused. "Wait a minute, Greenberg, you don't know what you're talking about."

And Graham came to his own defense. "What do you mean, insinuating something like that?" he shouted. "I'm an assistant district attorney! I brought you down here! People like Vinny Rose should go to jail!"

"Then stay here until we've gone through with the plan," Dave said.

"Okay," Graham shouted, "I will! If you don't want me to go, I'll just call my office!"

"No, no," Golden said to him. "That's all right. You can go."

"Mr. Golden," Dave said, his voice shaking, "if you allow this man to leave this building, our whole deal is a complete washout!"

But Golden was firm. Dave and Bob watched in disbelief as Graham left the Office. They turned back to Golden, who said that now they would proceed with the plan.

Golden paid no attention to their warning. But it's not as if we made accusations behind Graham's back, Dave thought. We said what we felt about Graham while Graham was in the room! So Golden must know that we honestly believe Graham is going to sabotage this arrest if he can. He could have said to Graham, "Listen, stay here until this is over," and that would have solved it! The whole plan would take no more than an hour, Dave was sure. If Golden believed Dave and Bob about Vinny Rose, why wouldn't he give them just a little more faith in reference to Graham? Probably because Graham was an assistant district attorney.

On the way to the wire room to have the miniphones installed under their clothing, Dave hoped for a miracle. Elliott Golden was, after all, second in command of the D.A.'s office for all of Kings County; he and Bob were just two patrolmen. We can't possibly know as much as Golden does. Something, somehow, would prevent Graham from getting to Rose.

A fellow named Johnny Morris was assigned to take care of the wiring. Dave and Bob were searched. They gave over all their possessions in return for a receipt, so there was no way for them to have money in their pockets when they met Rose again. Rose would be in no position to charge that he had been framed with money that wasn't his.

Forty minutes later, with the miniphones strapped to their chests, they left the Municipal Building with Morris and walked back to the courthouse. On the second floor, Morris led them into the men's room, where he turned on their machines.

"I don't want either of you guys to touch anything involving this equipment," he said. "When the time comes to turn them off, *we'll* turn them off."

They went downstairs and approached the door of the courtroom. This was it. If Vinny Rose hadn't been warned, the transaction would be made and he'd be under arrest for bribery.

Dave pushed open the door of the courtroom. He and Bob walked in together, miniphones running, pulse rates rising. The courtroom was crowded with lawyers, cops, defendants, prosecutors. Dave glanced around, trying to spot Vinny Rose. Suddenly he heard the judge's voice.

"What do you mean, you went to the District Attorney's office on a special assignment? How dare you leave my courtroom for any reason without informing me?"

All the faces in the room turned toward them. And there was Vinny Rose, smiling with satisfaction.

They walked toward the assistant district attorney, who was standing near the judge's bench. "Listen," Dave whispered to the

A.D.A. "We were, uh, instructed to do something concerning the guns, the shotguns."

"Tell the bench," the judge shouted.

Dave stared at the A.D.A., silently pleading with him to do something.

"Your Honor," the assistant district attorney said out loud, "these officers were attending to matters concerning the weapons, in order to safeguard them."

The judge scowled. *"Don't hand me that,"* he said. *"These men were up at the Municipal Building, at the district attorney's office! How dare they go up there and leave my courtroom without authority from me?"*

The assistant district attorney looked at Dave and said, "Were you there?"

Dave stared back at him. They had been instructed to tell no one about where they had been. In the silence, he felt a rush of panic, as if they had been trapped by everybody. Then he saw Vinny Rose get up and walk out of the courtroom.

"Okay, Bob," Dave said. "Let's go."

They headed for the door of the courtroom. Rose was in the hall, the money actually hanging out of his pocket.

"Judge Rose?" Dave said. "You want to see us?"

"Want to see you?" Rose answered. "What would I want to see *you* for? Who are you?"

"Don't you remember what you said to us upstairs? About the money?"

"What money? What are you talking about? I don't even know you!"

Rose turned and walked toward the staircase. "Listen," Dave called out, "if you don't want to do this, then *tell* us, and we'll take care of it the way we *were* gonna do it." He hoped they could get something—anything—on the miniphones.

Vinny Rose glanced back and muttered, "You're nothing but two bums."

What to do now? Dave was shaking, sweating. Bob's face had become pale, then flushed. In a daze, they went back to the men's room, where Johnny Morris switched off their miniphones. Then they walked back to the Municipal Building, and into Elliott Golden's office.

"What happened?" he said.

Neither of them could answer. Just what we *told* you would happen, Dave thought. The whole thing blew up in our faces! You allowed us to walk right into a trap! Everything we've done by ourselves has worked out, but we trusted your judgment, and look what happened! *If I had any strength left in me I'd kill you with my bare hands!*

But neither he nor Bob could speak. They just shook their heads. The room seemed to swirl with confusion. Detectives played back the useless tapes and gave Golden the details of what they had seen. "Okay, fellas," someone was saying. "Greenberg? Hantz? That's it for you guys. The rest will be taken care of by this office. You can go back to work."

They went back to the courthouse to see the three prisoners hired to assassinate them. One of them shouted, "Did our lawyer take care of you?"

"No," Bob said. "He doesn't want to make a deal."

"What do you mean, *no deal?* We were *told,* man! We're supposed to be gettin' out of here!"

"Your friend Rose backed out," Bob said.

The prisoners began banging their fists on the cell bars. "Go out and see my wife," one of them yelled. "Go see my wife! She gave Rose the money!"

It figures, Dave thought.

They went out to the hall, where the prisoner's wife was waiting. "What's wrong?" she said.

"Well," Dave told her, "your friend Rose won't go through with it."

"What? I gave him fifteen hundred dollars! We had a deal!"

"Well, he didn't want to give *us* the money," Dave said. "So there isn't any deal."

"That sonofabitch," the wife screamed, hurrying off.

Dave gripped Bob's arm. He could still see the judge glaring at them. He had to know how the judge had learned of their secret trip to the D.A.'s office.

"Let's go," he said.

They went back to the courtroom and waited for the judge to finish with a case. "I was on the bench," he told them in his chambers, "when Vinny Rose came up to me and asked for his case to be called. When I did, he told me that you two were over at the Municipal Building on a special assignment for the district attorney's office."

Then Rose had moved that the case be dismissed for lack of prosecution and "total disrespect by the two police officers who have left this courtroom in such a manner."

The mission was doomed from the start, Dave thought.

Luckily they had a few days off. Dave held on to a slim hope that it might end well after all. The evidence could be introduced to a grand jury and he and Bob would go in and testify. It would be obvious that Arthur Graham had been responsible for things having gone awry. The D.A. could have Graham indicted, and Graham would turn evidence against Rose.

Dave made some calls to the D.A.'s office, but was told that no indictments of any kind were forthcoming concerning Graham and Rose. It was bad enough that the three gunmen, although held on bail, were being charged with gun possession, not attempted assassination; now it was clear that the district attorney had no plans for moving against either an ex-judge who had attempted to bribe them or a member of the D.A.'s office who may well have destroyed one of its own operations.

When Dave and Bob wearily returned to the precinct for work, they could feel the cold stares from the other men. Even guys who had been friendly were now backing away. Word had come back that Greenberg and Hantz had nearly made a deal with three prisoners and a defense lawyer, but that it had blown up. Either they were corrupt or, worse, they were informants who could not be trusted. They were probably working for the Police Commissioner's confidential investigating unit, spying on other cops. They were either crooks who made money from drug pushers or they were stoolies. Or both. Maybe they had been caught planting drug evidence or shaking down pushers, so they were working as informants under the threat of going to prison.

Captain Levitan was waiting for them. He closed the door of his office and asked them to sit down and relax.

"Now," he said, turning up the radio, "fill me in."

Bob was shaking his head. It's a sure thing, Dave thought, that we won't be able to go back to narcotics work for a long time. As close as we were getting, having tried to do the right thing, the pushers—and their main suppliers, the Hayes brothers—have won.

"What happened?" Levitan was saying. "Bob? Dave?"

"Captain," Dave said, "I . . . we, uh . . ."

He couldn't go on. He rubbed the tips of his fingers against his forehead and closed his eyes.

BOOK
3

15

Captain Levitan leaned back in his chair and looked up at the ceiling while Dave finished relating the whole grim story: the Hayes brothers, the three men with shotguns, Vinny Rose, Arthur Graham, Elliott Golden.

"Unbelievable," Bob said. "Never expected it to turn around like that. Maybe we ought to have instant replay—see what we did right wrong. Or maybe just laugh it off."

"I'll say one thing," Dave went on. "As far as we're concerned, Captain, that D.A.'s office is a fucked-up, corrupt piece of shit. And we're fast becoming believers that this whole city is corrupt."

"Take it easy, Dave," Levitan said. "You guys are just too good to go under now, because of what *other* people are doing. If you really are against certain things as much as you're saying, then you'll stay here to do something about it."

Levitan told them that he had once been accused of doing something he hadn't even known he had done. It was probably the reason he was still a captain. If they could believe anyone in the Police Department, it had to be Levitan. He was laying it on the line, not just as their captain, but as a man who understood and to some degree shared their feelings.

"I've been frustrated a *lot* more than you two, over the years," Levitan said. "Stick with it."

In their radio car once again, on the day shift, Dave figured they should avoid the heavy narcotics areas altogether. Then he thought about the Hayes brothers, the invisible men who had paid to have them killed, who supposedly operated out of the candy store–restaurant at Rochester Avenue and Sterling Place.

"We shouldn't go near there for a while," Dave said.

"Right. Let's bounce around. Loosen up."

"Absolutely."

Dave made a left turn, then a right, and headed straight for Rochester and Sterling. "I can't resist," he said. "We'll just drive past, to let them know we're still around."

Bob had begun to laugh. "I *knew* you were going to say that," he replied.

As he drove into the area, Dave noticed a group of young blacks waving to him. He slowed down and heard them singing:

"Dada dada dada dada, *dada* dada dada dada, *Batman!"*

Dave waved back to the kids. This, he realized, was the easiest way to let the Hayes brothers know that he and Bob were working again. These youngsters would spread the word.

"That's where the nicknames came from," Bob said.

"Yeah. And that's why those guys with the shotguns called us Batman and Robin."

It was a boost to the ego—not enough to start the tedious work of rooftop surveillance again, but a pleasant surprise nonetheless.

When they returned to the station house, a package was waiting for them in the back room, addressed to "Batman" Greenberg and "Robin" Hantz. Dave opened it up to find a pair of white Batman T-shirts emblazoned in red with figures of the comic-book characters. There was no return address on the package.

Dave held one of the T-shirts up against Bob. "Perfect fit."

For a while after the assassination attempt, Greenberg and Hantz were content to do their jobs at a less frantic pace. Much of their time was spent in court, where they testified in the trials of their prisoners, earning an almost perfect record of convictions. Dave and Bob were becoming known as "professional witnesses" in court; anticipating how the defense lawyers would try to trip them up, they covered all the bases.

They stayed clear of narcotics work, instead making stolen-car arrests—felony arrests, good for citations—to maintain some level of activity on their records. Once they had taken three or four cars, their colleagues in the precinct starting reacting again. "They're into something else already! Going after stolen-car rings, eh?" But to Dave, it was as if they were beginning all over again.

One night in early June, he realized that they had made a grand larceny auto arrest on each of their last three tours of duty. "Now," he said, "we have to go out and bring in *two* cars at a time."

They went on the four-to-midnight shift; but by eleven o'clock they hadn't come up with anything. Dave was beginning to panic. "We'll blow our whole record," he said to Bob. "Let's go see one of our boys."

Lloyd, a young drug addict, had given them information previously. Hoping to find him, Dave steered the radio car through a couple of darkened blocks, then slowed down. Two blocks away they saw Lloyd standing on a corner with two other guys who were probably junkies as well. Dave circled the area a few times, watching Lloyd from a distance. At last, he was alone. Dave pulled up next to him.

"Lloyd, how're you doing?"

"Hey—Batman!" Lloyd was grinning.

"Listen," Dave said, grinning back. "We need a hot car."

"You need a hot car?"

"Well, no, we want *two* hot cars."

"Yeah? Two! What for?"

"We gotta have two hot cars, and we gotta have 'em right away."

It looked as if Batman and Robin were up to something very big. "All right," he said. "Meet me in an hour."

Around midnight Dave and Bob drove the radio car back to the station house and changed into civilian clothes. They got into Dave's car. Lloyd was waiting for them at the same spot.

"Okay," Lloyd said. "I know where there are two hot cars, but there's no one driving them."

"Wait a minute," Dave said, "you've got to have guys driving them. What good is it to find stolen cars if we don't have the drivers?"

Lloyd shrugged and said okay, they should meet him several blocks away in half an hour. Thirty minutes later, they met Lloyd again. "Okay," he said, "we gotta go over to the Seventy-ninth Precinct, man. The two guys with the stolen cars are gonna get in them and drive me somewhere. They're at a party. Take me over there, and I'll go up and they'll both get in their cars and drive around."

"Yeah," Dave said, "but we'll need a reason for stopping

them—especially since we're off duty." He paused, thinking. "How about if we get the two guys to drag race?"

Lloyd was confused. "How do we do that?"

"Well, you're gonna be riding in one of the cars. So just say to one guy, 'Is this car faster than the other one?' That should get it started."

"All right," Lloyd said. "I'll try."

"You're sure these are the two guys with the stolen cars?" Bob asked him.

"Yeah, man. I went to the party, and when they came in they were telling everybody they got two hot cars, and saying who wants to go for a ride."

"Now, listen," Dave said. "First of all, you have to get them to go from the Seventy-ninth Precinct to the Seventy-seventh Precinct. Then, you have to be out of the car when we apprehend them, because if you're in the car we'll have to lock you up for being in there."

They decided Lloyd would volunteer to referee the drag race, enabling him to be out of the car. The racers would start at one corner, and Lloyd would be down at the other end of the block to see who got there first.

They drove to the building where the party was going on. Lloyd went up to the apartment, returning moments later with the two young men, who got into the stolen cars. Dave followed a short distance behind the car Lloyd was in. The other one was up ahead.

A few moments later, both cars stopped at an intersection. Dave and Bob could see the drivers yelling back and forth to each other through the windows. Then both cars made U-turns and headed toward the Seventy-seventh Precinct.

"That Lloyd is really something," Dave said.

"Better not stay behind them, though. We're two white guys riding around this section at night. They must have seen us once or twice already."

"Okay," Dave said. He turned onto a narrow street and lost sight of the stolen cars.

"Just go to where the drag race is going to be," Bob advised. "It's taking a chance, but they'll probably show up."

When they came to the broad avenue in question, Dave pulled into a parking space and shut off the motor to wait. A few minutes went by. Ten minutes. Half an hour. "Shit," Dave muttered. Forty minutes. Nothing. Forty-five. "Might as well wait the whole hour," he murmured.

Just then Lloyd came walking down the street, holding a red hat in his hand. He went out to the middle of the intersection, gave a shrill whistle, and ran to the sidewalk. The two cars roared toward him, side by side.

Dave and Bob glanced at each other, wondering how to stop them. One of the cars suddenly went out of control. The cars scraped against each other. Both drivers slammed on the brakes, and one car went spinning around, landing on the sidewalk. The other one wound up facing the opposite direction, still in the street.

The two drivers, dazed but unhurt, slowly opened their doors. Dave jumped out of his car and walked toward the scene. And although both he and Bob were in civilian clothes, the drag racers immediately figured they were policemen, turned, and ran.

Bob, wearing sandals, was hardly in a position to chase after two men wearing sneakers, but that was his part of the teamwork.

"Off you go," Dave said.

Bob sprinted down the block; suddenly he broke stride and rounded the left-hand corner, now out of sight. A few seconds later, Dave heard two thunderous gunshots.

When he turned the corner, he saw Bob sprawled on the sidewalk, his gun pointed at the two young men, who were standing up against the wall of the building across the street, shaking. Bob's feet were bleeding profusely.

Almost as soon as Bob had started to run after them, the sandals flew off his feet. Running barefoot, he turned the corner and saw that the sidewalk was covered with pieces of broken glass. Rather than stop, he sped up, running over the glass and cutting his feet open with each step. The two young men were about to duck into an alley, and Bob couldn't bear to run any more. Falling in pain, he fired two shots in the air. The two froze immediately against the building.

"Stay up at that wall!" Bob was yelling.

Dave helped him up. "You're bleeding all over the place," he said.

"Couldn't stop in time," Bob mumbled.

They collected the two prisoners and marched them back around the corner to where the drag race had ended. The police were already responding, undoubtedly because of the warning shots. One of the three radio cars that responded called central command and checked out the license plates. Both cars, they learned, had been stolen just three hours ago.

Meanwhile, a small group of young men had gathered across the street. "Motherfucking pigs," one of them yelled.

Dave looked up at them, then down at Bob's feet. Blood was still pouring out. When one of the young men hollered something abusive again, Dave nodded to Bob and they both started across the street. Two other young men who happened to be passing by, thinking Dave and Bob were after them, opened their hands and dropped a batch of heroin envelopes on the ground.

Startled, Dave turned to them and said, "You're both under arrest for possession of junk."

One of the men still had a glassine envelope in his other hand. He reached up and stuffed it into his mouth. Bob grabbed his throat. "Go ahead, swallow it!"—and, to Bob's amazement, he did.

"Whether we like it or not," Dave laughed, "we just got back into narcotics."

Lieutenant O'Shea was on the desk when they walked into the station house. A pair of sergeants and several other officers were also on hand.

The lieutenant had come on duty at midnight, after which time Dave and Bob were supposedly not working. Seeing them walk in, he scowled. "What have ya got? Narcotics?"

"Yeah," Dave said.

"For what? Sale? Possession? What?"

"Which one?"

"What do you mean, which one? How many prisoners do you have?"

"Four."

"Four for narcotics?"

"No."

"No? Well, what d'ya got?"

"Four prisoners."

"For *what?*" O'Shea screamed, pounding his fist on the desk. The other officers had begun to snicker.

"Stolen car," Dave said.

"I thought you just said narcotics!"

"Oh, yeah. We got that, too."

"Let me get this straight," O'Shea said. "You arrested some people for stealing a car? And you found some drugs in the car? Right?"

"Which car?"

"What do you mean, *which car?* The *stolen* car!"

"Which one?"

"What? How many cars? How many prisoners? Which for narcotics? Explain it to me!"

"Okay," Dave said, keeping a straight face. "We have two stolen cars, with two perpetrators. And two guys for narcotics. In approximately the same time period, but different times. In about the same place, but in different actual locations."

The onlooking officers were now holding their stomachs, they were laughing so hard. O'Shea had stood up, nearly in tears.

"If you think I'm gonna try to put that in the book," he said, "you're out of your mind! You're off duty! You got four different people, two different locations, two stolen cars, and two narcotics, *and you think I'm gonna put that in the book? Uh, uh, not me!* I'm going out for my meal! Come down tomorrow, in the daytime, and let the *next* desk officer book your prisoners."

"But, Lieutenant, you can't just leave us here and—"

"Watch me!" O'Shea screamed, marching out the door of the station house.

"Here we come," Dave was saying as they rode to work after two days off. *"Fuck you, boys,"* he said aloud to the invisible Hayes brothers. "You tried to hit us, so now we're really gonna nail you! We got ourselves together, and we're *vengeance-minded!* You thought we were making drug collars *before,* man? Well, this time we're doing *five times* as much, and we're gonna wipe you out!"

The first thing to do was to contact an informer. It was early afternoon, still a few hours before they had to report for duty, so

Dave drove straight to the corner of Rochester Avenue and Sterling Place. Among the men on the sidewalk was Roy—the one who had been convinced that other people had informed on him. Roy was good for more than mere information; he would be able to set up an actual arrest.

Okay, Dave thought, there's no way for him to know that we want to see him. With these other dudes standing around he'll ignore us. And if we just call him over, everybody'll know he's a stoolie.

Dave and Bob jumped out, walked up to Roy, pushed him against the wall, slapped him in the face, grabbed his arms, threw handcuffs on him, and whisked him into the back seat of Dave's car.

They drove over to Eastern Parkway and removed the handcuffs from him. "Thanks," Roy said. "You guys made that look real as shit! Man, everybody thought I was being got by Batman and Robin!"

"We just need a little information," Dave said. "We need a collar, baby, and I figure you can set us up." Together, they worked out a plan whereby Roy would help them trap one of the drug dealers at Rochester and Sterling.

In the meantime, one of the people who had seen them grab Roy off the corner went running to tell Roy's sister, who in turn raced to the station house. There she found out that he had not been arrested. When she went back to the corner and told everyone what she'd found out, someone shouted, "Then they *kidnapped* him."

Half an hour later, when Dave and Bob reported for work at the station house, twenty-five angry people were inside screaming at the desk officer that Greenberg and Hantz had kidnaped Roy, robbed him, beaten him up, and thrown him in the river.

Captain Levitan was pacing the floor. As soon as he saw Dave and Bob come in, he motioned for them to go into his office.

"All right," Levitan said as he closed the door. "Now, *I'm* gonna tell *you* the story. Because I don't believe *any* of what they're saying out there. You were probably wrong, but as far as I'm concerned, you *can't* be wrong. So," the captain improvised, "I've been made aware of the fact that you are looking for someone in connection with a past robbery. You thought you saw him on the corner of Rochester and Sterling. You got out of your car. You put him in your car to bring him into the precinct. And before you got here, you realized that he was the wrong guy. He identified himself properly; so you released him. Right?"

"Right," Dave said.

"Fine," Levitan said. "Wait here and I'll get rid of this crowd outside."

Within an hour everybody had left the precinct.

They were discussing the fact that the setup with Roy was off when a call came in. Dave took it. Bob watched his partner's face growing pale as the call went on.

"What is it?" Bob asked when Dave hung up.

"Heavy stuff," Dave said. "Heavy, heavy stuff. That was Internal Affairs."

"Internal Affairs?"

"Uh-huh. They want our memo books, covering a big period of time. Nothing else said."

"Oh, man."

"Looks like the rise and fall of the Roman Empire, Bobby. Now we'll never make detectives. Once Internal Affairs gets after you, it's all over. They'll bury us."

"For what, though?"

The Internal Affairs Department's function was to investigate cops on the job and bring them up on charges. Exactly what offense Dave and Bob had committed or would be accused of, they had no way of knowing. All civilian complaints against them—about a dozen, all related to previous narcotics arrests—had proved unfounded. But this was different.

Many of the "dumped" cops in the Seventy-seventh Precinct were happy to fill in the grim details: "Internal Affairs goes around and puts the scare into you, and that's to shake you up so you do something wrong, and they keep gathering evidence, and all of a sudden they swoop down and grab you!"

"That's Gestapo tactics," Dave said.

"Listen," Captain Levitan advised, "don't go near Rochester and Sterling. Stay away from the street over there, until I find out

·211·

what's happening."

"We will," Dave said. "You want to see two paranoid people, Captain, you better look at us."

They went on the midnight-to-eight shift, determined to avoid narcotics again, to just behave well and please everybody and hope that the I.A.D. investigation would wind up, one way or the other. Like the Hayes brothers, Internal Affairs was an invisible enemy that could strike at any moment.

In the radio car at two in the morning, they passed an apartment building that had been burglarized more than a dozen times over the previous two weeks. "Uh-oh," Dave whispered as a man emerged from the cellar doorway to the sidewalk. "Looks like we found the burglar."

They walked up to the man, who had some tools stuck in his back pocket.

"What are you doing?" Dave said. The man was reeking of liquor.

"None of your fucking business."

"Where do you live?"

"None of your fucking business."

"What were you doing down there?"

"None of your fucking business, whitey!"

The discussion went downhill from there, and Dave felt he had no choice but to arrest him. "Okay," he said calmly. "We're taking you in." Nice and easy, Dave thought; no need to do anything rash.

Suddenly the man threw a punch at Bob, hitting him in the jaw and sending him backward over a garbage pail. Dave forgot all about Internal Affairs and started punching the man; and Bob got to his feet and joined in. The man fought back, so the two young cops continued until he was flat on the pavement.

A woman came running out of the building. When she saw what was happening, she started to scream hysterically.

Dave and Bob stopped. By this time the man was curled up on the sidewalk, thoroughly battered.

"What did you do to my husband?"

"Your husband?"

"Yes! *My husband!*"

"Where does your husband live?"

"In this building!"

"In the building?"

"Yes!"

"Well, what was he doing in the cellar?"

"He just took the garbage out! What have you done to him?"

"He took the garbage out at two o'clock in the morning? And he comes out the cellar?"

"Yeah," she sobbed. "If you goes down to the basement with the elevator, you drop the garbage off and come outside. . . ."

Oh, God, Dave thought. It was just a misunderstanding. Wait'll Internal Affairs hears about it! What the hell is *happening* to us?

By the following night, a new charge against them had gone to the Civilian Complaint Review Board: they had "brutally attacked an innocent bystander" during the course of duty.

"The I.A.D., and now C.C.R.B. again," Dave said. "So now that's at least two going after us." Bob tried to shrug it off.

The matter of the burglar who had turned out not to be a burglar was eventually resolved when Captain Levitan convinced him to drop his complaint. Still, Dave and Bob were almost afraid to go out on patrol again.

Levitan was on their side, but the mysterious, ongoing Internal Affairs investigation was taking its toll on their confidence. Over the next few weeks, Dave and Bob heard more and more horrible tales about what happened to cops whenever I.A.D. went after them.

One afternoon Dave decided to call the Internal Affairs Department directly. "Can you tell us why you wanted our memo books?"

"Is that what you called here for?" came the reply. "Don't ever call us again like that."

A week later, the captain called them into his office. "I tried to find out," he said. "I called the I.A.D. office, even went over there. But they won't even speak to me."

"It's hard to believe," Dave told him. "All that work, down the drain. We'll never make detectives with this on our records."

"I don't know what it is," Levitan said, "but I'll back you a hundred percent. And believe me, nothing will hurt you unless it's something involving a crime you committed."

"Captain, we didn't do anything that would warrant criminal charges."

Another week passed. Dave told Levitan, "This Internal Affairs thing is affecting us to the point where we can't function. We can't concentrate on what we're doing. We're jeopardizing one another's lives by going out in the street. And for the first time, I'm afraid to *be* in the street."

It was hard for Dave and Bob to believe that the Police Department would allow two officers to work with the threat of a major accusation over their heads. Other cops would tell them, "If it's a small thing, it would be handled on a division level or by the Civilian Complaint Review Board. But if I.A.D. takes on something, you've had it. Even if you're right, you're wrong. Once they're doing an investigation, they'll make sure you're guilty. It's a matter of time."

As they were changing out of their uniforms one night, Dave strolled over to a fellow officer to ask him something. "Hey, listen," the other cop whispered, "I think I'm being watched. You'd better not talk to me."

That was the limit.

16

Still no word, through July and into August.

"If they'd only tell us what they think we've done," Dave said. "It wouldn't hurt them at all to say, 'Listen, it's not a criminal charge, it's just a violation of the regulations.'"

Even Captain Levitan, despite his words of comfort, probably had some doubts. He had to figure that Internal Affairs couldn't be totally wrong about them.

The captain decided not to allow one of them on the street without the other. In the first place, they were too controversial. Second, too many people—mostly drug pushers—were looking to hurt them.

"It would be unduly jeopardizing another officer's life to have him in the street with either of you," Levitan said. "Besides, while the two of you are together, you're fully capable of looking out for each other, and the chances of your being hurt are very slight."

Thereafter, whenever Dave or Bob happened to be off duty, the other was assigned to clerical duty, prohibited from leaving the station house. If one of them had to go to court alone, the other would take the day off.

One Friday morning, Dave went to court so Bob went to the beach. Dave got out of court early, and returned to the station house.

"Hey," Levitan said when he saw Dave come in. "Put on your civilian clothes—we're going over to the Famous for some lunch."

The Famous Restaurant on Eastern Parkway was one of the cleanest places in the area. The owners apparently were in love with cops from the Seventy-seventh Precinct; they would never take the cops' money. The food was great, but the prices for policemen were even better.

Dave and Captain Levitan were getting settled at a table when one of the owners approached them. Levitan shook his hand. "I guess you know Dave Greenberg here."

"No," said the owner. "I've never met him."

Captain Levitan shot a glance at Dave. "You're kidding me."

"No, I've never had the pleasure of meeting him," the owner replied.

The captain refused to believe it. "Maybe you just don't recognize him. He's Bob Hantz's partner."

The owner shook his head.

"Captain," Dave said, "he's not going to know us, because we've never been in this place."

"Well," Levitan went on, unable to hide his amazement, "I want you to know that this man and his partner are the two very best cops that I've ever had under my command. I'd appreciate it if you'd treat them accordingly."

When the owner left, Dave said, "You're wasting your time, sir. Because this is the first and probably the last time I'll come into this restaurant, unless I'm with you again."

"Really? Why?"

Dave explained that he and Bob didn't want to be associated with cops who came into the Famous, because the officers were taking advantage of the owners.

The captain shook his head. "I never figured you guys carried things that far," he said. He added that while he wouldn't order his men not to come into the Famous, he wished they wouldn't take advantage of the proprietors. "Coming here for a meal is one thing," he said, "but otherwise, I'm gonna see that it's stopped."

When they left, Levitan picked up the check and paid for himself and Dave, in full.

The shadow over them lifted just as suddenly as it had appeared. Again there was very little explanation.

"Come and pick up your memo books," said the caller from Internal Affairs.

"Well," Levitan told them when they repeated the latest development, "they're leaving you alone."

"What do you mean, leaving us alone?"

"If they're telling you to come up and get your memo books, if they haven't come to your house and arrested you, if they didn't get you suspended, then you beat them!"

"We did?"

"Sure. Let me tell you guys—you're the first two men I've ever known that beat I.A.D. I'm delighted."

It turned out that the investigation had started because of the trouble with Roy, the stoolie they had taken off the street that day. Unreal, Dave thought. That misunderstanding could have been cleaned up in a few minutes! For that one little incident, they kept us hanging for weeks and weeks and weeks!

"One good thing came out of it," Bob said. "If *they* couldn't frame us, no one can."

"You're right. This is the last time, Bob, we're going to be disturbed by that shit. It'll disturb us, I guess, but it won't affect our work, our output. Let's go, man. We've got a lot of catching up to do."

He drove the radio car directly to Rochester Avenue and Sterling Place. Dave wanted to jump out and declare war on everybody in the "drug exchange"—the Hayes brothers, the pushers, the junkies, all of them. Then he saw one of their stoolies—a young man they had helped into a rehabilitation program in lieu of jail. The kid was probably back on the junk by now. Dave called him over to the car.

"Meet us later," he told the stoolie, giving him an address where they could talk without being observed.

To go on the offensive again, they would have to do something different. Make a splash. The key was to use control, forethought, advance planning. It was nice to be back.

They told the stoolie that they were going after something big, preferably one of the Hayes brothers' top dealers. The stoolie clammed up about the Hayes operation, but he mentioned a man named Victor Woods. "He's one of the biggest guys over there," the stoolie said.

"Where?"

"Rochester and Sterling, man. Everybody's doing one, maybe two bundles a day, but Victor Woods is doing *five*, man. And he's been tellin' everybody that he paid off Batman and Robin. He says that's why you never got him."

"He's telling people that he paid us off?"

"Yeah, man. He's bragging about it."

That was all Dave needed to hear. They thanked the stoolie and went for a meal at a diner on Fulton Street.

"I want that Woods guy so bad I can taste him," Dave said.

"Sounds pretty slick," Bob commented. "He's doing a big business for himself."

The stoolie had given them a description of Victor Woods' operation. The setting included two tenement buildings facing the sidewalk, several feet apart, separated by an alley, *below* sidewalk level, down a flight of five concrete steps. Woods would wait for his customers at the top of the steps, on the sidewalk and between the two buildings. When a verbal deal was made, Woods and his buyer would go down the steps into the alley, almost out of sight, to complete the exchange of heroin and money.

"The problem," Dave said, "is to find a place to hide so we can see this guy make a transaction and also be in a position to grab him right away."

They went off duty at midnight. After a few hours of sleep at Dave's apartment, they got up and drove into Bedford-Stuyvesant again at five thirty in the morning. They parked several blocks away from Rochester Avenue and walked to Victor Woods' place of business.

The street was deserted. Dave knew they had to conceal themselves quickly; two white men in this area would be noticed immediately. They noticed that there was a huge pile of garbage several feet high, starting about fifteen feet from the bottom of the steps. Apparently the people had been throwing garbage out of the windows over a long period of time.

"Am I reading your mind right?" Bob said.

"You know it, baby. We've got to become gophers."

It took them several minutes to get far enough into the mountain of garbage so they were concealed.

"Phew," Bob whispered. "The smell, man. The smell!"

"The trouble is," Dave said, "I can't see a fucking thing."

"Neither can I."

"Wait here," Dave said, crawling out again. He brushed himself off and walked up the steps to the sidewalk. Four blocks over, he found a twenty-four-hour Puerto Rican *bodega*, where he purchased two rolls of toilet paper. It was just past six in the morning. When he got back to the alley, he saw that Bob was hidden under the garbage. Then he noticed something moving—Bob's nose, which had a clothespin stuck on it.

"Hey, Pinocchio—I'm back."

"Can't take the smell, Dave."

"Listen, I got two rolls of toilet paper."

"What for? I'm not staying in here *that* long."

Dave unwound the toilet paper down to the two cardboard cylinders. "Binoculars," he said, burrowing back into the mound of garbage. Concealed again, he handed a cylinder to Bob, so that now they could both see outside.

"You're right about the smell," Dave said. "Hey, these telescopes are pretty good."

"Oh, Dave, they're terrific. Wonderful. I couldn't be happier, man. They never told us about this in the Academy, how exciting it is to be a cop."

After a couple of hours, Bob had to take the clothespin off his nose to breathe. "You sleep awhile," Dave said. "I'll keep watch. Then, if nothing happens, we'll alternate." The only interruption during the next few hours happened when someone tossed a bag of garbage out of a window and it landed near them, startling Dave and waking up Bob.

All morning and into the afternoon they waited. It was getting close to four o'clock, when they would be expected to report for duty. Dave had left a message on the captain's desk, explaining that he and Bob would be starting work early, so they would miss roll call.

Daylight dragged on until past eight o'clock at night. Still no Victor Woods. Maybe the stoolie had given them the wrong information. They had been hiding under the garbage for at least fourteen hours. The later it became, the less Dave wanted to leave, simply because it would mean that they'd wasted their time completely.

At about twenty minutes past nine, a tall, thin man appeared at the top of the steps. He fit the stoolie's description of Victor

Woods. Through the cardboard cylinder, Dave watched as another man approached. Then the two of them came down the steps into the alley, walking right to the edge of the garbage pile, less than three feet away from Dave and Bob.

"Okay," the buyer said. "How's the shit?"

"Dynamite. Two bags should take you right off."

"How much, man?"

"They're fours."

"Four bucks apiece?"

"Yeah, man, it's great stuff," said Victor Woods, reaching into his pocket and taking out one packet of heroin. He turned to the wall of the building, reached up to a ledge, and brought down what looked like more than fifty full glassine envelopes. "How many you want?"

"Fifteen, I guess."

"Sixty bucks."

The transaction was made. Victor Woods stuffed the other envelopes into his pocket and counted the money. Still hiding under the garbage, Dave and Bob watched the two men start to walk out of the alley.

Then Dave remembered his stunt with the box in the garment district. He put the toilet paper cylinder to his mouth: *"Wwwwooooooooooooooo!"*

Bod did the same thing. *"Wwwwwoooooooooooo!"*

Victor Woods and his customer stopped short and turned around. In a husky voice, Bob called, *"Come closer!"*

The two men looked around, too afraid to run, their eyes widening.

"Closer!"

"Wwwwwoooooooooooooooo!"

"Victor," Bob sang. *"This is your conscience!"*

Dave started shaking with laughter. From the outside, the entire mountain of garbage seemed to shake. Victor Woods came closer, as if in a trance. Dave reached out and grabbed his ankle. And Victor Woods proceeded to faint, falling forward onto the pile of garbage, pinning Dave down.

The other man let out a shriek and seemed to fly up the stairs. Like some gargantuan beast rising from the ocean, Bob lunged out of the garbage and caught him at the sidewalk. Dave managed to work his way out of the garbage, from beneath the still unconscious Victor Woods.

Among the people living in the Seventy-seventh precinct, the legend of Batman and Robin picked up where it had left off. Batman and Robin, it was said, had dug a tunnel and had come up through the ground to catch Victor Woods. Batman and Robin had flown off a rooftop. Batman and Robin had stood at the door of an apartment and had allowed a man to fire a gun at them, over and over, and yet they had been unharmed. Batman and Robin had taken revolvers in their hands and crushed them into dust. Batman and Robin had picked up a three-hundred-pound man by the throat and had held him suspended in midair. Batman and Robin were indestructible.

"Hey," a patrolman told Dave and Bob. "I locked up a guy, and he tells me these wild stories about Batman and Robin! So I say, 'Why are they called that?' and he says, 'Oh, man, those guys come from *nowhere*, out of the sky!' And he goes on and on! He tells me, 'There's *no way* you can hide from them, if they want to get you. They're bad-asses,' the guy says. How do you like that?"

Dave didn't mind at all. The junkies were afraid—but now the nicknames were even being used by the junkies' victims. They had begun to believe that a miracle was happening, that Batman and Robin had come to their neighborhoods as saviors.

"We're safe, now," an elderly black woman told Dave.

"How come?"

"Haven't you heard 'bout Batman and Robin?"

"No, tell me," Dave said, grinning.

"Well, I *saw* them. Myself! Up on the roof—and *whoosh*, they flew down and took those bad peoples off the street corner! *Whoosh!*"

More junkies were calling the station house now, asking for Batman and Robin—to the mild annoyance of the switchboard officers:

"You mean Greenberg and Hantz?"

"No, man! Batman and Robin!"

"Okay, okay. *Batman! There's a phone call for you!*"

One night Dave parked the radio car near the pool hall. Wearing their uniforms, he and Bob walked inside, and faced about three dozen men. Without drawing their guns or even making the typical provocative move of adjusting their belts, and without speaking, they moved slowly into the crowd. Dave knew that drug transactions took place here in the poolroom itself, and that some of these men were armed. Several in this crowd would have drugs in their pockets. The objective was simply to frighten someone into dropping his weapon or dope or both, since searching without sufficient cause was illegal.

They chose one particular man whom they recognized from their rooftop observations. They singled him out, stared at him awhile, then headed slowly toward him. The man panicked and reached inside his pockets, taking out several envelopes of heroin and throwing them to the floor. They scooped it up and grabbed him by the arm and marched him outside.

The method worked. Every other night, now, they were appearing at the door of the pool hall. *"Batman and Robin!"* someone would shout. *"They're coming in!"* Guns, knives, drugs would come out of pockets and onto the pool table almost immediately. Dave and Bob made collar after collar this way, in the Heartbreak Hotel, in nightclubs and bars, even on the street.

An informer would tell them, "There's a guy dealing heavy shit on the corner, man. Wearing a gray Panama hat and blue pants." Dave and Bob would pull up in the radio car, get out, swagger toward the crowd on the corner, spot the dealer in the Panama hat, and walk right up to him—knowing there was nothing they could do to him unless he became frightened enough to either run or drop the heroin or try to throw it somewhere. Once the pusher did panic, they made the bust.

Their arrest record soared; more important, they were hurting the Hayes brothers. "You know," Dave said one night, "in a way we're really in debt to the Hayes brothers. I mean, that hit they set up has *made* us, man. That contract made us Batman and Robin! They've probably already saved our lives a lot of times. We're walking into places where any other cops would get their heads blown off. We're walking in and out with prisoners like going to the supermarket!"

17

Each night they seemed to move closer to the Hayes brothers. They concentrated on Rochester Avenue and Sterling Place and on Albany Avenue and Bergen Street, another spot infested with drugs.

"At some point," Dave said, "we're gonna see a crack in the wall. And we'll be right there to jump in."

The Hayes brothers, who still supplied most of the drugs, were behind that wall. But Bob had the feeling they were on some larger adventure together, too. He had come to see Dave Greenberg as a kind of modern Don Quixote, either a genius or a fool; his own life was inextricably bound up with this friend, so much larger than life. He was the second half of the team, the one who would have to back up Batman in every respect. He spent more time with Dave than Dave's own wife did; he knew more about Dave's current thoughts and emotions than Irene could know.

At this point Dave and Bob were making three fourths of the narcotics arrests in the entire precinct, forcing the other cops to step up their activity. Sometimes they scheduled six or seven cases at the courthouse for one day, so they would have time left in the week to get back on the job. They were meeting with informers, building up new leads, helping prisoners with their personal problems. Meanwhile, complaints were pouring into the Review Board from pushers and their families who were trying to get rid of Dave and Bob by tying them up in investigations; but they ignored the complaints, cooperating only when they could find the time.

Suddenly the first crack began to appear. The Hayes brothers, they learned, had put out the word to their pushers to find new ways of avoiding Batman and Robin. Dealers had been advised to make their sales away from the street, using alleys and rented rooms, and to make their transactions in "stages" rather than all at once. For example, a pusher might make a verbal deal at first, then hide the heroin inside a cigarette box, under a radiator in the hallway of a building. That done, he would go outside, through an alley to the next building, and meet his buyer, who would hand over the money. Now the dealer would retrace his steps, pick up the junk, and go put it somewhere else, where the buyer would find it later. This way, Batman and Robin would not be able to see the transaction take place.

Dave saw the shift in strategy as a challenge. When he got word that a Hayes pusher named Clarence Smith had moved his operation into a second-floor room in the Heartbreak Hotel, he and Bob decided to seize the opportunity.

Near midnight they left the radio car, changed clothes, and walked into the dingy hotel posing as a pair of derelicts. In front of each door on the second floor they paused to listen for sounds of activity. Nothing. Perhaps they would wind up hiding for a while, pretending to be winos sleeping off a binge, and try to see which way the junkie traffic was heading. Suddenly Dave stopped and glanced at Bob. They both heard it: *"Click . . . click . . . click . . ."*

Someone behind the door to Apartment 2F was loading a gun. Dave hesitated; they couldn't just barge in without a warrant. Besides, the man would probably open fire once they cracked the door. Then Dave spotted a master-switch box along the wall nearby. He looked at Bob again and winked.

He pulled the lever. The lights went out in the hallway and in several rooms on the floor. They listened in the pitch-black silence. The gun had stopped clicking. After several minutes, Dave turned the lights back on. Still no response. He grabbed the lever, throwing the place into darkness again, and they waited ten minutes more. "Aw, fuck it," Dave said, and he started flipping the lights on and off, on and off, on and off. . . .

"What the hell's going on?"

"Bingo!" Dave whispered.

The door to Apartment 2F flew open and Clarence Smith himself stood there with a loaded, cocked gun in his hand and a hypodermic needle stuck in the other arm, where it had missed the vein because of the lights. Bob kicked the gun out of Smith's hand as Dave's fist crashed into the dealer's face, sending him backward to the floor.

Smith had a lot of junk inside his apartment, having just moved in with it. He picked himself up, shaking his head and saying it was impossible for Batman and Robin to have busted him so fast.

"One of those Brewer cats put you on me, right?"

"Who?"

"The Brewer people, man. Where you been, anyway? Shit, them Brewer brothers are out for blood, man."

Brewer people? What the hell is this guy telling us? Who is Brewer? Then he said to Smith, "Yeah, man, those Brewer people tipped us off. We didn't *ask* for the information, so I don't feel we're ratting on 'em right now. But they just came to us and said, 'Clarence Smith is dealing in shit.' They nailed you."

Clarence Smith started to talk. They listened, carefully, fascinated.

What emerged was a picture of a war between two heroin suppliers in this part of the city. The Hayes brothers, the big suppliers over at Rochester and Sterling, had several pushers working on each corner at any given time.

The Brewer brothers—a much larger, more established operation—were in business all over Brooklyn; they had sent some of their pushers over to Rochester and Sterling to compete for the Hayes brothers' business. In fact, Dave discovered, some of his and Bob's informers were actually working for the Brewers. No wonder they were volunteering information to get the Hayes pushers off the street.

The intriguing part, though, was that the Hayes brothers were picking up steam despite the competition. While the Brewers brought their heroin down from Harlem, the Hayes brothers had begun to import a higher quality of narcotics from Latin America. A man known as the Cuban was said to be the Hayes brothers' new connection. It was "just a matter of time," they were told, before the Hayes brothers became bigger than the Brewers. People were coming from other parts of New York City to buy this high-quality dope, and even some of the junkies loyal to the Brewers had begun to buy it. The Hayes brothers were supposedly getting ready to invade sections controlled by the Brewers!

Dave wondered how far all of this went. Who was the Cuban? Was organized crime involved? How far could two young patrolmen go to find out? How would he and Bob use all this information? The only answer lay in going ahead.

One way to put the pressure on was to play one side against the other. At Rochester Avenue and Sterling Place, there were dealers on all four corners, working for either the Hayes brothers or the Brewer brothers. Dave and Bob showed up at times deliberately to provoke them. In full view of everyone, they would walk up to one of the Brewers' pushers, grab him by the shoulder, and say, "Come over to the car." They would stand there chatting with him, laughing out loud and slapping him on the back, making double-talk. Then, hopping in their car, they would shout, *"Thanks a lot, baby, we'll return the favor!"* Fifteen minutes later they would drive back and pick up one of the Hayes pushers, making it appear that the Brewers' man had informed on him. They would reverse the procedure next time around, and so on, back and forth, until none of the junkies and pushers on either side could trust each other.

More and more calls came into the station house from heroin dealers asking for Batman and Robin and offering new information. A Hayes pusher would say, "Got a Brewers cat for you—cold! He's dealing right now in the alley. . . ." Dave and Bob were getting more leads than they knew what to do with.

Suddenly the pushers changed tactics. Now they called, asking for Batman—not to give information, but to find out what tour Dave and Bob would be working. If they found out Batman and Robin were scheduled to be on patrol from four to midnight, the pushers would stop all activity during that time.

Dave and Bob countered with a scheme of their own. If they were going to be working from four to midnight, they would go right out at four and grab a junkie off the street in front of everyone. The other pushers would figure that Batman and Robin would be finished for the night, because of the tedious paperwork and procedures following any arrest. But Dave and Bob would simply take the junkie back to the station house, tell someone to watch him, and then go back out to begin their real work for the night.

The dope pushers and Batman and Robin had to become inventors, constantly changing the rules of the game. Dave curbed his impulse to go straight to the Hayes brothers' candy store at Rochester and Sterling; it was still not the right time. He and Bob had learned the value of patience, of preparation. It was too easy to spoil the big moment on impulse. What if they crashed into the candy store but the heroin supply wasn't there? It was much better to be absolutely certain. Meanwhile, the best way to hurt the brothers was to keep taking all their dope and their pushers on the street.

Then word came that the Hayes brothers had assigned various lieutenants to take quantities of heroin to new locations in Brooklyn, away from Batman and Robin.

"We're getting close," Bob said one evening. "They can't put the dope out fast enough. As they put it out, we get it. The dope is going out and there's no money coming in. Now they're digging into their *own* pockets. The panic will start to set in."

"Okay," Dave said, "let's increase the pressure some more."

They decided to concentrate on the pool hall, still a major dealing center. The pushers, who now expected frequent visits from Batman and Robin, were posting guards up front. At a warning signal, they would jump out the rear window before Dave and Bob could get inside.

One night they told another patrolman to call the police emergency number at nine o'clock and report that a man with a gun was inside the poolroom. A dozen or so cops would arrive at the front door, while Dave and Bob would be waiting in back for anyone who jumped out. The plan went awry, because they got down inside a courtyard and found they had to climb up the next wall and go over a rooftop to get to the yard behind the poolroom. Stranded in the first courtyard at nine o'clock, they heard the squad cars arriving but could not get to the scene.

When Dave picked up Bob the next day at four to drive him to work, Bob was holding a coil of rope with a grappling hook at one end.

"You *gotta* be joking," Dave laughed. "Where'd you get that thing?"

"Oh, just tripped over it somewhere. I figured we should get scientific about our work. After all, why not use some equipment?"

That evening they asked the same cop to call the police emergency number again at nine o'clock with the fictitious report that a man with a gun was in the poolroom.

When they got to the edge of the first courtyard, six stories high, Dave wondered if they might not be going too far. How in hell were they going to climb all the way up that opposite wall? Bob threw the grappling hook to the other roof, where it caught on the tiny wall along the edge, and tossed the other end of the rope into the yard so it hung down alongside the other building.

They descended the fire escape to the courtyard and looked straight up at the six-story building, the rope dangling in front of them. "You go first," Dave said. Bob grabbed the rope and began pulling his way up, pausing every few feet to catch his breath. He made it to the top in about ten minutes.

Now Dave tried it. He grumbled and cursed, straining, and finally jumped back down. He was rubbing his hands together when he noticed Bob pulling the rope up. "What are you doing?" Dave called. "Tying knots for your feet," Bob shouted down at him. When it was time for another try, Dave grabbed the rope and pulled himself up as if his very life, or Bob's, were at stake. He got up to the fourth floor and paused to rest on a window ledge. He looked in the window and saw a man and a woman, both naked, staring at him in disbelief.

"Excuse me," Dave said. "I'm just passing by. Carry on."

When he got near the top, Bob reached down and pulled him onto the roof. Time was growing very short, so Dave had only a moment to rest. Then they took off across the roof and down a fire escape into the second courtyard, right behind the pool hall.

Well, Bob thought, we've made it this far. He never ceased to be amazed that although he and Dave usually started out with a specific plan, there was always a point beyond which they couldn't predict anything. Whatever happened, they had to depend on their own instincts and reactions. The trick was to keep preparing and refining the plan, then be ready when reality took over. At that moment he always felt alone. He knew that Dave was with him, but he knew, too, that Batman and Robin were far from supermen.

Dave was making some steps out of milk crates, so they could stand tall enough to see through the back window.

"What time is it?" Bob asked.

Before Dave could answer, they heard sirens from the street and a great commotion inside the poolroom. The rear window opened and a silver gun came flying out, followed head first by the owner of the gun. The man landed hard on the milk boxes, crashing and tumbling to the ground.

Bob grabbed the silver gun. He was laughing, as much out of relief as at the sight of this man flying out the window into their obstacle course. Interesting, he thought—we set up the milk crates for one reason, but it turns out they served a whole different function! Better to make preparations than not, even if they're never used for the purpose you had in mind. Meanwhile, Dave searched the man and found forty-seven envelopes of heroin.

Rumors spread afterward that Batman and Robin had been scaling walls all night long. It was said they had been carrying machine guns strapped on their shoulders, and that they had raided several apartments—all this from "eyewitnesses."

The panic was on, at least among the pushers who used the poolroom. The junkies who frequented the place never knew whether Batman and Robin would show up at the front door or through the rear windows. They began posting guards at all the windows, rooftops, alleys, fire escapes, and doors in the area.

Dave relished the challenge. He stayed up nights when he was home, working out new strategies and countermoves; then bounced his ideas off Bob during their long waits at the courthouse. At last they came up with what Dave called "the ultimate caper" to get the two of them into the poolroom *before* anyone else. "They'll be watching for us outside," he said, "but we'll be right there under their noses!"

At about five o'clock in the morning, off duty, they drove into Bedford-Stuyvesant in Dave's car. The pool hall was closed. They climbed a fire escape to the roof of the one-story building that faced the sidewalk. Dave had planned to go through a hole in one of the two skylights, but when he discovered that the one over the bathroom was unlocked, he opened it and eased himself down into the bathroom. Bob followed, shutting the skylight before dropping all the way in.

Now the problem was where to hide. In the far corner of the poolroom, there was a trap door used to stash drugs. When Dave went over and opened it, he discovered it was just a hole full of pipes.

"That's terrific," said Bob. "Just great. What now?"

"Hold it," Dave said. "Think we can fit in there?"

"Oh, man. I guess so, but—"

"Let me try," Dave said. The hole was about four feet deep, not counting the pipes that ran through it at various angles. "Come on," he said, crouching. "Get in and close the door behind you."

So Bob stepped in, shutting the trap door over them. "This is ridiculous," he murmured, trying to make himself reasonably comfortable.

They waited all day. Whenever someone in the building turned on the hot water, the pipes heated up and nearly burned them. They listened to people walking around and conversing above them. Cramped in this small, dark hole, they began to lose all sense of time. The longer they hid, the more firmly they resolved to stay there and wait.

Dave was just beginning to worry—not much seemed to be going on above them—when he heard someone say, "Wade here yet?" Bob stiffened. Another voice said, "Here comes Wade. Hey, Wade! You know this brother? This here's Joseph. He wants to cop, man."

If Dave wasn't mistaken, the guy up there was Wade Gary, a Hayes brothers pusher and a regular at the pool hall. They waited a minute more, hearing the sound of money being counted near the wall along one side of the room, then threw open the trap door and jumped out. *"Okay, that's it, you're under arrest!"*

Wade Gary and his buyer just stood there, utterly shocked. Dave and Bob marched them outside to get help. Word spread quickly around the neighborhood that Batman and Robin had done it again. No one would go to the pool hall any more, not even to play billiards. Within a few days the owners simply shut it down and put huge locks on the door.

"There's a couple of dudes on Fulton Street, doing the Hayes brothers' stuff. One of 'em is Ossie Mayfield, I don't know him personally, but he hangs around the park. Always wearing pretty clothes. . . ."

Dave and Bob listened to the informant, who worked for the Brewer brothers, give a complete physical description of Mayfield. And when they went off duty at four in the afternoon, they decided to stop by the park on their way home.

They sat in Dave's car for about half an hour when a man in a silky purple shirt and darker purple pants, with a stunning white hat, came out of a building and headed directly into the park.

"That's Ossie for sure," Bob said.

"Stay here," Dave answered. "Keep an eye on me. I'm going to go sit on that bench, to get a good look at him. He'll have to walk right by me."

Dave strolled over to the bench and sat down. Casually, he put an arm over the back of the bench and watched Ossie Mayfield out of the corner of his eye. A very good-looking black man in his early twenties, Dave thought.

For some reason he made eye contact with Mayfield, who looked away and then abruptly looked back. Dave crossed his **legs**, turning his head, wondering if the man had recognized him as a policeman. Mayfield sat down next to him and said softly, "Hi!"

Dave glanced at him and said, "Hi?"

"How are you?" Mayfield's voice was seductive.

"I'm fine," Dave said.

"That's good," Mayfield replied, rubbing his knee against Dave's.

"Nice day." Dave felt himself blushing.

"Well," Mayfield said, "what are you doing around here?"

"Just waiting for someone," Dave said.

"Someone special?"

"Actually, I'm waiting for a connection. I met some dude downtown who said he could cop for me. And he told me to wait here in the park. He took my bread and he split. And he hasn't come back yet."

"What were you looking for?"

"Some stuff, man."

"Are you uptight?"

"I'm getting there."

"Well, how much are you shooting?"

"I'm not shooting, man, I'm snorting."

"Oh," said Mayfield. "One of those. Well, if you like, *I* have some fairly good stuff."

"But I don't have any more bread, man. The guy took all my money."

"That's all right." Mayfield smiled and touched Dave's arm gently. "Come with me, okay?"

Dave wondered how far things would have to go before he could make a drug arrest. He stood up and started walking along with Ossie Mayfield, sure that Bob would follow.

In Mayfield's basement apartment, he sat on the couch and tried not to squirm as Mayfield sat down next to him and put a hand on his leg.

"Listen," Dave said, "if you'd like me to stay here, you're going to have to unlock that door. I don't know you, and I don't want to get taken off."

"You know what I want," Mayfield said.

"Right, but at least let's wait until I see what's around the apartment, before you lock the door on me."

"If you insist," Mayfield sighed, getting up and unlocking the door. Now, Dave thought, at least Bob'll be able to get in here if things go wrong.

Mayfield's apartment was large and well furnished, no doubt the result of the money he was making as a drug seller. Dave noticed a large amount of narcotics and works on a table in the hall.

There was a knock at the door. Dave followed Mayfield through the living room again. Maybe it was Bob, posing as a jealous fag, Dave thought with a smile. But the door opened and it was another black guy, coming to buy some heroin.

"You straight?" he asked Mayfield.

"Yeah. This is a friend here. How much you want, Larry?"

"Four."

Dave noticed the tips of Bob's blue sneakers across the hall behind the open stairway door.

"Okay," Ossie Mayfield said, "I'll be right back."

He went into the kitchen to get the heroin for Larry, who remained in the doorway, staring at Dave. When Mayfield returned, he handed the drugs to Larry and asked for his money.

"Now," Dave yelled, and Bob grabbed Larry while Dave took hold of Mayfield's arm. Dave and Bob walked them back inside the apartment and collected the rest of the drugs—sixty bundles of heroin.

By early November 1969, Dave and Bob had put more than half the Hayes brothers' pushers in jail. The brothers were forced to send their lieutenants out on the street to hustle and make sales. More money was needed for bail and legal fees. Meanwhile, the street situation was worsening every day for the Hayes brothers; junkies, afraid of being locked up for buying from them, were taking their business elsewhere. A confrontation with the brothers could not be postponed much longer.

One night, at home, Dave got a call from an informant. "Hey, man," said the caller. "One of your stoolies got a knife in his throat."

"What?"

"He's dead, man."

"Who?"

"Willie."

"Willie!"

"Yeah, man, I think the brothers had him killed, I don't know. Right up at the top floor of 230 Rochester, they found him with a knife to his throat."

"No kidding," Dave whispered.

"Hey, listen, I got something for you."

"Go ahead."

"The brothers, man, they moved all their stuff out of the store."

"Yeah, I know."

"Well, now they're moving it all back in. I'd say they're dirty as shit, man."

"Yeah?"

"No doubt about it. And I hear that about two kilos of stuff are coming in tomorrow. They're gonna be cutting it up and bagging it tomorrow night."

"In the store?"

"Right."

"Thanks, man," Dave said, hanging up.

He thought of Willie, the stoolie who had been killed. With a knife in his throat! Because of his relationship with *us*. It was impossible for Dave to feel guilt: only a sinking, bitter sensation in the pit of the stomach.

It took an hour for Dave to collect his thoughts and decide to call Bob.

"The store is hot," he said on the phone. "It's time."

"I'm ready," Bob replied.

18

Dave parked the radio car three blocks away from the candy store at Rochester and Sterling. He and Bob were in uniform this evening, the seventeenth of November. They had never been inside the candy store. They had never seen the Hayes brothers. But there was no doubt in their minds that this was the moment they were going in there to capture them.

Bob thought of that evening more than a year and a half ago when they had dressed up in Texaco uniforms and had made their first narcotics arrest. All their work since then seemed to have brought them up to this point. When this act is over, Bob thought, we'll have to begin again on some other level.

In preparation for their entrance into the store, Dave had gone to see an informant, a young man named Hershell. Hershell's wife had been arrested for possession of drugs, and Dave had agreed to go to court and inform the judge that her husband was giving him information and that it was Hershell's supply of dope that she had been holding. In return, Hershell had become a trusted friend. Earlier today he had agreed to go into the candy store to make sure the door was unlocked, so Dave and Bob would not have to break in. They still had no idea how to apply for search warrants or even how to use them; besides, they didn't want to involve the detective squad.

They went through an alley and into the back door of a building, down a hallway and out the other side, next to the store, whose entrance was exactly at the corner. It wasn't going to be a great surprise attack, but at least they could avoid being seen by everyone on the block. If the door was unlocked, they would be able to walk right in and make the arrest in a matter of seconds.

Dave pushed the door and it opened. He and Bob stepped through, expecting an immediate and possibly violent reaction. Instead, the inside of the candy store looked like a stage setting. The players were all in position, waiting for the curtain to open. A counter ran along the left wall; three or four tables were at the right and toward the rear; and there was a back room. A young woman behind the counter was serving Hershell coffee. From the descriptions Dave and Bob had been given, they recognized all three Hayes brothers. The heavy-set man in dungarees and a sweatshirt, seated at the counter, was Joe; the second brother, wearing fancy clothes and reading a newspaper at one of the tables, was Frank; and John, also dressed smartly and sporting a wide-brimmed black hat, was standing at the entrance to the back room. Another woman stood behind him.

No one spoke. Dave walked straight toward John while Bob covered the front door. "Excuse me," Dave said, and John stepped aside to let him into the back room. On a table next to the woman were measuring spoons, scales, and glassine envelopes. Nothing illegal so far, Dave thought, but then he remembered that, according to their informants, there were two kilos of heroin in this store and at least one or two guns.

"Where is it?" Dave said softly.

"Where's what?"

Trying not to panic, Dave walked around the store, pulling out drawers and looking for likely hiding places. He glanced only once at Bob. He opened one refrigerator, scanned its contents, closed it, moved it away from the wall. He did the same with the second one. Then he went into the bathroom and pulled the sink out, checking the pipes. He leaned down and ripped the toilet bowl out of the wall. Water poured out all over the floor. I must be losing my mind, he thought.

He reached down and pulled up a floorboard. Then another. And another. He moved through the store, ripping up loose boards, tearing the place apart. *Fuck the law*, he was thinking. No dope! No guns! Nothing! This was supposed to be the bust of our lives, and they're clean, absolutely spotless!

He finished searching and stood there in the middle of the store, breathing heavily and feeling the fury rise in his throat and behind his eyes.

Dave faced the three Hayes brothers. "You're it," he said quickly. "Gonna get you. If it's the last thing either one of us does, we're gonna catch you. If we have to take every dope pusher and every junkie in this entire borough, and put them behind bars, so that you're the only people left, *we're gonna get you!*"

"Whatcha talkin' about, man?"

Dave stared at them for a few moments. "Right now," he said deliberately, "I'm going to give you some names. I'm going to give you a list of a hundred guys that we've locked up, all of them working for you. I'm going to name all your lieutenants, and tell you what they look like. I'm going to tell you about twenty civilian complaints made by your people, and how each one of them has been disproved. I'm going to tell you about our reputation, if you don't already know. I'm going to describe your car, and give you the times when you're getting your drops. I'm going to name the apartments where your people are keeping your stuff. I'm going to name the Brewers' people and your people, and then I'm going to tell you how we're going to go after you until you pack your suitcases and leave town or get locked up for thirty years!"

He rattled off names and places and facts he and Bob had put together during the previous months. This was a personal war that could not be avoided, and Dave wanted them to know it.

At last, one of the brothers reacted. "Hey, man, don't come down on us, man! We're *cool*, man. Listen, let's get it together, ya know? No *reason* for all this heat."

Dave picked up on it. "Okay—what's happening?"

"Hey, man, you're *killing* us. We know that, man. You're driving us out of business!"

"Yeah," Dave said. "So what's on your mind?"

"Take care of our people, man."

"What do you mean, take care of your people?"

"We'll cut you in. We're doing all right."

"What are you doing?"

"Fifteen thousand a week."

"What do you want us to do?"

"Lay off."

"How much?"

"We can discuss it, man. We'll put you on a weekly take."

"Yeah," Dave said, "but we need the collars. So you've got to give up all of Brewers' people—connections, drops, everything."

"That's cool."

"All right, look—we'll have to discuss it by ourselves. We could use some bread. And if we can have the Brewers, it might be a deal. We'll be back."

Dave turned to Bob, and the two of them walked out of the store.

In the radio car again, they slumped down in silence. Dave had no energy to drive. Bob felt his stomach tightening.

"Wouldn't have believed it," Bob said, shivering.

"How about going on the pad?" Dave asked. "Didn't expect *that*, baby. Whoo, shit!"

"We've been knocking their brains out, and they're still doing fifteen thousand dollars a week! Can you imagine what they were doing *before?* Or what they *would* be doing, if we hadn't locked up so many of their people?"

"They know how to spend it, too," Dave said. "They don't want to give it up, man."

"What should we do?"

"Let's go back there, Bobby. Let's see what kind of figures they're coming up with."

To Bob, it sounded for a moment like a replay of the Vinny Rose encounter. He asked Dave for a cigarette, the first one in months.

They sat around one of the tables in the store with the Hayes brothers.

"First, we want to know what it's worth in bread."

"Give us a price, man."

"No, man, you tell us what you're into, so we know what you're making. And then we can give you a price based on that."

"Well, look—you know, it's not our operation."

"Not yours?"

"No, it's the Cuban's."

"What's the Cuban, man?"

"The supplier. He brings the stuff in. He's got one of the biggest things going on the East Coast. It's coming in from Florida. We only work for him."

"Okay, then," Dave said, excited. "Come up with a figure, man."

"Five hundred a week."

"Listen, from what you're talking about, man, you're down in the dumps. We want to show you our good faith. And if you're willing to go for five hundred dollars, I'll tell you what—rather than make you bankrupt, we'll do it for maybe three hundred."

The Hayes brothers looked at each other.

"Listen," Dave went on, "we figure it's worth more to us later than if we try and shake you down now, or hold you up for five hundred a week."

"Okay," Joe answered. "Three hundred a week, if you want."

"Fine. We'll get back to you and let you know whether we agree, man. But let's get down in detail what *you* want."

"Just don't bust our pushers, man. Don't harass 'em. We'll tell our people to wear a certain color hats or shirts or pants—and those are the guys you don't touch."

"What about the Brewers?"

"We'll keep giving you information on the Brewers' people. That's agreed."

"Wait a minute," Dave said. "What happens if we can't nail one of the Brewers, and we need a collar? Would you give one of your guys up?"

"Let you bust one of our people?"

"Yeah. Because we still want the collars, man. And then, for an extra amount of money, we'd cut your man loose in court, with our testimony."

"Sounds okay. You got it."

"Good. Now, we're gonna split, and we'll have to think it over. Call you tomorrow."

That same night they went to see Captain Levitan. Neither Dave nor Bob really knew where it all might lead. If they could actually become part of the Hayes brothers' operation, they might not only lock them up but get to the Cuban as well.

"This is hot," Levitan said. "Too hot for me. In fact, it's too hot for the department. Let me call my own supervisor, the chief inspector, and the Narcotics Division. And let's go right to the D.A.'s office with it."

The next morning, Dave and Bob went to the Brooklyn district attorney's office with instructions to see Sergeant Peter Perrazzo.

"Okay," Perrazzo said enthusiastically when they had finished explaining. "Now we've got to go to my boss."

His boss, Assistant District Attorney Martin Hershey, was also excited and went to see his boss, Chief Assistant District Attorney Elliott Golden. The latter name was quite familiar to Dave and Bob; Golden had left a bad taste in their mouths from the Rose-Graham episode. But this situation with the Hayes brothers would involve a completely different part of the district attorney's office. This was narcotics, and the men assigned to it would be the elite.

When Hershey returned, he reported, "I've been instructed to follow this through. But we don't want any minor arrests. We want to go all the way with this. Whatever the costs—wiretaps, manpower, anything necessary—"

"Does that include going on the pad?" Dave asked.

"Right. Get on the pad. You're covered."

"How?"

"The best thing to do is make the call from here," Hershey said, "so we can tape it. Set up a meet to get your first payoff."

In the wire room, Dave put in a call to the Hayes brothers.

"Hey, Joe," said Dave.

"Yeah. Who's this?"

"Batman."

"Yeah, man, what's up?"

"Listen, we thought over what you were talking about. You want to set up a meet?"

"Yeah."

"You gonna bring the bread with ya?"

"Yeah."

"How much?"

"Three hundred dollars."

"Okay, fine. Where's the meet?"

"Tonight. Eight o'clock."

"Where?" Dave asked.

"Buffalo and Park."

"Okay."

That was it. The tape was played back. Members of the district attorney's staff held various meetings and discussions, in which Dave and Bob were not included, and finally they were told to get wired up with miniphones.

"Now," said the detective in charge of the wiring, "which one of you wants to wear the miniphone?"

Dave was startled. "Which *one* of us wants to wear it?"

"We only got one. The rest are out of order."

"What if we split up or something?" Dave said. "What do we do then?"

"Yeah, that's a point. I know what to do. Use your attaché case."

Dave had an attaché case that he carried with him a great deal, containing notes and photographs.

"Use my attaché case for what?"

"Put the miniphone and recorder in the attaché case. We'll wire it up so it works out of that."

It seemed a little silly, but Dave said nothing.

The detectives threw the miniphone and tape machine into Dave's attaché case and showed them a rubber device to turn it on and off. "Now, when you want it to play, just hit the outside of the case. When you want to shut it off, hit it again."

"That's all there is to it?"

"That's all."

"Do you want us to try it out or something?" Bob asked. "Or show us how to check it out so we know if it's working or not?"

"Don't worry," the detective said. "These machines always work. Besides, we don't want you playing around with it. Don't open this attaché case."

They went back and spoke to various officials again, including A.D.A. Hershey and Sergeant Perrazzo. Dave and Bob were told to show up at the meeting place in Dave's car, wearing civilian clothes, and make the deal. "Take the money," they were told, "and get as much conversation as possible on tape. See if you can get them to talk about what you're *doing* for the money. See if you can get them to talk about the Cuban again. We don't care what you have to do, just go with it. If it falls through or something happens, you can make an arrest. But don't worry about where it goes. And don't try to get in touch with us. We'll contact you."

"Wherever you are," another of the D.A.'s men added, "that's where we'll be. Don't be surprised if a neighborhood drunk walks up to you. He may be one of us. You'll be watched all the time."

With an hour to go, they sat facing each other in a coffee shop, discussing it one more time. Dave glanced down at the attaché case beside him on the seat. It would have been much better if both he and Bob had been wired up. Only one recorder available? Well, the district attorney's men had to know what they were doing. They were experts. Dave figured that at least twenty agents had been assigned to this case. And the F.B.I. was probably involved as well. Maybe even the Secret Service and the C.I.A.

One thing was certain—they were covered. The man sitting over at the counter, reading a copy of the *Daily News*, was probably a plant, Dave thought.

Dave let his mind wander. He and Bob would get into the Hayes brothers' operation as top lieutenants. They would meet the Cuban, who would take them to see the Havana connection in Florida. From there, it was on to Marseilles, France, to the top leaders of an international drug ring. He and Bob would explode the entire worldwide operation. Two young guys from Coney Island, on the police force for only a year and nine months, would be responsible for winning the war on heroin. There would be an invitation to the White House to be greeted by the President . . .

"Let's go," Bob said.

They paid their check and Dave glanced back to see if the plant at the counter was watching. No, his face was buried in the *Daily News*. Good, Dave thought. He doesn't want to blow his cover.

19

It was about eight o'clock when they pulled up at Buffalo Avenue and Park Place in Brooklyn. The area seemed deserted. As they sat in the car, a man crossed the street and stopped at the corner. He looked toward them a moment and Bob gestured with his hand as a sign of recognition. The man turned and walked down the block out of sight.

Meanwhile, Dave was checking out the rooftops. He couldn't see anybody, but he was certain that there were agents all around, providing cover. A curtain moved behind a window on the third floor of an apartment building.

"Holy shit," Dave whispered. "Covers all over. These guys have a whole army out watching us." A woman carrying a baby in her arms walked by the car. "I wonder which one it is," Dave laughed. "The baby or the woman."

"See that cleaning store across the street?" Bob said. "That store is never open this late. I'll bet the D.A.'s men took it over for this operation."

A bus went by. Dave waved to the driver. "We're so well covered, it's amazing," he said. "We don't even need our guns."

A green Chevrolet, about five years old and battered, came around the corner and made a U-turn, swerving into the space in front of them. Two men, not three, were inside the car. Joe and John got out. Where was Frank? The two brothers motioned to Dave and Bob to follow them to the door of the corner building.

Dave hit the side of the attaché case and listened a moment. "It's working," he said.

"Don't you think it's making too much noise?" Bob whispered.

"Nah. Let's go."

They caught up to the two Hayes brothers and went into the darkened hallway with them. "Hey, man, what's happening?" Dave said. "Everything's cool—we haven't taken anybody in the last few days. Where're your heads, man?"

"Okay," Joe said. "Our people will be wearing black Derringer hats. Lay off them. Here's the bread." The brothers counted out separate piles of bills and handed Dave and Bob a hundred and fifty dollars apiece. "Okay, everything's cool?"

"Yeah, man," Dave said, stuffing the cash in his pocket.

There was a momentary silence; Joe and John seemed to be waiting for Dave or Bob to arrest them. When nothing happened, the brothers visibly relaxed.

"Great," Dave said. "We're partners, man. And from now on, we want to know everything coming down, baby, because like I said—we gave you a break on the price. But it's only until you get on your feet. And the only way we'll know you're on your feet is by your telling us what's coming down."

"We dig it, man."

"So from now on, when you're making drops and you're making pickups, we want to know how much you're paying for it, how many people are in the street, when the stuff's being cut, when it's being bagged. We want to know everything there is. And we'll see to it that nobody takes you off. But if we find out you're fucking us, just once, baby, we'll take this operation and put you in the electric chair with it."

Joe and John nodded. Dave figured they had bought his act, but there was no way to be sure.

"Listen," Joe said, "we're making a pickup tonight. You guys want to make a little extra bread?"

"Go ahead, man," Bob said. "Where's it at?"

"We're going by car to a place, man, and we're picking up some stuff from the Cuban. One of you come with us. That way we'll have some protection. If we get stopped for speeding or something, one of you will be in the car to flash your tin and cool it."

Dave felt a surge of excitement at the prospect of meeting the Cuban in person. The first night on the job and we're going right to the top!

"Yeah, man," Dave heard himself saying. "What do we get?"

"A hundred dollars. Just to take a ride."

"Just one of us?"

"Yeah, man. Two white guys and two black guys—that would draw suspicion."

"Okay, that's cool," Dave said, still gripping the attaché case. "I guess I'll be the one to go."

The four men went out to the sidewalk.

"I'm gonna go meet my chick," Bob said. "Listen, Dave, I'll catch you tomorrow. Why don't I leave your car at the precinct? I'll give the keys to the guy at the desk and tell him you'll pick 'em up later."

He turned to the two Hayes brothers. "Joe? John? Good doing business with you. Take care."

Dave and Bob looked at each other for a second. Then Bob turned and walked toward Dave's car.

Dave was told to get in the front passenger seat of the Chevrolet. He put the attaché case on his lap. John was at the wheel and Joe climbed in the back seat. Confident that Bob would be following, Dave decided not to look back. Besides, there were other agents involved.

He tried to relax as the car lurched forward and down Utica Avenue. They came to a red light, but John went through it. At the end of the block, they passed another one.

Dave chuckled. "I guess you guys are just feeling big because I'm a cop, eh? I mean, I'm in the car, so you don't have to sweat the red lights."

Neither one answered. John sped up to nearly seventy miles an hour, took a right turn, then a left, that nearly tipped the car on its side. He stopped, made a U-turn, and headed back to where they had begun, passing two more red lights. Dave looked for his own car with Bob driving it, but the streets were empty. John sped the wrong way through a one-way block, circled around, and then got on the Belt Parkway.

Dave kept silent. Were they trying to lose Bob? Afraid of a take-off? Or some competition tailing us to steal the dope when we make the pickup? He turned around to Joe, hoping to get some more conversation on tape. "Tell me about the Cuban, man." Joe began tossing out some details about how many times a week they picked up heroin from him, what he looked like, the size of his operation. As Joe talked, Dave was wondering how many of those cars on the highway belonged to the D.A.'s squad, and whether Bob was among them. He began to worry about the other agents reacting too fast. He hoped they wouldn't jump on the Cuban right away. Once we get an identification on him, Dave thought, we can always find him. Meanwhile, we should follow this thing as far as we can.

The car took the Coney Island exit off the Belt Parkway. The area was familiar: the amusement park, Surf Avenue, Mermaid and Neptune Avenues, the boardwalk, the shops and stores and tenements, the newer high-rise buildings. Dave knew these streets and buildings as well as anybody did, even in the dark.

They cruised along Surf Avenue—no cars or people around at all—and turned left at West Twenty-seventh Street, a dead-end road that led to the boardwalk. The car slowed to a halt. A police car was parked fifty feet straight ahead of them on the boardwalk. It was a radio car from the Sixtieth Precinct. Cops often drove up and down the wide boardwalk on patrol.

"Turn around," Joe said from the back seat. "He'll be gone in a while."

Dave tensed, thinking Bob was probably following behind. If we go back out of the dead end, he thought, we'll run right into him. But the U-turn was completed and what Dave saw was a deserted street. Empty, desolate, dark, no sign of life. No agents' cars, no Bob. Nothing.

They rode back out of West Twenty-seventh Street, away from the boardwalk, and made a right turn onto Surf Avenue again. Then a left over to Neptune Avenue. Still no sign of anybody following them.

The moment the Hayes brothers had suggested that only one of them ride to the pickup, Bob Hantz began to worry. He hadn't protested because, after all, Dave had the attaché case with the recorder; besides, the brothers would have been suspicious if he and Dave had made a stink. So the moment had passed, and Bob had played along, inventing the story about a girl to meet.

He was alone. Once again Dave was in the center of the action and he, Bob, would have to remain on the sidelines and make all his decisions in a kind of vacuum. If anything happens to Dave, Bob thought . . .

When Dave left with the two drug suppliers, Bob got behind the wheel of Dave's car. He watched the Chevrolet drive off and waited to see how many agents' cars would be trailing it. None appeared. I'm going anyway, Bob said to himself, with or without the D.A.'s men. He started following, staying far enough back to avoid being seen.

The brothers seemed more concerned about shaking off a tail than about anything else. Through all their traffic infractions—jumping lights; driving down a one-way street the wrong way; speeding and making spontaneous U-turns—Bob stayed three or four blocks behind, straining to pick out details that would stand out: one taillight on the Chevrolet was a bit brighter than the other; the rear window was made of some sort of clear plastic.

Picking up speed now, they headed into the fast-moving traffic on the Belt Parkway. On the highway, Bob stayed three or four car lengths behind them. They were doing some fancy lane-changing, moving out as if they knew this route by heart.

Suddenly the Chevrolet jumped a lane and turned off into Coney Island. Bob slowed down, then swerved over in time to make the exit. On Surf Avenue, he stopped three blocks away as the Chevrolet turned into West Twenty-seventh Street, the dead end. There were no obstructions, so he could see the lights of their car. Heading right toward the boardwalk, Bob thought. That must be where the pickup is going to be.

Then he saw the radio car on the boardwalk. The Chevrolet was making a U-turn and coming back to Surf Avenue again. Bob turned into Twenty-fourth Street, another dead end leading to the boardwalk. The brothers must have been scared off by the police car. Dave is covered, he reminded himself, so I can go down here and speak to the cops. The brothers'll be coming back to Twenty-seventh Street, anyway, to make the pickup. He was staking his entire life—and Dave's—on the assumption that Twenty-seventh Street was where they would meet the Cuban.

Bob watched the Chevrolet go by and turn away toward Neptune Avenue. At the end of Twenty-fourth Street he jumped out of the car and ran up on the boardwalk. At the radio car, he held out his shield and said, "Listen, do me a favor and move. Go have your coffee somewhere else."

"What's the matter?" one of the cops asked.

"Listen, I can't discuss it with you. Just leave the area, if you will."

"Need any help?"

"No," Bob said. "But you could hang around a couple of blocks away, if you like. At this point we got more help than we need. But I appreciate your offer."

"What's your name?"

"That's irrelevant. Take the shield number and go!"

When the radio car pulled off down the boardwalk, Bob raced back to Dave's car and drove out to Surf Avenue again. He circled a few blocks, searching for the Chevrolet, but it was nowhere to be seen. Don't worry—Dave's covered. Somebody else has picked him up.

For the past five minutes Dave had seen not a single other car. It was about nine o'clock at night. Nothing happened around here in November. No snow, but it was getting cold and damp and misty. The two brothers had been quiet. Now they were back on Surf Avenue, heading toward Twenty-seventh Street again. The radio car up on the boardwalk was gone. John turned into the dead-end street, slowed down about fifty feet from the boardwalk, under a streetlight, and turned the engine off.

"Okay," John said. "Let's go."

The three of them got out. Dave felt a blast of salt and spray and took a deep breath. He left the attaché case on the floor of the car. No sweat, he thought. Both of them are out of the car, where I can see them. Too awkward to keep carrying that case around with me, anyway.

Don't want any trouble at this point. I guess I'm alone. We must've lost everybody. Well, I still have my gun. They know I've got it stuck under my belt, because they know I'm a cop and a cop carries a gun. Now we'll go meet the Cuban, come back to the car, make the transaction. No problem. Easy does it.

He followed the two brothers toward the boardwalk. Suddenly Joe stopped and said, "Hey, I'll wait in the car."

Shit, Dave thought to himself, wishing he had taken the attaché case with him. Joe was probably just playing it cool, dropping back as a lookout. No sweat. So Dave stayed with John, who was continuing toward the boardwalk. Instead of going up the ramp, John walked under it.

"Doesn't look like anyone's here," Dave said.

"The stuff's here. Don't worry about it."

Okay, Dave thought. If the stuff is here, then the Cuban has to be here.

They went down the steps to the sand, beneath the boardwalk, to a small brick building that housed men's and ladies' rooms. John walked slowly along the length of it. About three fourths of the way, he stopped, reached into the sand, felt around with his fingers, and pulled out a plastic bag full of white powder.

"Pure, uncut stuff," John said.

"I guess the guy isn't showing up, eh?"

"He don't, man. Only once a month we meet him, and that's to pay him."

Dave looked around at the desolate beach. The air was so wet that it might have been raining. He glanced back at the large amount of white powder. Maybe it's just as well Bob isn't here, he thought; I'd really be tempted to make the arrest.

They walked back over the sand and climbed the steps to the street. The Chevrolet was still there. No other cars were around at all. Dave slipped into the front passenger seat again. John was getting behind the wheel. Joe was in the rear seat. That's it for tonight, Dave thought.

Dave's foot was on the attaché case. Something felt strange. Was it open? He started to bend down to see. Suddenly a hand grabbed his hair, pulled his head back. He strained forward but an arm came around and he felt the tip of a knife pressing into his throat.

"He's got a tape recorder!" Joe screamed. *"He's gonna bust us! What're we gonna do? It's a setup!"*

Then Dave felt a gun being jammed into his left side. It was John, at the wheel, with a silver-colored automatic.

"Put your hands up!" Joe was screaming. *"Put your hands up!"*

Dave slowly brought his hands upward and put them behind his head, hoping that Joe would stop pulling his hair. At the moment that pain seemed more important than either the knife or the gun.

"What are we gonna do?"

"I don't know! I don't know!"

"Kill him! He ain't gonna lock me up! Kill him!"

Amid the jumbled shouting, Dave felt as if he were drowning, trapped with the hand yanking his hair and the knife pressing at his throat and the gun hurting his ribs. He wanted to scream, *Kill me, you motherfuckers!* He was sure he was going to die. Images of his mother and father and his wife rolled by. Visions of a thousand faces from the past appeared and exploded like fireworks inside his brain. He remembered that he wasn't even twenty-six years old yet. He knew he was going to die, wanted to die. *Kill me,* he thought. *I deserve it. Get this over with!* And then he had a dream. He could see an image of Bob running toward him frantically like a madman, gun waving around in his hand.

Dave turned his head around just a bit. The dream was real! It *was* Bob! He was racing toward the back of the car, his hair flying. Dave felt the gun leave his side. John was swinging the automatic around to take aim at Bob. Got to warn him, Dave thought.

"Bob!" he yelled. *"Watch it, he's got a gun!"*

When Bob had left the radio car on the boardwalk, he had driven Dave's car back onto Surf Avenue. He went around several blocks, finding no sign of the Chevrolet. Good thing Dave's still being covered by the D.A.'s men, he thought.

Suddenly he saw the Chevrolet through his rear-view mirror. He pulled quickly around a corner and let it pass by. From that angle, he could see the Hayes brothers—and Dave—turn again on West Twenty-seventh Street. Then he waited to see how many detectives or agents were following. No car was behind the Chevrolet.

Holy shit, he thought, there's nothing, nobody, behind him at all. What the hell is going on?

Bob was furious. Why had there been no explanation from the D.A.'s men of just how all this "coverage" was going to be provided? It was the same old story: you were told to trust that the people in charge knew what they were doing. Shut up and obey orders and stop thinking for yourself. What a sham!

And now Dave is all alone. I can't let him down.

The Chevrolet had turned into West Twenty-seventh Street, heading toward the boardwalk again. Bob followed, stopping a block away on the other side of Surf Avenue.

He leaned out the window. The Chevrolet had parked near the boardwalk, about a hundred and fifty yards away from Bob. He scanned the darkened area, shivering. I'll be a son of a bitch, he thought. There's nobody here. There *can't* be anyone here. No detectives, no F.B.I., no D.A.'s squad, no Secret Service, nobody. If they're here, they're invisible. No bums drinking liquor. No women with baby carriages.

Where the hell is everyone?

He grabbed a pair of binoculars out of the glove compartment and adjusted the focus. Good thing the car is under a streetlight, he thought. He could see three men getting out of the Chevrolet. Joe, John, and Dave. Dave doesn't have the attaché case with him. The three of them are walking toward the boardwalk. Wait a minute—one of them, Joe, is going back to the car. He's getting into the rear seat again. No problem. If it's a one-to-one situation, Dave can handle himself.

Don't worry, Dave—I'm here. You're covered, baby. Come on, man, pick up the old mental telepathy. You're not alone. It's together, Davey.

He waited, still a hundred and fifty yards away, straining to see where Dave and John would emerge. There—they were coming out from under the boardwalk. John is getting back into the driver's seat. Dave is jumping into the front again with him. Fine. But hold it—his hands are going up behind his head. Only two kinds of people do that—P.O.W.'s and guys that get locked up. Never seen Dave do that. Something's going down, and it's bad.

Bob opened the car door quietly and stepped out. He put his elbows on the hood and focused the field glasses again. Dave's hands are staying on his head. That's a bad sign, Bob thought. He threw the binoculars into the car and hustled across Surf Avenue. Now a hundred yards separated him from the Chevrolet. It seemed like a mile. It was harder to see without the glasses, but somehow he was able to concentrate on what he'd seen before. No movement yet, and Dave's hands were still up. Bob broke into a trot, heading toward the car. Then he started to run. I'm coming, Dave, I'm coming!

Within a few strides, he was running for all he was worth, practically flying over the wet ground. He was within fifteen feet of the car when he saw a hand pulling Dave's head back. Then he heard Dave's voice: *"Bob! Watch it, he's got a gun!"*

Bob saw a knife, not a gun—at Dave's throat. Even if I shoot the guy with the knife, what's to prevent him from slitting Dave's throat as he goes down? Have to hit him with enough to make him stop what he's doing, make him fall forward, not backward.

He had come closer to the side of the car, from the rear. He took quick aim at the guy with the knife, wondering about the gun that Dave had yelled about, but there was no time to do anything except open fire. In that one second as he pulled the trigger he remembered how he had despised violence all his life, in Brooklyn or Vietnam or wherever, and that he had never killed a man or even shot anyone, and yet he was about to do it, do it, do it . . .

In that split second, Dave instinctively reached down and grabbed his gun out of his pants. *I'm going to die, but this motherfucker with the gun is coming with me!* Gunfire exploded around him. The knife came off his throat. Am I bleeding to death? He's already slit my neck! He jabbed his gun into John's side and squeezed the trigger. *Is Bobby safe?* John fell across Dave's lap, and Dave put the gun at the guy's head and pulled the trigger again. He fired over and over, thinking he was going out of his mind. Blood was rolling down his own neck and chest. He kept firing and firing into the man's head, lost in the deafening sound, not knowing whether it was the noise of everyone firing at once or of madness or of his own violent death.

Bob was firing at Joe in the back seat. Joe had kept the knife at Dave's throat. Bob fired into the side of his face. Joe shook it off. The knife moved away from Dave's throat, still in Joe's hand, but now the man was actually rising up to stab Dave on top of the head! Stunned, Bob fired again, hearing another gunshot at the same time. Then another, and another. *Why isn't this guy with the knife laying down and dying? He's not even limp, he's still moving!* Bob stuck his gun inside the car with one hand, trying to push Joe with the other, but the guy was pushing back! Bob fired again and again and again and again—until Joe went limp.

Echoes seemed to crowd in from all over, as if bouncing from buildings miles away. Cloudy—misty—and now the air was filled with gunsmoke. The smell of salt and spray, and now the stench of gunpowder. Blood and shit and vomit. Bob hesitated, allowing it all to settle. *Am I the only one left alive?*

Everything had stopped. Silence. No movement in the car. He stumbled toward the front passenger door. Three dead bodies. He bent down, weeping, and saw Dave's face. His throat wasn't cut. Dave had both men's blood all over him. His eyes opened!

"Are you hit?" Bob whispered, crying. "Are you all right?"

Dave looked up at him like a little child. His lips were moving. "Thanks." And for the first time, Dave realized that he was still alive. "I'm not dead," he whispered.

Bob pulled him out of the car, slowly, carefully. They stood facing each other, both of them covered with blood. The bodies in the car were twisted, wrecked. They looked at each other without speaking, touching themselves to make sure their own bodies were intact. Blood covered everything—the car, the street, them.

Bob took a few steps toward the middle of the road. He peered into the darkness of this deserted section of Coney Island, feeling the silence all around him. No movement anywhere. He lifted his head and yelled louder than he had ever done in his life:

"There's no cover here! There ain't nobody here! We're alone, man, there's nobody here! We're alone!"

BOOK

4

20

Dave Greenberg sat, covered with blood, on the curb of West Twenty-seventh Street. In the cold darkness of this November night it seemed as if his entire life had stopped right here in Coney Island, where it had begun twenty-six years ago. A salty wind was coming in from the pitch-black water, over the boardwalk, and two men lay dead in the Chevrolet several feet away from him.

He put his head in his hands. We killed two men—to save our lives, but why did it have to happen that way? The echo of the gunshots still pounded inside his head, all mixed up with the sound of Bob's voice, which was just settling over the street, blending with the fog and the mist.

Bob sat down next to him, shivering. A radio car from the Sixtieth Precinct turned the corner from Surf Avenue and came toward them, its top light swirling around. It stopped in front of them, behind the Chevrolet. The two uniformed officers who got out were the same ones who had been parked on the boardwalk earlier. They recognized Bob from their brief meeting.

"You guys all right?"

"Yeah," Dave replied.

"I'll go check the car."

"I don't think you ought to go look in there," Dave warned.

"Why not?"

"Two dead bodies, man. It's a mess."

"So what? Shit, I been on this job twelve years, and I've seen that stuff a thousand times."

The officer walked to the Chevrolet and yanked open the door. He looked inside, turned away, and promptly threw up on the street.

"Jesus, I'm cold," Bob murmured.

Radio cars were pouring into the dead-end street. Dave looked around at the commotion—sergeants running around, ballistics people arriving, ambulance pulling up. A cop wandered over and threw his winter jacket over their shoulders.

"They *are* dead, aren't they?" Bob whispered.

"Christ, if they're not dead from the bullets, they must've *bled* to death. They've *got* to be dead by now."

"No question about that," Dave said. "Those two guys are going straight to the morgue."

"Oh, man," Bob said. "I'm cold as hell."

The ride into the Coney Island precinct house was a blur. Inside, the faces of men speaking of them, the voices—everything—seemed far away and disconnected.

Ballistics men arrived to examine the weapons. The silver-colored gun, a .25-caliber automatic, was cocked but the one remaining bullet had jammed. The knife was recovered, and the heroin.

"They made killers out of us," Dave whispered. "Paid assassins, Bobby. I don't think it ever entered my mind that we were gonna have to kill anyone."

When the questioning began about an hour later, neither of them did much talking.

"I'm not speaking to anyone, man," Dave was saying. "I don't give a fuck if the Mayor himself comes in here."

He thought of Captain Levitan. At this point, Levitan was about the only person he could think of trusting. Dave placed a call to the Seventy-seventh Precinct, but the captain was not there. Five minutes later, Levitan rang up from home. "Dave," he said, "don't do anything until I get there."

Dave went into the bathroom to splash some water on his face. When he came out again, Levitan was already coming through the door of the station house. Dave jumped up and gave him a bear hug.

"Come on," Levitan said, directing them both into a side room where they could be alone. "Now, tell me exactly what happened." They went over it all, from the meeting with the Hayes brothers and the ride to Coney Island, to the shooting itself.

"You'll have to make statements," Levitan said.

"Listen," Dave said, "they can take their statement and anything else they want to know, and fuck themselves to death! We're not talking to anyone. We're going home."

"No, wait," Levitan urged, explaining that the statements had to be made for several reasons—the press, the grand jury, the dead men's families. "You're not going to do anything but make things really bad for yourselves, unless you're willing to talk," he told them. "Just tell them what has to be said, and don't worry about a thing. I'm behind you a hundred percent. And I won't leave until you're finished."

They ended up making statements to everybody who came up and asked—the inspector on patrol, the man from the detective division, the D.A.'s staff, the borough commander, the division commander. Martin Hershey from the D.A.'s office had tried to play back the tape that had been recovered from the attaché case. But the batteries were dead by now, so everyone had to wait while new ones were brought in.

When the tape finally was played, nothing was on it. Someone suggested that it was Dave Greenberg's fault. He probably had never turned on the recorder in the first place. Then someone else pointed out that the tape had run all the way through from one end to the other.

"Then he must have had the recording volume down too low."

No one mentioned that the D.A.'s office itself had set up the tape recorder, and that Dave had been told to not even open the attaché case.

As for the backup cover they had been promised, there had been none. The two teams of detectives dispatched by the D.A.'s office had become busy on different cases, each thinking that the other would stick with Greenberg and Hantz. Only Bob's extraordinary effort had saved Dave's life.

As the D.A.'s men were leaving the precinct house, one of them came up to shake Dave's hand. "Drop dead," he muttered, turning away.

Irene was still in bed asleep when he got home around dawn. He didn't want to wake her up and be forced to tell her what had happened, and he certainly didn't want her to get up in the morning and see his pants, covered with blood. So he hid them in the corner of his closet, showered and changed clothes, and went outside again.

Later that afternoon friends called to tell Irene about the shooting. Then Dave phoned to say that he and Bob were all right and not to worry, and anyway it was over.

By the time he and Bob went to the morgue that day to identify the bodies, he was no longer angry at the Hayes brothers. The two drug pushers had been playing a dangerous, cruel game, but their deaths had not been inevitable. Dave was angry at the D.A.'s office. With a minimum of cooperation from them, the violence and the deaths could have been avoided.

At the morgue, several relatives of the dead pair came in, among them their two common-law wives, the third brother, Frank, and four or five children. The women, hysterical at the sight of the bodies, stood cursing and screaming at Dave and Bob, who made no response. Dave knew that they, too, were selling drugs, so he was not totally sympathetic. But he did feel bad for the children. The kids were being supported by their parents' illegal drug trade, and now that that source of support had been largely cut off, the children would suffer.

The third brother came up and apologized for what had happened. "I didn't like what was coming down," he said. "That's why I never showed up. I just didn't know what was gonna happen." Dave wondered what the real reason had been. After the pickup, were John and Joe going to lead him into a trap of some kind? Had the original plan gone awry when Joe discovered the tape recorder? Dave would never know.

They were reassigned from the Seventy-seventh Precinct to the Borough Office of Brooklyn South and were told to be available for any further questioning and appear before the grand jury. When someone was killed because of action taken by a police officer—if for no other reason than to have it declared justifiable homicide—all of this was standard procedure. Dave and Bob were anxious to have the entire chain of events, especially the part about the D.A.'s role in the affair, put on record.

There was no word of any pending grand jury investigation. At the same time, they began to realize that few people were on their side. Each member of the D.A.'s staff refused to accept blame for any specific part of the original operation. Chief Assistant D.A. Elliott Golden hung his hat on Assistant D.A. Hershey, who in turn shifted the weight to Sergeant Perrazzo, who issued a statement that he had "left the office convinced that my orders would be carried out." The detective in charge of the wiring claimed that Dave and Bob "must have misunderstood" his suggestion to use the attaché case.

Previous conversations that had taken place in the D.A.'s office were now being denied. When the question about backup coverage arose, everyone had a different answer: "Oh, that's not my department . . . I'm not in charge of covering . . . Well, I thought *you* would handle that . . ."

"Just wait'll we get to the grand jury," Dave said.

They sat in the Brooklyn South offices for a couple of weeks, waiting, telling themselves that something like the shooting would never happen to them again. "We're that much smarter now," Dave would say, but then he and Bob would go home and have their separate nightmares.

For Bob, it was the thought of having allowed a third party—in this case, the D.A.'s office—to get involved. He would wake up in a sweat, then go back to sleep and return to the nightmare of the shooting itself, his body jerking and his hands flailing.

Dave came down with hives. He kept wondering if the D.A.'s office would try to frame him and Bob in order to clear itself.

By the third week, Dave and Bob felt like caged animals.

"I *gotta* get you guys out of this office," the inspector said. "You're dragging us down in here! Nobody wants to look you guys in the face!" He made some phone calls, but with no results. He reported to them that they probably would be reassigned to some precinct far away from Bedford-Stuyvesant.

"What?" Dave shouted. *"Why?* Because someone *else* made a mistake? Because the district attorney's office didn't want to admit its own errors? If we're going back at all," he told Bob, "we go right back to the seven-seven. And that's a *promise."*

If they were transferred to another part of New York City, the record would show only two things: "Shooting . . . Transferred." Dave Greenberg had never run away from anything in his life—especially when he knew he was right—and he was not about to begin with this case.

At the Seventy-seventh precinct house, Captain Levitan phoned various superiors telling the inspectors and everyone else, "The only people who hate those two men are the junkies." He even put his request for their return to his precinct in writing, but there was still no reaction from the bosses.

Help finally came from an unexpected source. When residents of the precinct discovered that Batman and Robin had been reassigned and transferred somewhere else, block associations and neighborhood groups were outraged. Community leaders from the area got together and a crowd of nearly two hundred blacks stormed the station house one night to complain. The unprecedented demand by ghetto residents for the return of two white cops turned the tide in their favor.

Dave and Bob received orders to return to work the following day.

Captain Levitan greeted them on their first day back. "Come into my office," he said. "Sit down, fellas. As far as I'm concerned, you guys are great. In fact, I'm recommending you for the detective bureau. No reason in the world why you shouldn't make it. Every boss in the city knows you guys. They'd all like to have you guys working for them. So go back to work and give 'em hell."

"Thanks," Dave said, rising out of his chair.

"There's just one problem," Levitan said.

"What's that?"

"Well, I can't have you guys going back to Rochester and Sterling. You can go anywhere else but there."

Dave sat down again. Not go back to Rochester and Sterling? Not go back there and wipe out the Hayes brothers' operation completely? Allow the whole narcotics traffic there to be built up all over again?

"Why?" Dave shouted.

Levitan said he was having trouble with narcotics in other parts of the precinct and wanted them to be his troubleshooters, who would go anywhere on a moment's notice.

"Whenever something's happening," the captain said, "I'm going to send you in. Anywhere—except Rochester and Sterling."

He explained that they had become targets for angry drug dealers who had worked for the Hayes brothers, mostly in the Rochester and Sterling area. Word spread that Batman and Robin had been on the Hayes payroll for about a year prior to the shooting. When the brothers stopped making payments, the story went, Dave and Bob had assassinated them. According to another version, the Hayes brothers had been working for *them;* when the two brothers wanted to quit, they were murdered. Rumor also had it that the brothers had been carrying large sums of money on them when they had been killed, and that Greenberg and Hantz had taken it.

Dave walked into the D.A.'s office in the Municipal Building and confronted the first person he saw. "I want to find out about a grand jury hearing," he said. "There's been a delay, and I need to know why. My partner and I have been restricted because of rumors and threats that are getting out of hand, and yet we've done nothing wrong."

Dave was ushered from the office without being able to speak to anyone in authority. Each attorney he saw at the courthouse said that "something was wrong," because all incidents like the Coney Island shooting are brought before the grand jury. At last Dave caught up by accident with a senior member of the D.A.'s office in the hallway of the court building.

"Listen," he said, "what's the story? When are we going before the grand jury?"

"Well, we have no reason to bring you before the grand jury. The only time we'll take someone before a grand jury is when we suspect that a crime has taken place. And we leave it to the jury to decide whether or not there's reason to bring that person to trial. But as far as we're concerned, everything was done legitimately. So there's no reason to bring it before the grand jury."

The judges Dave discussed it with had the same opinion: "Don't worry, there's no evidence of anything wrong."

"But that's not the point," Dave argued. "I want things put on record! The incompetence and the lack of know-how, and the chain of events, supervised and condoned by the district attorney's office—I want it all put on that record! But in my opinion, that's exactly why they're *not* bringing it before a grand jury. I'd rather have them say, 'We're not bringing this before a grand jury because we think you committed homicide, and we want to be able to indict you on it when we're able to prove it.' That would be a good enough reason—if they really did think we did something wrong."

Then Dave learned that even if a grand jury hearing were held right away, and if the shooting were declared justifiable homicide, the case could be reopened if evidence to the contrary was uncovered. So why not hold a hearing right now?

"We're right back to my theory," he told Bob. "They're covering their own asses."

Other rumors were circulating by this time. Greenberg and Hantz were a pair of crazy cops looking to shoot junkies on sight. No grand jury hearing: did that mean Greenberg and Hantz paid off somebody to avoid a hearing? Before Dave and Bob could digest that rumor, another bomb was dropped, this time by the family of the dead Hayes brothers.

The common-law wives filed a complaint with the Civilian Complaint Review Board charging that Greenberg and Hantz were actually the big drug suppliers. The two dead men, they charged, had been working for Dave and Bob, and when they wanted to get off the payroll, Greenberg and Hantz killed them. Besides that, Dave and Bob had stolen the Hayes brothers' money and jewelry after killing them.

The investigation the Civilian Complaint Review Board would conduct, lasting at least several months, was another reason Dave and Bob had to stay away from Rochester and Sterling: it was feared that the two cops would harass potential witnesses who would be involved in the investigation.

The D.A.'s men were asked by the Review Board to appear and make some sort of statement at least to substantiate the fact that Greenberg and Hantz had been working for them during the time of the shooting. They refused to appear.

When Dave and Bob were called to appear before the Review Board, the attorney from the police union advised them, "Dave, Bob, I'm telling you, off the record, and I'm telling you on the record as well, don't make any statements."

"Why not?"

"Because you haven't had a hearing, and anything you say to

the Review Board can be introduced before a grand jury as a statement made by you. The district attorney hasn't said a word to back you up."

After an hour or so of arguing, the inspector in charge of the Review Board joined them and said, "Greenberg and Hantz, if you don't make a statement, give me your guns and your shields." He showed them a regulation stating that all officers were required to cooperate with the Review Board and that anything they said could not be used against them in a court.

"That's bullshit," the union attorney said.

"Fuck it," Dave said. "We don't need any lawyers, we don't need anybody! We'll make our statements and tell the truth and that's that."

He and Bob testified about the shooting, drawing a sympathetic reaction. But there were months of investigating to come. What new accusations would be made? And would the rumors and speculation among the junkies *and* cops continue to grow?

They had been on their own that night of the shooting. They still were.

21

In January 1970, they cruised back into the Seventy-seventh Precinct—this world of four- and six-story tenement buildings, of sprawling poverty and overcrowding, a world that seemed to have a permanent grayness about it, even when the sun was shining.

Now it was dark. The junkies were out in droves, looking for their connections or feeling high or wondering how to scrape up the money for their next fix. Of the young people in this area between the ages of fifteen and twenty-two, about seventy-five percent were involved with hard narcotics, most of them shooting heroin. For a young man of twenty, long since out of school, with no education and no job prospects, there was little to do but get high with his friends.

He gets strung out, becomes a thief, gets busted, maybe goes to a rehabilitation program upstate. During his eight-month stay, while he is off narcotics, he dreams of that first high and believes he can have it all over again. He comes back to the slums, returns to the drug scene, gets into far worse crimes to pay off the pushers, and winds up with nothing but a habit.

"George!" Dave called from the radio car. "How're ya doing, man?"

The young drug addict looked startled. Then he recognized Dave and Bob, shrugged, and came to the side of the car.

"Hop in the back," Bob said.

"I'm clean, man!"

"Don't worry," Dave said. "We just want to talk."

George climbed in.

"What's happening?" Dave said.

"Ain't nothing happening, man."

"Nothing?"

"Well, there's a little action up on Rochester and Sterling."

"Later for that. You got no information to give us?"

"I *told* you, man. I'm clean!"

Dave stopped the car. "Okay, George. Thanks, man, and we'll see ya."

They watched him walk away. "You hear that?" Bob laughed. "George is clean."

"Clean, my ass," Dave said. "Let's follow him. If we can avoid busting him, fine. But he's gonna go cop somewhere, that's for sure, and maybe we can get his connection. Just one splash, baby, and everybody'll know where we stand."

George wandered around for at least an hour. Around nine o'clock that night, he headed for an apartment building on Eastern Parkway. Dave parked the radio car about a block away; then he and Bob rushed to the doorway in time to see which apartment he was entering. They went into the hall and hid under the staircase. Five minutes later another young junkie came in and knocked on the same apartment door.

"What do you want?" came a woman's voice.

"You straight?"

"Yeah. What're you doing?"

"Two bags."

The door opened. Two bags of heroin were handed out, and the young man handed in his money. When the door closed again, Bob ran over and grabbed him. "Quiet," he whispered, leading him back down the hall and behind the stairs. They took the glassine envelopes and handcuffed him to the radiator under the staircase.

"Now," Dave told the junkie, "we are going to insert the barrel of our gun in your mouth and pull the trigger if you say one word."

George was still in the apartment, making his buy. Having witnessed a sale at the door, they could enter the place without a search warrant. They left the young man under the staircase and positioned themselves on either side of the door. As usual whenever they were going through a doorway, Dave would go "high" and Bob would take the "low" route, so that if any shots were fired only one of them would get hit.

When the door opened, they crashed through, knocking George to the floor. Bob grabbed the woman while Dave checked the kitchen. No one was there, so he passed that doorway. Both he and Bob had their guns drawn as they came into the living room, where they found a man facing them, holding a .45-caliber automatic.

"Drop it," Bob screamed. *"Drop it before we blow your fucking head off. Now!"*

The man went limp and the gun fell out of his hand. Dave scooped it up and they started looking around for drugs. A pile of envelopes was on a table. They went through the other rooms, although to search any further would be illegal. The initial sale was what counted, as well as the gun and the drugs on the table. Dave didn't care—if they found dope in another room, even if it was not admissible in court, at least they could take it away from them.

He and Bob turned on the man who had dropped the gun, Walter, and pushed him against the window at the far end of the living room. "All right," Dave said, "where's the rest of the shit? Come on, man! *Where is it?"*

Behind them, they heard a click—unmistakably, a gun being cocked. Without a word, Dave and Bob split up and dove for either side of the room. They wheeled around to see the woman standing there, waving a gun from side to side so she could keep them covered. Finally she held it in position with both hands, trembling, aiming it at Dave.

Bob tried to calm her down. "Baby, you can't get both of us. You take him out and you're dead, sweetheart. Think about it, baby—if you pull that trigger—"

"Don't do it," Walter screamed. *"You're crazy, Flora, don't do it! They'll kill us!"*

The young woman had a lot more nerve than Walter did. "Drop those motherfucking guns," she said, "or I'll blow your motherfucking head off."

It was a standoff. Dave and Bob refused to drop their own guns, and so did she.

Flora was uncertain how to proceed from here, but she was determined. "Get their guns," she told Walter. "Go ahead, man, get your own gun back at least. Go on, go on!" Walter refused to move. *"Get their guns,"* she repeated. *"Then I'll blow these motherfuckers away! Hurry!"*

Walter still hesitated. Flora had the gun on Bob and she started swinging it back toward Dave, shouting again. Bob grabbed a flowerpot next to him and threw it at her before she could swing the gun all the way. The pot hit her in the face. She fell backward and Dave was there to grab the gun.

"Boy," said Walter, shaking. "You are some crazy son of a bitch."

At the station house after arraignment, they met with Captain Norman Weiner, the shoofly for the entire Thirteenth Division. Weiner, whose job was to catch cops doing things wrong, had mixed feelings about Greenberg and Hantz. He had been told to stay clear of them, because Captain Levitan had made them his "special" patrolmen, whatever that meant. Besides, he liked Dave and Bob; he knew the volume of work they were doing. But Weiner couldn't let them get away with infractions of the rules, because then everyone else would try it. So Weiner tried to maintain a balance, knowing he was damned if he did and damned if he didn't.

On this day, when he came into the precinct house, all the cops stood up and saluted him. You could never know what the shoofly was up to. But Dave and Bob were in too good a mood to be reverent, shoofly or no shoofly.

"Hey," Dave yelled, "here comes the rug!" (A reference to Weiner's toupee.) "How're ya doing, boss?"

Weiner walked up to the pair and examined their uniforms. "Listen," he said, "come over here. I'd like to talk to you two guys."

They followed him into a corner of the room. "What is it?" Bob asked.

"Your hats. There's something wrong with your hats."

Bob took his hat off and looked at it. He shrugged. "Nothing wrong with this sturdy piece of clothing, sir."

"Yes, there is. It's a *summer* hat. You're both wearing summer hats!"

"What do you mean, a summer hat?"

"That band, that webbed band around your hat," the shoofly said. "That signifies summer!"

"Ah," Bob replied. "That band has nothing to do with the weather. The *hot weather* signifies summer, sir."

Whenever Dave and Bob got caught doing something wrong, one of them would start doubletalking until the other could think of a halfway plausible excuse. The idea was that if they couldn't talk sense, then one of them had to talk nonsense. "If you can't win 'em," Bob would say, "confuse 'em."

"What'd you say?" Captain Weiner asked.

"Summer or winter," Bob said, "it's the thing about my grandmother, who's very, very sick at the moment, and of course the hat is used for my brother, whose hair is falling out, sir, and I know that this is my normal hat, some cop was wearing lipstick the other day and, uh, too much hair on his chest for that role, so we wear these hats now as before and in the future—"

"Wait a minute!" Captain Weiner was saying. "Wait, hold on! Tell me again, now. *Why* are you wearing a summer hat?"

"It's part of the uniform," Bob said. "I can't go into the street without a hat, Captain. You should know that."

"Look, *something's* happening now. But I just can't figure it. Once more—why a summer hat?"

Dave started to laugh.

"What's so funny?" Captain Weiner asked.

"Well," Dave said, "here you're the shoofly, and you're supposed to go around enforcing department regulations, and you don't even *know* the regulations."

"What do you mean, I don't know the regulations?"

"Well, the T.O.P. came down last week, saying that there's no longer any difference between summer and winter hats. Summer hats became optional all year long."

"What?"

"Yeah," Dave bluffed. "And that's what I'm laughing about."

"Oh, yeah," Bob said. "That's right. I remember reading that. Captain, you should know about the new orders."

The discussion went on for another half an hour. Captain Weiner asked everybody in the precinct house if they had seen the new Temporary Operating Procedures. They all said no, but then, few cops ever read them, anyway. Weiner ran downstairs to speak with the desk officer. Dave and Bob followed halfway down the stairs and gave a high sign to the officer.

"Is there a new T.O.P. on the wearing of hats?" Captain Weiner asked him.

"Well, I seem to remember reading something, Captain, but I'm not sure."

Nobody in the precinct house wanted to admit to Weiner that they didn't read Temporary Operating Procedures. When approached, the officers wandered off in different directions, leaving him standing there. At last a cop came back with some T.O.P. sheets. "There's two or three missing out of here, Captain," he told Weiner. "They might be the ones."

"Wait a minute," Weiner said. "I'll solve this. The property clerk's office will know if there's such a thing. No, wait—the equipment bureau! *They* would know about it."

He telephoned the equipment bureau, said a few words, then hung up. He turned to Dave and Bob with a smirk on his face. "I knew there was no such T.O.P."

"What do you mean?" Dave asked.

"I just spoke to the equipment bureau!"

"Who'd you speak to?"

"I didn't get his name," Weiner said.

"Well," Dave went on, "why don't you find out who it was?"

Weiner called the equipment bureau again. He hung up and reported, "It was Bill Saunders."

"Saunders?" Dave said. "Gee, Cap, he just started working there last week! How would *he* know?"

"Really?" Weiner said. He placed the call again. "Let me talk to the supervisor." A sergeant got on the other end of the line, and the shoofly explained his problem.

"I don't remember those orders," the sergeant replied. "But I don't think that's correct, sir."

"Are you sure or aren't you?"

"Well, to tell you the truth, I'm not sure."

"Let me talk to your captain," Weiner said.

"The captain isn't in, sir. He'll be back in half an hour."

Captain Weiner waited by the phone for thirty minutes and then called the equipment bureau for the third time. "Captain? I'm interested in finding out if summer hats are optional."

"*What?*"

"Yeah, I have two men here, and . . ." The shoofly repeated his story.

"You called me back from lunch to find out if summer hats are optional?"

"Yes, I—hello? Hello?" the shoofly repeated. Then he looked at Dave and Bob and said, "He hung up on me!" So he called back once more. This time the captain at the equipment bureau said, "No, there's no such T.O.P."

Captain Weiner hung up, triumphant. "I *knew* you guys were bullshitting me," he announced. He was so happy that he went around the precinct house telling everyone, "I caught them! I caught them!"

Meanwhile, he forgot that Dave and Bob had violated a regulation. By the time he came back looking for them, they were gone.

The street had changed. There seemed to be far less drug peddling outside. Most of the action, they learned, had gone indoors. Word of their encounter with the Hayes brothers had produced a widespread paranoia on the part of the pushers. Most major connections were operating now in houses and apartments, with new locks and bars on their doors. Strong gates had gone up on the windows of all ground-floor apartments. And code words were being used. Some connections required buyers to show up wearing red scarves or other designated pieces of clothing as identification.

The Hayes brothers' common-law wives and other relatives had picked up the Rochester-Sterling operation where it had left off, but indoors. The Brewers' pushers, meanwhile, had taken over most of the street activity there, using house connections in other areas of the precinct and all over Brooklyn. Dave and Bob were still intent on wiping out the Hayes people entirely and then concentrating full time on the Brewers. But to do so would mean to disobey orders. They would have to go after the Brewers' house connections first, which meant learning how to get inside those apartments despite all the locks and bars and gates and code words, not to mention the fact they were white and known by reputation, if not by appearance.

22

Dave stood at the front door of his new Staten Island home, looking over the marshland across the street to the Verrazano Bridge, Brooklyn, and Manhattan beyond. He was waiting for Billy Metz.

"Where is that guy?" he said aloud to himself as he walked back to the kitchen, where Bob was sitting at the table with Irene.

"Relax," Bob said. "He's probably shooting up dope somewhere."

"No, no," Dave murmured. "Billy's off the junk. He's kicked it, man."

"Sure, sure. Tell me another."

Dave slumped down in a chair, tapping his fingers on the table.

Damn it, where was Billy? The whole plan was getting off to a bad start. Billy had helped him and Bob make their first arrest in Bedford-Stuyvesant—the Earl King collar, when they had hidden inside the cardboard box. Billy had served time for his previous narcotics convictions; Dave had gone to the judge and the district attorney on his own case involving Billy, explaining that he'd been an informant, and had gotten Billy paroled in his custody. Dave had agreed to take him into his new house and be responsible for him.

Dave groaned. "I should never have let him out of my sight!"

Billy had agreed to come to Dave's house, but he had pleaded for a few days on his own, out in the street, and Dave had relented.

"Actually," Bob said, "I hope he doesn't show up."

"Well, fuck you, man!" Dave yelled at his partner.

"But what's the purpose, Dave? Why bring any more trouble

into your life than you already have? Why jeopardize everything for a junkie? Why?"

"Listen, he ain't a junkie any more! He kicked, I tell you! But he needs help, man."

"Dave, the guy was shooting a hundred bucks' worth of heroin into his veins every day for seven years!"

"I know, I know. But if I can keep him indoors for two or three months, get him healthy, then maybe I can find somebody who'll hire him. I can put him on his feet."

"It's just going to be trouble," Bob said.

Dave stood up again and went to the door. It had been three days since Billy had gotten out of jail—three days and nights.

"Come have dinner," Irene called.

Dave wondered if he had been conned. If Billy leaves town or something, what'll the judge and the district attorney do? He poked at his food.

"What do *you* have to gain?" Bob pressed him.

"It's what *we* might gain, nutmegs! We'll rap with him, get information, get him to tell us what drug addicts think about. How do they get their stuff? Where do they normally hide it? Do the major pushers all have guns? What are the different methods of making a buy? Do they have any plans of escape? How far will they go in order not to be apprehended? How do we get to the pusher's pusher? Billy can give us a lot of tips on that kind of stuff."

"Maybe you're right," Bob said.

"I'm always right."

The doorbell rang. Dave jumped up and raced to the door. Billy Metz was standing there, a suitcase in his hand, his eyes glazed.

"Where've you been?" Dave said.

"I'm wrecked, man. I'm sorry. Just shot two bags."

"Oh, no."

Billy shrugged. Dave brought him into the house and took him down to the cellar playroom. Billy would have to kick it all over again.

"No problem," Bob said.

He was standing on a wide wooden plank about twenty feet above the ground, ready to carry a sheet of aluminum across to the opposite side of a building that was under construction.

"It's too windy," Dave warned. "Whatever you do, don't try it by yourself. Wait for me."

"Hey, I can do it myself. Watch!"

"Don't turn it into the wind!"

According to the second part of Dave's plan, they had become temporary steelworkers, taking jobs on actual construction sites. Dave had been a member of the steel union prior to joining the police force. Through a friend, he got work for himself and Bob.

While they were learning from Billy Metz, who was off the junk again, they would develop their ability to scale walls and walk across ledges. This first job involved "decking," or "sheeting," on a Long Beach construction site, next to the water. Each sheet of aluminum was about nine feet long and three feet wide; the idea was to carry the sheets up and lay them down in place.

"Watch it!" Dave yelled. "Bob, you're turning it into the wind! Move the other way!"

"Ahhhhhhhh!"

The wind lifted Bob up off the building, and he began to sail out over the beach. He held on to the huge sheet of aluminum with both hands, his feet flying upward, like Superman. Near the ground he let go, falling onto the sand.

"You're right!" he called back up to Dave. "Don't turn it into the wind!"

Dave lounged on one of the beds in his downstairs playroom, listening to Billy Metz describe some of the activities of his junkie friends. It was eleven o'clock at night and Dave was tired. He and Bob had worked all day on another construction site, carrying wooden planks nearly two hundred feet up. It was strenuous, dangerous work. Dave wanted to sleep, but Billy was really talking now, revealing more and more about the personal side of his addiction.

"Explain it again," Dave said. "I mean, the steps leading up to where you're only psychologically hooked."

Sitting next to Billy was another junkie, Bernard, who was also staying in the house. A local newspaper reporter had learned of Dave's efforts to rehabilitate Billy, and wanted to do an article. As he was completing his research, the journalist said he knew of another addict who needed help. Would Dave take him in as well? So Bernard had moved in and had kicked his habit, like Billy.

The two young men were not allowed to leave the house unless accompanied by Dave or Irene or a neighborhood youngster hired to guard them. They slept on the beds in the basement playroom, and had become part of the household. They called Dave "the colonel" and viewed him and Irene almost as their father and mother. Irene cooked for them and washed their clothes, and gave them chores to keep busy. When friends asked her how she put up with two junkies, her answer was simply that this was part of Dave's work.

The newspaper reporter's story, headlined "Policeman Plays Two Roles in Handling Drug Problem," began, "David Greenberg is an enigma—a twenty-six-year-old cop who not only arrests addicts but shelters them." Billy Metz had been quoted as saying of Dave, "He's really beautiful. He saved me from going back to the street. We goof around, and Irene takes us serious. She's like a mother or sister. Both have the patience of a saint. We'll never come by another shot like this, or someone like Dave."

"What else you wanna know?" Billy was saying.

"Nothing. Gotta get some sleep. See you."

He got off the bed, pleased about what he was accomplishing during this period of time off from work. Tomorrow there would be more steelwork with Bob.

"Hey, Colonel," Billy called to him as he started up the stairs.

"Yeah?" Dave said.

"There ain't nothing in the world we wouldn't do for you, man."

"Thanks," Dave said.

Nothing in the world, except stop using drugs. Dave had no idea that once he was asleep, either Billy or Bernard would sneak out the basement window to find a connection for heroin and shoot it into their veins.

"No!" Dave shouted. "Bob, don't do it!"

Once again, Bob was feeling too confident for his own good. They were on a bolting job, high above the ground, requiring them to walk around on wide steel beams. During the past week, Bob had gained self-assurance gradually, learning not to look down. The first day, he had sat down on one of the beams the entire time; but now he was goofing around, playing the expert.

"That's a stringer!" Dave called. "You can't just run across it, Bob!"

"I'll just tiptoe lightly."

"I don't think you should, man! If you're gonna go across a stringer, straddle it and crawl!"

"Everything's under control," Bob laughed.

Dave watched him start across the stringer, a long, thin beam from one side of the building frame to the other. It was ninety feet long, attached at both ends, but only four inches thick. Under Bob's weight, it immediately started wobbling.

"You sure you want to do this?" Dave yelled.

"Yeah, man. Positive!"

"Don't forget—if you're gonna fall, fall *in*. That way, you'll only go down one floor, and hit the planks. If you fall out, baby, you're heading all the way down!"

Bob was now about ten feet out on the stringer, balancing himself as if he were on a highwire. When he got twenty feet out, the stringer began swaying from side to side.

"What do I do?"

"Get down! Sit on it!"

The long, thin beam was swaying like a tree branch in the wind.

"Fall forward!"

"Here I go!"

Bob let himself fall onto the stringer and held on with all his strength.

"Okay," Dave called. "Now throw your legs under and straddle it like a horse!" Bob obeyed. "Don't move. Let it stop shaking. All right—now just swing around, if you can, and crawl back here."

"Bullshit! I ain't turning around on this thing! I'm going to the other side!"

Bob started crawling across in the direction he was facing. The stringer began moving from side to side again.

"Stay still!" Dave ordered. "Let it stop shaking again!"

"I can't get *myself* to stop shaking!"

Other workers came to the rescue, throwing ropes around the beam and pulling so it would no longer shake. When it was firm again, Bob stood up, turned around, and in one last act of bravado, tiptoed back to the edge. His legs were trembling as he climbed down the ladder to the ground.

"That's it, man!" he shouted up to Dave. "Going home! Thanks a lot, but let's be cops again! It's safer!"

23

"It's against my better judgment," Captain Levitan said, "and I really don't want to do this. But you don't have a sector any more."

"No more sector?"

"That's right. From now on, you're my two precinct plainclothesmen."

Dave couldn't believe it. Plainclothes? The plainclothes detail in this precinct had been eliminated some time ago.

"It's a special assignment," the captain explained. "Despite all the trouble you've caused, you've earned it. Anyway, I have a good excuse."

"What's the excuse?"

"Well, see, you guys are targets. Everybody's out to get you. Say there's two guys looking to hit you, waiting across the street, and you turn out with thirty-five other men. From a distance, everybody in uniform looks alike! And what's to stop them from shooting two other men in uniform, thinking it's you? So in order to protect the rest of my men, I'm putting you guys in plainclothes."

On the rooftop, alone, Bob Hantz hooked up his safety line. He dropped the ropes and adjusted the belt. The people on the fourth floor below him worked for the Brewers. Dave had posed as a junkie and had made a few undercover buys from their street pushers, but that was small stuff compared to this. The house connection was what counted.

He lowered himself down from the roof, avoiding the windows, and positioned himself beneath the window that he and Dave had agreed on. The pushers in the living room up there had a habit of throwing their junk out that window whenever the cops came to the door.

Inside the building, Dave strolled down the hallway and knocked on the door to the same apartment.

"Who is it?"

"Police!" Dave yelled. "Open up!"

Bob heard commotion. The window opened and the drugs came flying out—right into his lap. He stuffed the envelopes of heroin inside his shirt and started pulling himself up on the safety line.

Dave knocked on the apartment door again. This time a woman named Joyce opened it a crack. "What do you want, motherfucker?"

"You work for the Brewers, right?"

"What's your business, man?"

"Well, I've got you on possession of a whole lot of shit."

"Yeah? You wanna look around?"

"No, baby, *you* look around."

She turned around and saw Bob climbing through the window with her drugs.

It turned out that Joyce didn't work directly for the Brewers, but through a middleman she met every evening on the Long Island Rail Road subway platform at New York and Atlantic Avenues. They immediately decided to pursue it further.

"Maybe you'd be willing to give the guy up," Dave said, "if we promise to talk to the D.A. and the judge about your case."

Joyce said she was afraid to become a stoolie, afraid for her safety, but at last she agreed.

They took her down to a phone booth, and she called the middleman to set up a meeting on the subway platform an hour later. Dave and Bob took Joyce for coffee and then drove her to within a block of the station. They watched her walk toward it and positioned themselves on either side of the platform. If the guy made a break, he would have to come down one set of stairs or the other. The middleman had not yet arrived. Dave hid in a doorway and waited.

Moments later, a tall man, fitting Joyce's description of her connection, went past him and up five or six steps. He turned, glanced across the street, and spotted Bob, who was trying to keep an eye on Joyce as well.

Frightened, the man pulled out a gun and started running the rest of the way up the stairs. Dave went after him, yelling for him to stop. Just as he got to the platform, he saw the man jump down onto the railroad tracks. He followed him down onto the tracks. Near the opposite platform, the man wheeled around and pointed his gun at Dave.

Dave froze, his heart pounding. He glanced to his left and saw a train heading into the station—on the track he was standing on. He looked at the gun, the train again, back to the gun. *If I move, he'll blow me away! If I don't move, I'm dead.*

Suddenly Bob was up on the opposite platform, running, now diving head first onto the gunman from behind. Dave jumped backward, hit the ground and rolled under the platform. *Just enough room!* He straightened himself out, face against the wall, and the train went thundering by, the sound filling his head.

The police had responded to someone's call. Sergeant Regan was the first one on the platform, on Dave's side of the tracks. Regan looked down at the tracks and saw one of Dave's Indian moccasins—that was all.

"Get him out of there!" Bob was holding on to the gunman by his hair and pointing at the edge of the platform opposite him. "He's under there!"

Sergeant Regan and the other cops bent down and looked under the platform. "Dave? You all right? Dave?"

Dave spoke without moving. "Yeah, I'm all right. Get me the fuck out of here."

Dave Greenberg, shirtless under the blazing summer sun, paced around the rear patio of his house, waiting for Bob to show up. *No doubt about it,* he thought, *I become obsessed.* It had been three months since the incident on the train tracks. He and Bob had made more than forty arrests since then, using an assortment of new disguises and tactics. Just the thought of wiping out the rest of the Hayes operation had kept him going; now it was time to go back to Rochester and Sterling.

He looked down at the table, where he had spread out some crude maps marked with crayon and pencil designs—the entire layout of the forbidden Rochester-Sterling intersection, all the alleys and courtyards and fire escapes. He had circled one specific building on Sterling Place, where the Hayes people had their main narcotics operation.

Bob arrived and looked down at the maps. "What is this, the War Room at Omaha Beach?"

"Right," Dave said, pacing around the table. "Listen, I got it worked out pretty well. The best time to make this attack is when they're all together in one place. Agreed?"

"Sure."

"Okay. Now, that whole crew of people who worked for the Hayes brothers—they celebrate every holiday, regardless of ethnic background or whatever. Right?"

"Uh-huh."

"And what is tomorrow?"

"The Fourth of July."

"Independence Day! Why not? Make it when they least expect us. Like the St. Valentine's Day Massacre. The Fourth of July Raid—how does that sound?"

Bob was smiling. "Not bad."

"We hit 'em tomorrow evening, while they're celebrating, and maybe we clean out the whole operation!"

Bob studied the maps. "We can't use any equipment," he said. "No?"

"Nah. Better to go up the rear fire escape—here."

"Great. That'll be easy."

"Yeah," Bob said, "but hopefully we're not observed. As soon as anyone sees two white guys climbing the building, it's all over."

"They won't see us. We leave the car here, and walk this way, through the alley, and we come out here. Now," Dave said, putting his finger on one of the maps, "we walk the ledge to this point, to the courtyard, and then to the fire escape. No problem."

For a moment he thought of the time he first met Bob in the Police Academy. Who would have thought we'd be planning to wipe out a complete narcotics operation only two years and four months later?

He'd probably have trouble sleeping that night.

It was six o'clock in the evening, the Fourth of July. Dave and Bob entered the courtyard behind the six-story building on

Sterling Place and positioned themselves under the fire escape. When Dave reached up, he discovered he was not tall enough to reach the metal stairs.

"All that preparing," he said in a low voice, "and we can't even get onto the fire escape."

They looked around the courtyard for something to stand on. Nothing, aside from an old box spring with a mattress. Not high enough, Dave thought. Of course, if we jumped on it and bounced . . .

They dragged the box spring to within several feet of the fire escape. Dave got up on the ledge jutting out from the building and leaped off onto their makeshift trampoline. He was catapulted upward and forward, high enough to grab the bottom of the fire escape. He swung back and forth, then chinned himself up so he could stand.

"Now you," he said.

Bob got on the ledge, jumped, hit the mattress, and was standing on the fire escape with Dave in seconds. They looked up at the six-story building. If they just walked up the metal stairs, people in the apartments would surely see them.

"We'll have to go up the outside edges," he said. "Can't use the regular part of this fire escape at all."

"Okay. Hell of an easy plan we made, you know?"

To climb up the outer sides of the fire escape, they would have to grab each bar and pull themselves up, stand on the bar, and then go on to the next one. The task looked simple, until Dave realized that they could not reach the first bar above them by just standing on their toes. They would have to stand on the edge of the bar, balance, then jump up four or five inches to grab the one above. If we miss, Dave thought, there's only one place to go: straight down.

Thank God for the steelwork, Bob thought as he stood on the first bar. He got on his toes, balanced himself, crouched, and sprang. His hands gripped the next bar and he hung there a moment, relieved. Then he chinned himself up. Was the whole thing really worth this risk?

On the other side of the fire escape, Dave went from one bar to another, straining but making it look easy. Well, Bob thought, he's now about ten pounds lighter than I am, and besides, he's had more experience at this. This is like a circus act—each jump is a new gamble, more dangerous than the one before it. The higher I go, the greater the risk. And with each jump and chin-up, a certain amount of strength is gone.

By the time Bob reached the fifth floor, it seemed he might not make it to the roof. Dave was already up there, breathing heavily, but grinning. That does it. Bob leaped to the next bar, but as he hung there he realized he no longer had the strength to pull himself up. He had enough power in his wrists and fingers, but not in the arms.

Dave looked down. "What're you waiting for?"

"I don't know, man. My arms are weak."

"Well, wait—hold on."

Dave knelt at the top edge of the fire escape, hooked his feet, and hung over the side, upside down, trying to grab him. He slapped Bob's pants, grabbed the belt, and pulled. Bob got his arms bent and was able to chin himself up the rest of the way. Now he was up there, but Dave was still hanging down by his feet.

"Give me a hand," Dave whispered.

The two of them nearly pulled each other off the top of the building in the process of getting themselves up there together. Once on the rooftop, they collapsed out of sheer exhaustion.

Nobody had seen them. There was one structure on the roof, about eight or nine feet high, containing the door leading down into the building. As they rested the door opened and out came a junkie who seemed to be sick. They remained still, watching him vomit. Maybe he won't see us, Dave thought; just then the drug addict noticed their presence. No way we're gonna let this guy blow it, Dave told himself.

He and Bob ran over to the young man. "I ain't got nothin' on me," the junkie said. "I just got a stomach ache, that's all."

If we let him go, Dave thought, he'll tell everyone in the building we're up here. We can't risk it.

"Bob," he said, "see those milk boxes? Let's make some steps."

They put two of the crates next to the doorway structure and Dave climbed up to the top. "Now," he said, "boost our friend up."

"Hey," the young man said. "What're you doing?"

"Just a little insurance," Dave replied as he pulled the junkie up. He handcuffed the young man's left hand to his right ankle, so there was no way for the captive to move. Dave swung himself over the side and jumped back down to the roof. They pushed the milk boxes away.

"You leaving me up here?" the young man asked.

"Right," Dave said. "We'll be back later. If you try to get down, man, you're gonna fall and break your ass. That's a nine-foot drop, baby, and I'd hate to see you get hurt."

They ducked through the doorway and into the building. Now the problem was to get inside the top-floor apartment where the Hayes relatives and friends would be gathered. Dave figured that he and Bob should wait at the top of the stairs leading from the roof to the sixth floor until a drug buyer came up and went inside. Then he and Bob would sneak down and wait by the door until the buyer came out. At that moment, they would crash through into the pad.

In the hour that followed, they saw five transactions at the door, whose chain was never unlatched. Now, Dave thought, we can go in there legally.

They watched four more transactions take place over the next half hour; again, the door never opened all the way. Dave got so restless that he walked down the stairs and knocked on the door himself, putting his hand over the peephole.

"Yeah?"

"You straight?" Dave asked.

"I can't see you," came the voice.

"I'm strung out, man."

"Ain't nothin' happening. Split."

Dave shrugged. So it didn't work. He went back up the stairs. "Must be *some* way to get inside that place," he said to Bob.

At last they saw one of the Hayes' pushers come down the hall. "It's Rico," Bob whispered.

Rico'll be going inside that apartment for sure, Dave thought. He and Bob crouched, watching, ready to spring.

"Who is it?"

"Rico."

"Okay, brother. One minute."

The chain inside was being unlatched. As the door began to

open, Dave and Bob jumped downward, missing all twelve steps and landing on the hallway floor. They pushed Rico ahead of them into the apartment. This better be good, Dave thought.

Inside, eight people, including the common-law wife of one of the dead Hayes brothers and a number of pushers who still worked for the operation, were lounging around. Clearly, they were stunned. Nobody said a word.

Loads and loads of dope, Dave was thinking as he and Bob searched everyone. Bundles of the stuff, all over the place. It was a narcotics factory, where they cut the heroin and bagged it for other pushers who worked in different apartments or on the street. Dave recalled four of the prisoners' faces from his and Bob's rooftop operations months before. Dapper Dan was here. And Gypsy Rose. T-Bird. Rubber Legs.

"Hey, Bob, have these fine people just relax a while. Or else blow their fucking heads off. In my opinion," Dave went on, "we ought to get the rest of them."

"Sure. Why not?"

"I mean, let's wrap 'em all up, because you know we're not going to be able to come back here a second time. The Old Man is going to be mad enough that we came here the first time," he added. "I'm going out for a while. You keep 'em all company in here. Explain to them how this is the Fourth of July Raid."

"Good idea. Current history in the making."

Leaving Bob with the eight prisoners, Dave closed the apartment door behind him and started down the stairs. He planned to pick up some of the street dealers who got their drugs from the factory upstairs. The information he had was that the sellers out in the street took their buyers into the hallway on the ground floor to make all transactions. When he got down there, he hid himself behind the stairway and waited.

Two men walked in from the sidewalk. He listened and watched as the drugs and money were exchanged.

"All right!" he shouted. "This way, folks!"

"Hey—Batman?"

"Fuck you. March—up the stairs!"

Leaving his gun tucked in his belt, Dave made them walk up the five flights. When they reached the top floor, he was exhausted.

"Down the hall. Okay, stop. Right here," he said, pushing the apartment door open. "Two more," he said. "Let's see, that makes ten. Okay, I'll be gone for a little while again."

He went back downstairs, caught another buyer and seller, and brought them all the way up as he'd done before. The third time he did it, he felt dizzy.

"That's fourteen, so far," he said. "Listen, Bob, this is getting ridiculous, walking up and down those steps. How about *you* trying it?"

Bob went downstairs and returned ten minutes later with one seller and two buyers. "Bravo," Dave said. "Seventeen! Give it another shot, man! We're all up here just celebrating the Fourth of July. Let me turn up the radio here." The prisoners stared at him sullenly, two of the women cursing him under their breath.

When Bob came back with two more collars, Dave decided that nineteen prisoners was enough. The place was getting crowded, and he and Bob had only one pair of handcuffs between them. In fact, Dave thought, I forgot all about how the hell we're supposed to get all these people out of here. March them into the street? There'd be a lynch mob in five seconds! Neither one of us is going to leave without the other to go call for help.

He glanced over at Bob, who apparently was having the same thoughts. Nineteen of them, two of us. Why don't these people have a phone? Why didn't we bring walkie-talkies? Dave made a face.

He looked at the faces of the men and women they had caught: the entire remaining Hayes operation in one room. One of the women, Lucille, had been an informant for them several months ago. She must know, Dave thought, that if she helps us now we'll do everything we can to have the D.A. and the judge take it into account when her case comes up. Maybe she'll give us a hand.

"Let's have a game," Dave said, turning down the radio and looking around the room. "I want someone to yell out the window for help. I don't care who—Lucille, you do it. Go to the window and call out to the people down there that you're getting robbed."

"What for?"

"Just do it. I want to see what happens."

Lucille went to the windows and yelled, "Help! Help! We're being robbed! Somebody's sticking us up!"

"Tell them to call the police," Dave said.

"Police! We're being robbed! Get the police!"

Down in the street, dozens of people ran to call the police emergency number to report a robbery at the building on Sterling Place. When the radio cars started arriving, Dave leaned out the window and yelled, "Up here! Up on the top floor!"

Several junkies looked up from the street. One of them cried out, "Hey, it ain't any stickup! It's Batman! Batman's up there!"

Dave sat down in one corner of the room, a satisfied smile on his face. Minutes later, cops were swarming into the apartment on the top floor.

24

They took a long vacation that summer, not knowing whether they might become detectives at any moment, or whether they would receive word that the Review Board had swallowed one of the many charges of brutality or corruption against them.

Dave's situation at home with the two junkies, Billy and Bernard, had been shaky at best. Somehow, they had smuggled a set of works into the house, and at three or four in the morning they were sneaking out the basement window to go buy heroin from someone on Hylan Boulevard. Whenever Irene was taking a shower or otherwise occupied, they would make phone calls to set up their connections. Bernard had a girl friend on the outside who was supplying the money.

One evening Bernard called Dave down to the basement. "Can't handle it, man."

"What's the problem?"

"We're using stuff."

"I thought so," Dave said. "I knew you guys were getting high, but I had no way of proving it. It's taken a little longer than I expected for you to come and tell me about it."

Bernard confessed that he and Billy had even taken Dave's car over to Coney Island to get their drugs. Dave drove the two of them to Coney Island to point out their connection. Dave stopped the car, walked over to the young man, about Dave's age, who had been selling them their dope.

Without a word, Dave slugged him and continued beating on him until the pusher was sprawled on the sidewalk, unable to stand up.

"If I ever find out that you sell dope to either one of these guys again," Dave said, "I'll kill you."

The next step was to get Billy and Bernard unhooked again and find them some work. Through a friend in the steelworkers' union, he got them jobs paying three hundred and fifty dollars a week. He arranged to take them to work in the morning, drop them at the job, and pick them up in the afternoon. They were otherwise still confined to his house.

It seemed to be working out well for a while. They were off the junk, and each had a bank account that Dave had opened for them. They were saving every penny. Dave allowed them to go out with their girl friends, and soon they began driving to work by themselves in a used car Dave had bought for them.

Within months, they each had a few thousand dollars in the bank. They were working steady, with no problems. Dave let one of them buy his own car. The only minor setback occurred when Billy got some heroin and took an overdose on the job. Dave had to start all over again with him, to get him back on his feet. The union men complained, but Dave took the weight himself.

By now the two young men were ready to move out, Billy to get married and Bernard to go back to a wife and child he had left because of the drugs. And Dave had become an expert on narcotics. There wasn't anything that a junkie could do that he didn't know about.

The only trouble was that Billy and Bernard were destined to go back to the dope.

The letter from the Civilian Complaint Review Board was brief. "The Board has reviewed this complaint and found that the allegations have not been substantiated and has recommended to the Police Commissioner that no further action be taken. . . . The fact of this complaint is confidential and no notation of any kind shall be made in your personal folder on file with the Department. Thank you for your cooperation in this matter."

That was all. One piece of paper, ending months of waiting and wondering. Dave stuck the letter in his briefcase.

In less than three years on the force, they had made about four hundred arrests, earning a ninety-five percent conviction rate in court. They had survived more than thirty investigations of them.

Perhaps because of that very success, they were still not free of suspicion. Dave and Bob had no way of knowing that at the moment, the American Civil Liberties Union, the F.B.I., and the Knapp Commission on police corruption were also looking for whatever they might have done wrong.

They sat in their radio car on Prospect Place, watching an empty truck parked up the block. The truck had been hijacked earlier in the day and now, at six o'clock in the evening, Dave and Bob were following instructions to wait there and see if the hijackers might return.

During the past few months they had steadily chipped away at the Brewer brothers' narcotics operation, hoping to wipe them out as they had the Hayes people. As they sat drinking coffee, names and faces of people they had arrested over the past few months popped in and out of Bob's mind. What he and Dave had done in Bedford-Stuyvesant seemed like a surrealistic movie, filled with faces, names, words, one scene merging into the other . . .

Once they had dressed up as house painters to go into a drug pusher's apartment to paint the kitchen, with the superintendent's permission. While waiting for a narcotics sale to take place in their presence, they became very involved in the painting. Dave was up on a ladder, spreading turquoise paint over the ceiling. It dripped down onto the refrigerator, so Bob painted *it* turquoise. This went on for an entire day.

The woman who lived in the apartment was suspicious, so she was making her heroin sales out in the hallway. Dave and Bob returned the next day, and the next, until they had painted four rooms—turquoise, yellow, pink, brown. By then the woman figured that they had to be real painters, so she began conducting her business inside the apartment again. When they arrested her, she cried—not because she was going to jail, but because it was the first time that her place had ever been painted.

"You motherfucking cops did a real nice job," she said, wiping her eyes. "Too bad I won't be around to enjoy it." Only in a place like Bedford-Stuyvesant, Bob thought.

Another time, he had come up with the most original of all their disguises: a cop in uniform, directing traffic. Since traffic cops never made drug arrests, the disguise was perfect. They had been able to observe drug sales without any suspicion. Again, such was the world of Bed-Stuy, where things became all mixed up and, to those outside it, perhaps, incomprehensible.

It looked as if the hijackers would not be coming back to the truck. Dave tossed his coffee cup out the window. It was cold, and he felt cramped and restless. Just as he was about to light a cigarette, he glanced across the street and saw three black people come out of an apartment building. One was a heavy-set man; the two others were women. All three were acting strangely. The young women were staggering around on the sidewalk. Suddenly one fell. The other sat down next to her.

"Stay here," Dave said. "Watch the truck."

As he approached the trio across the street, the man hurried away. Dave bent over the girl who had fallen. She and her friend were only ten or eleven years old. She was unconscious. Dave put his ear to her chest, but there was no heartbeat. He held her wrist; no pulse, either. The other girl, semiconscious, was screaming incoherently. "Heroin!" she was saying. "Heroin!"

"What happened?"

"Heroin!"

Dave turned his head to see Bob running toward him. "Bob— these chicks have taken an overdose."

"What'll we do?"

"Got to get to the hospital," Dave said, looking around. St. Mary's Hospital was three or four blocks away. One of them had to stay on the truck with the police radio in case the hijackers showed up. "Give me a hand," Dave said as he lifted the unconscious girl. Bob helped him throw her over his left shoulder. Dave grabbed the other girl with his right arm, holding her next to his waist, and started walking toward the hospital. Midway he thought that he might not make it, so he tried running with all his strength.

Staggering through the hospital doorway, he shouted to the nurses, "Two O.D.'s here!"

Teams of nurses and doctors went into action immediately. One of the girls had gone into a coma. Dave collapsed on the floor from exhaustion, and the next thing he knew there was an oxygen mask over his face. He had been unconscious for three minutes.

On the third floor of the hospital, the eleven-year-old girl would not come out of the coma. The other one was sitting up, then passing out, gasping for breath. Every time she awoke, Dave tried to ask what had happened. Eventually she was able to tell him that the man they were with, known as Fat Larry, had enticed them into the hallway of the apartment building. He forced them to snort heroin, so they would get high and he would be able to rape them. But they had taken overdoses, and he was trying to get them outside to the fresh air when Dave saw the three of them.

Dave got a description of Fat Larry. Then he called the family of one of the girls and told them what had happened. Within minutes, a crowd of at least sixty angry people showed up at the hospital. Dave repeated what had happened, and they all stormed out to look for Fat Larry.

By now, Bob had arrived at the hospital. They kept checking on the two girls, one of whom was receiving shock treatments. Twenty minutes went by without any success in bringing her out of the coma.

Dave turned around to see two men rushing into the room.

"You'd better go down there," one man gasped. "They're outside—they're gonna kill him!"

They went to the window and looked down. A mob of more than two hundred people was standing outside the hospital with Fat Larry.

"Batman! Hey, Batman! Come down here! We got him!"

"It's a lynch mob," Dave said as he and Bob raced downstairs and outside. *"Don't do it,"* Dave screamed at them.

"Here he is! The dirty fuck!"

"We're gonna tie him to a car and drag him down the street!"

The mob was almost out of control. "You people know us," Bob said. "You know we've never bullshitted you! We're in the street and we've helped you as much as we can! Do something for *us*, now! Let us take this guy and we'll see to it that he gets justice! If *you* punish him, you'll get nothing out of it!"

"Listen," Dave yelled, "if you don't give this guy up, if you don't give him to us, we're gonna split, and we're not coming back! Because if you ain't helping us, we don't want to help *you* any more!"

At last the mob relented and let them arrest Fat Larry. He was held in fifty thousand dollars' bail. The girls remained in the hospital, one of them unconscious for three days, but they survived.

In court, Fat Larry got three years on probation without having to go to jail.

25

They had just gone through a month-long Criminal Investigation Course, to which a certain degree of prestige was attached. Maybe they were going to get the promotion after all. As it was, they were already more like detectives than regular cops, wearing plain-clothes and roaming the entire precinct, getting the cooperation of more informers or stoolies than any other two cops in the city could claim.

One of the stoolies told them, "Hey, man, while you been gone, this dude who goes by the name of Leon, he set up business over at Rochester and Sterling!"

"Nobody's dealing over there any more," Bob said.

Dave thought a moment. "Yeah," he said, "but that means he figures there's no competition, so he might as well go in there."

"We all told him he's crazy," the stoolie said. "Everybody told him, 'Batman and Robin are gonna nail you,' but he comes on with a big scene. He says, 'Hey, man, those guys ain't doing *nothing* to me. See this?' he says, and he shows us a gun and he takes a bullet and says, 'See this bullet? This got Batman's name on it. And this one here—it's got Robin's name on it.' That dude got a big mouth. He says he's gonna hit you guys and be a hero, man."

"Well," Dave laughed, "instead of letting him become a hero, Bobby, why don't we just make him a schmuck?"

"You gonna come get him?" the stoolie asked.

"That's right, baby."

The informer went off to tell his friends that Batman and Robin were coming to get Leon, the loudmouth. Dave and Bob went back to the precinct house to put on some old clothes. As they walked to Rochester and Sterling, pushers and junkies came out of the doorways and off the street corners to follow them. They all knew Dave and Bob by sight—all except the unsuspecting Leon, over on Sterling Place. By the time they got there, a huge crowd had formed on both sides of the street.

"This is just like opening night on Broadway," Dave murmured as they walked along.

To an outsider, the sight of a few hundred black junkies watching two white, bearded cops making a drug bust might have been puzzling. But in this case, the junkies actually wanted Dave and Bob to succeed. They had no doubt that Batman and Robin would be able to catch Leon, so why not have some fun watching? Also, Leon was from the other end of Brooklyn, and he didn't know what Batman and Robin had done. The junkies had told Leon all about these two cops; they had bragged that Batman and Robin worked in their precinct, even though Dave and Bob had locked up most of them at one time or another. Leon had scoffed at them and now they were lining up to see their own boasting proved right.

Dave approached two junkies. He glanced sideways and noticed the smirks on everyone's face: they all knew what was coming. "Hey, man," Dave said. "Arthur? Timmy? How're you doing?"

He had arrested both of them before for possession. They smiled at him, playing the game.

"What's happening?" Dave said.

"Hey, man, everything's cool. Where you been? Ain't seen you in a while."

"Yeah, well, we had a good connection down the other end of town. Had some dynamite shit, man. But the guy got busted, so we're looking for a new one."

"Well," the junkie replied, "there ain't nobody doing nothing. Not much happening."

"Yeah? Listen, we got the word. Rico told us to come see a dude named Leon. Where's Leon?"

The entire conversation was quite loud. Leon, standing nearby, heard his name and approached.

"Hey," Dave said. "Your name Leon?"

"Yeah."

"Well, man, Rico told us to come see you. You got some good stuff out in the streets, he told us. Tell me what you're doing."

"Fours."

"Can we do some short money?"

"No, man, straight four."

"All right. Turn us on to three, will ya?"

"All right."

"Hey," Dave said. "Wait a minute, though. Can you turn us on to half a load?"

"You got the bread?"

"Sure," Dave said, pulling out seventy dollars in cash.

"Cool, man. Come on with me."

Leon walked over to a parked car. Dave and Bob followed him. He opened the trunk and took the heroin out and handed it to Bob. "Well," Bob said. "Pay the man."

"Right on, brother," Dave replied.

He reached back into his pocket and took out his police shield. At the same time, Bob stuck his hand under Leon's belt and pulled out the gun. The crowd watching from both sides of the street burst into spontaneous applause.

Calls kept coming into the precinct house from stoolies competing with each other to see who could give Batman and Robin the best tips. "Okay," Dave would tell the informant, "we're gonna hit that place at nine o'clock tonight. By ten thirty, we should be out—there won't be anybody home."

The stoolies' main incentive for giving information was that they knew Dave and Bob would make their arrest and leave any money in the apartment behind. Just after ten thirty, the informant would burgle the place to get his reward.

It was unorthodox, Dave knew, but it got him and Bob more and better information. And it's a lot better than paying guys out of our own pockets, Dave thought. The only drawback was that every time he and Bob made an arrest and money disappeared, they got blamed for it. Other cops often did take money they found in such situations, so most of them believed Dave and Bob were doing it as well.

But they had vowed that they would never take money—not

bribes, not cash that might be in the apartments of people they arrested. If they found a thousand dollars in a pusher's room, they would leave it there for the stoolie. Why bring it in as property so the pusher could take it when he got out of jail? He would just use it to start up his business again!

It was dangerous; it was the reason for accusations from both cops and pushers that they were crooks. It was also a hell of a way to get information.

Dave wanted to concentrate on one particular building on Prospect Place. Of approximately one hundred and ten apartments in this building, probably two thirds were being used by heroin connections. He and Bob had hit the building off and on for about a year, mostly to catch pushers working for the Brewer brothers.

By now they had made arrests in nearly fifty of those apartments. After each hit, they would lock up the apartment and sometimes scrawl "Batman and Robin Were Here" on the door. Dave's goal was to close down the entire building. The vacant building would stand there as a monument, a warning, for everyone in the drug scene.

For each arrest, a great deal of planning was needed. He and Bob had become so well known that there were fewer and fewer places they could hide. After they used one spot to observe, the pushers would find out about it and look there before going ahead with any transactions. Dave and Bob would spend a week devising a plan; after it worked once, they had to think up a whole new method.

One night in the building they had ten prisoners face down on the living-room floor. There were bundles of heroin in the apartment, which was owned by Helen, the main connection.

While they were searching everybody and wondering how to get them all outside, five more junkies came to the door asking for drugs. Dave and Bob pulled them inside, one by one, until fifteen prisoners lay crowded on the floor.

Dave was trying not to show that he was worried about how to get them all to the station house. He and Bob had no handcuffs and no police radio. There was no phone in the apartment.

Bob was reading his thoughts. "I'll go call for assistance," he said.

Bob left him alone with one gun and fifteen hostile prisoners in this apartment. Dave made them put the bed and the couch and the chairs in one place and then told them to sit down, as a group, so he could cover everybody.

Three, four, five minutes went by. Someone was knocking on the door. Probably Bob. As he went to open it, though, something made him stop. What if it wasn't Bob?

He stepped into the living room again, still holding his gun. "Helen," he said, "go ask who it is."

She went to the door. "Who is it?"

"It's me—Jimmy."

"Ask him what he wants," Dave said.

"What d'ya want, Jimmy?"

"Listen," came the reply. "I got this here gun. I'm gonna go pull a stickup. But give me some stuff now, and I'll bring the money back when I'm finished."

Helen glanced at Dave. "Shit, man," she said, "he just wants me to open that door! When I crack the door, he's gonna take *us* off! He wants my money and my dope!"

"Calm down," Dave said. "Tell him to wait a minute."

"Jimmy? Wait a minute, okay?"

"Hey, baby, open up! I ain't lying—I got the gun right in my hand!" He began pounding on the door.

If I try to deal with this guy with the gun, Dave thought, what will the fifteen people behind me do?

"Listen," he told Helen. "I'll stay right here"—he was midway between the door and the living room, but to one side—"and you get by the door. When I give you the word, yank it open, but stay behind it. The door will shield you. I'll get the drop on him—if your friends don't get the drop on me."

When the door opened, he would open fire at Jimmy. He could hit him with two bullets and still have four left for the people in the living room. They'll jump me for sure, he thought. By sheer numbers, they'll have a good chance.

Dave got into position and cocked his gun. He gave Helen a signal with his hand.

"All right," she called to Jimmy. "I'll open the door!" She pulled it open, shielding herself. There was Jimmy, aiming the gun.

And Bob was standing right behind him in the hall, holding a gun at his head.

The building on Prospect Place was eventually closed down. Steel sheets were nailed up over the front door, and the windows were boarded up. Junkies would break inside there to shoot up in the hallway, and soon there were graffiti on the walls: "Batman and Robin—Wanted, Dead Only." One message read: "Batman and Robin—$1000 Dead, $1.19 Alive."

Dave Greenberg drove up and parked in front of his home on Staten Island. He had been working three days and nights in a row. It was just past four o'clock in the afternoon. He walked into the kitchen, took off his gun, and slumped down in a chair.

Irene put her hands on his shoulders, bent down, and kissed him. He reached up and gently pulled her head down to kiss her again. He was glad to be home. The world of Bedford-Stuyvesant was so far from his wife, his child, his home in Staten Island. Right now, he wanted to forget about the slums and the drug scene altogether.

The phone rang. He reached over and grabbed it off the kitchen wall. "Yeah?"

"Dave?"

"Yeah."

It was a sergeant at the Seventy-seventh Precinct. "Listen, Dave, we got a phone call here a little while ago, saying that some guys are coming to Staten Island to kill you."

"They said Staten Island?"

"Yeah. An unidentified male voice. I'll give you the quote— 'They're going out to Staten Island to get the Batman.' I told the captain, and he said make sure I call you right away."

Dave thought about it a moment. He was accustomed to getting threatening letters and calls.

"Fine," Dave said. "Sounds like another bullshit story."

"You gonna be okay?"

"Yeah. Thanks for calling."

He hung up and leaned back in his chair. The only thing that seemed authentic about this threat was the mention of Staten Island. People in Bed-Stuy weren't supposed to know where he was living. The call to the precinct house must have come from an informant—if the information was for real.

Dave could hardly keep his eyes open. Irene was cooking dinner, so he could eat and then maybe go to bed.

"What was it?" she asked.

"Nothing," Dave said. "It wasn't important."

After dinner he went into the next room to watch television. When he was home at night, he would usually collapse in front of the TV set and watch until the eleven o'clock news. He would switch off the set just before the news came on, and take his Great Dane, Shadow Bay, for a walk.

It was too early for the eleven o'clock walk. He decided that he would take out the dog an hour earlier, around ten, but there was still some time to kill. He tried to concentrate on the TV show.

"Are you sure that phone call was nothing?" Irene was asking him. "I mean, you looked worried when you hung up."

"It was nothing," he said. "A dude called the precinct and said there were some guys coming out here to kill me."

"What! David! Tell me the truth! Are you kidding?"

"Yeah," he mumbled. "I'm just joking. Take it easy." He put his arm around her and dozed off.

The next thing he knew, Irene was whispering, "Dave? Are you asleep?"

"No," he said, standing up and stretching. By his watch it was ten past ten. "I'll take Shadow out, and then let's go to bed."

He opened the basement door and the black Great Dane came bounding upstairs. Then he thought of that phone call. He took his gun out of the holster and stuck it under his belt. He had never taken the gun with him to walk the dog before. Just a precaution.

When he opened the front door, Shadow raced out into the night air. Dave walked down the pathway to the sidewalk and the street, watching him run along the edge of the swamp.

"Hey!" he called. "Shadow! Let's go! This way!"

After five or six minutes he was ready to call it a night. He clapped his hands and headed back toward the house. The huge dog ran by him up the walkway along the side of the house. He was standing a few feet from the corner of his house when he heard a loud click. He paused, his mind a blank. What was that sound?

He looked to his right, along the front of the house. A black man was standing in the garage, holding a gun. Pointed at him. Dave knew what was coming. There was nowhere to take cover but jump straight ahead onto the walkway, past the corner of the house. He dove forward. *Blam!* The bullet whizzed over the top of his head and the noise slammed into his mind like an explosion. He hit the pavement. It felt as if he had burned his hands with a torch. *Blam!* The second shot—

He pulled out his own gun and rolled into position at the side of the house, stood up, and looked around the corner. The man was running away! Dave watched him head toward the street and down the block. He took aim and fired. The man stumbled but kept running.

Did I hit him? Shadow had gone after the gunman. Shit, I've brought that violence right back here to my home! How many more men are there, out in that swamp?

Dave Greenberg started running into the night, chasing after the man with the gun, racing toward the trouble . . .

BOOK

5

26

The gunman stumbled as he turned the corner. Dave thought he might have wounded him. He took aim for a second shot, but the dog was in the way.

Dave reached the corner just as a late-model Cadillac sped away toward Hylan Boulevard. No headlights or taillights—can't read the license plate. Three men in the car, the interior lights still on.

He raced back up the block. They've got a huge head start. In the house, he grabbed his car keys off the kitchen table. Irene was hysterical.

"Are you hurt? David, they tried to kill you!"

"Call the police!"

She was holding onto his sleeve. *"Don't go! Don't go!"*

"Call the cops!" he shouted, breaking loose and running out to his car. He rolled backward out of the driveway, then forward and around the corner, down to Hylan Boulevard. He turned right toward the Verrazano Bridge, and sped two miles down the boulevard. The sound of sirens came from all over. Squad cars passed him going in the opposite direction, toward his house. Well, I lost them, he thought.

He made a U-turn and sped back. As he approached his house, he remembered Bob. Where's Bob? Maybe they're after him too!

Dave's street was clogged with radio cars. Cops were running around the grounds; some were wading into the dark swamp area to see if the gunman might still be there. Dave stopped the car and ran into his house to the phone. He dialed Bob's Brooklyn number. No answer. He tried Sonny's place in Manhattan. Still nothing.

"Find my partner!" he shouted, rushing outside again. "Listen," he told a sergeant, "my partner's phone doesn't answer. They could be after him while we're out here fucking around!"

He shut his eyes for a moment. Maybe they waited until we were split up, both tired out . . . . But the phone was ringing. He ran inside again, nearly leaping across the table to pick it up.

"Yeah!"

"Dave! You all right?"

"Hey, Bobby—I'm okay. Where are you?"

"Look, I'll be there soon as I can!"

"No, no—find a place to hide, man! I'm all right. They got away, but I'm fine. Don't come over! Hide somewhere!"

"You sure you're all right?"

"Yeah," Dave insisted. "Get out of sight for a while, and call me in the morning."

He hung up and saw that Irene was crying. "It's all over," he said. "Bob's okay."

Outside, the police were questioning a tow-truck driver who said he had seen two men with rifles coming out of the marshlands near Dave's home—but on the other side, at Hylan Boulevard. Maybe there were five men altogether. Two in the swamp across the street from the house, one in the garage. It seemed to have been a well-planned assassination attempt that had gone awry only because Dave had taken out the dog thirty minutes earlier than usual.

An extensive manhunt went on during the night. Twenty-five police cars and several emergency trucks and fire engines were on the scene. Headlights were turned into the marshland and woods, while policemen marched in rows, looking for the possibly injured assailant or some clue to his identity. A police helicopter came to help with the search. Interrogations lasted until nearly five in the morning.

Dozens of cops including detectives volunteered to stay on the case during off-duty hours. Dave and Bob were reassigned to assist the Seventy-seventh detective squad, each with different officers, to go through Bedford-Stuyvesant looking for possible motives, clues, suspects. Suspicions about Greenberg and Hantz surfaced again. The pair were shaking down addicts and dealers for money, some said, and maybe that was the reason for the assassination attempt.

Dave was driving down to the courthouse in the morning, three weeks later, when he passed a run-down hotel in Bedford-Stuyvesant and stopped. He sat in the car, thinking. And then it all came back to him. Three months ago, that hotel had caught fire. He and Bob had raced inside to bang on all the doors and get the people out. One woman wouldn't open her door, so Dave kicked it down. It was Joyce, the woman who had helped them by giving up her connection, the gunman up on the subway tracks. Dave had promised to help her in return, but the hearing had been delayed. When it was held, he forgot about his promise altogether. Completely, absolutely, totally forgot. He had hooked her up in his testimony without saying a single word in her behalf. Then the trial had been delayed—it still hadn't been held—and he had gone to find her and explain. But she had moved away, still selling drugs but somewhere else. He had been depressed by the whole affair. His and Bob's reputations were based on the fact that they stood by their promises, and he had sold this woman right down the river.

He looked over at the hotel. During the fire, he had seen her in one of the rooms, with the same man who had hidden in the garage and had fired at him. He's linked up with Joyce, and she definitely has a motive for wanting me killed.

Dave made a quick turn on the street and headed back to the precinct house. With the detectives, he went to get Joyce's arrest record to see who had been busted with her. Looking through photographs, he put his finger on one and said, "That's the guy."

An eight-day trial was held. But before the jury went out, the judge had a stroke and a mistrial was declared. The suspect took a plea of guilty, however, and the affair was over. No conspiracy was proved, but the twenty-four-hour guards posted at Dave's house were relieved.

When he and Bob heard rumors that they might be transferred to another precinct for their own protection, Dave said they were not about to be scared off. If they were going to make it to the Detective Division, they would do it right where they'd begun.

Dave was in court, so Bob asked for a foot post, rather than get into a car and go through a tour with someone else. He was on Schenectady Avenue, and he wanted to climb to a rooftop and make some observations in preparation for an arrest he and Dave would try in the near future. He started toward an alley, but a radio car was pulling around the corner. Bob paused, watching, and the car stopped in front of him. It was a sergeant who had been complaining every week to Captain Levitan about Greenberg and Hantz, mainly because they were making too many arrests in his sector, causing him a good deal of embarrassment.

"What are you doing here?" the sergeant inquired.

"Walking my post," Bob said. "In a military manner, sir, keeping always on the alert."

The sergeant ignored Bob's sarcasm. "You're off post."

"No I'm not."

"Here's the book," the sergeant said, holding up the memo book so Bob could see it. "It reads Post 37 for you."

"Yeah?"

"Yeah. And Post 37 isn't down this end. Post 37 is up the other way."

"I guess you got me. Simple mistake. I haven't got a map with me. We have a territorial-boundary dispute here, that's all."

"What were you doing?"

"Helping the responsible citizens of Gotham City, preserving the peace and so forth."

"What's that?"

"Rooftops," Bob said. "I was just checking the rooftops, making observations."

"Give me your book."

Bob shrugged, took out his own memo book, and handed it to the sergeant, who signed it. Then he took his book back and stood there on the sidewalk, waiting for the sergeant to pull away.

"Hantz!"

"Yes?"

"Don't you salute me?"

"Oh. Well, if that's what you need, man, you got it."

Bob gave an exaggerated salute and the sergeant drove off. The guy's more worried about his memo book than he is about making arrests, for God's sake.

Just then Bob saw one of his and Dave's informers coming up the block. "Hey, man," he said, "what's happening?"

"You know Debra?"

"Debra Keyes?"

"Yeah. She moved over to St. Mark's Place."

"So?"

"Well, she ain't doing any stuff. But if you went over there, you might find out on your own that her husband is."

"What's his name?"

"Jerry."

"He's in business?"

"I didn't say that, brother. I said if you went there you might find out. On your own."

"He's the same guy we've been hearing about," Dave said when Bob told him about his encounter. "You remember when I was wondering where Debra was? Well, she and Jerry moved over to St. Mark's Place. I put the word out that if Jerry doesn't stop dealing, we'd be coming to get him. I thought it would be warning enough. Let's get over there tonight."

He and Bob hid in the hallway of the building where Jerry and Debra lived. After a while, a junkie came in and went up the stairs. Dave and Bob took off their shoes and tiptoed up after him. They saw him knock on a door on the second floor. The drug sale was made quickly. Once the door had closed again, they stood up and faced the young man, who still had the heroin in his hand.

"Stay right there," Dave said. "We're going inside, anyway." Dave knocked. "Hey, Jerry! It's Batman and Robin! We got you! Open the door!"

Jerry, Dave thought, is the kind of guy that when you got him right, you got him and he's not gonna fight it. He'll say, Okay, you got me, I'll pay for what I did, and the next time I'll try it again.

The door was unlocking, but when it opened, no one was there. Instinctively Dave pushed the junkie down to the floor and he and Bob leaped for cover. At that moment, three shots in a row were fired.

On his stomach to one side of the open door, Dave yelled, "Are you crazy? We haven't even taken out our guns! Hey, Jerry, we're locking you up! It's us, man! We got you!" He saw Debra inside the apartment. "Debra, what's the matter with him? What is he, crazy or what? We're gonna kill him!"

"You ain't taking me," came Jerry's voice from behind the door. "You ain't coming in here! I'll blow your motherfucking heads off! I'll kill both of you!"

"Hey, Jerry," Dave called. "What is this, man? We got you on a lousy-ass junk collar, and you're shooting it out with the police?" But Jerry was screaming louder now, incoherently. Dave called to Debra again. "You know we can get a hundred people in here in five seconds! They'll probably come anyway, if they heard the shooting! Debra, tell him to throw the gun out! Give it up! Forget it!"

Debra became hysterical, begging Jerry to give up.

"Listen," Dave called, "we're giving him three seconds and then we're coming in shooting! And you know that he's the one that's going to die!"

Debra rushed toward her husband, but she tripped, and he ran past her toward the rear of the apartment. Dave and Bob got up and started through the door, guns drawn.

"Jerry?" Dave called. "It's all over, man. What are you doing this for?"

They saw Jerry standing at the window, crying. "All right!" he said, the tears streaming down his face. "I've thrown the fucking gun out the window! Put those things away and I'm gonna beat your motherfucking heads in with my fists!"

There had to be something wrong. Dave and Bob slowly put their guns away, and Jerry came at them, arms flailing. They struggled with him. "What's got into you?" Dave said as he grabbed a pair of handcuffs and tried to put them on Jerry's wrists, behind his back. At last he was subdued.

"Okay," Dave said. "Now, somebody better do some talking in a hurry. It was only an accident that none of those bullets hit one of us. What's the story?"

Jerry refused to talk. Debra was crying. "There's a reason," she whispered.

"What? What's the reason?"

"Three cops," she said. "Three cops beat me up and raped me. And robbed us."

"Three cops?"

"You heard me! Cops!"

Dave glanced at Bob and then turned back to Debra. "Go on," he said.

A month ago, Debra told them, she and Jerry had started selling drugs in their apartment on St. Mark's Place. One day three policemen came to the door and broke it down. Debra was there with her sister and the sister's baby. The three cops, in civilian clothes, displayed their shields, guns, and handcuffs. They asked for Jerry. "He's not here," Debra said. So they took the place apart and found some drugs and thirty-five hundred dollars in cash, plus a piggy bank with coins in it. Then the cops beat up Debra and made the sister commit sodomy. And they raped Debra. Then they took the money and the drugs and the piggy bank. When the sister cried, "That's my baby's money," they smashed the piggy bank, took all the money out of it, and left.

No wonder Jerry behaved the way he did! Christ, Dave thought, he probably wants to shoot every cop in sight!

"You sure they were cops?" he asked.

"They had shields," Debra said.

Dave put his hand on Jerry's shoulder. "Listen, man," he said, "we'll try to help. Whether they were cops or not, we'll get them."

They got descriptions of the three men from Debra, but no names. Not even a clue.

"I don't want to lock you up," Dave told them. "We'll go down and pick up that gun and bring it in, but we'll let you off. Jerry?"

Jerry looked up at him and nodded. Dave unlocked the handcuffs.

"We're going to need you both as witnesses," Dave said. "We won't even take you for this collar, man. But if I find out that you're still dealing, I'm gonna nail you. Okay?"

Jerry nodded again.

"I understand your feelings, man. We'll do what we can to get those guys. You know the way we treat people, right?"

"Right."

"Okay. And there are other cops like us, man. You can't shoot them all, anyway."

Dave and Bob left the apartment. They searched behind the building, but the gun was gone. In silence, they rode back to the precinct house. If someone had ever told me I'd want to lock up a cop, Dave thought, I wouldn't have believed it.

"Hey, Batman."

It was Frankie, a drug addict in his early twenties whom Dave and Bob had arrested for possession at one time. They had also helped get his younger sister off drugs and into a program.

"What's happening?" Dave said.

"Listen, man, the cop's name is Eric."

"Eric what?"

"Don't know his last name."

"Where does he work? Which precinct?"

"I don't know."

"Okay—thanks."

So now they had a name. Eric. Offhand, Dave didn't know any Eric on the police force. But then there were a hundred cops right in the Seventy-seventh Precinct whom he knew only by the last name. Who the hell is Eric?

Dave asked a girl friend in the Department's personnel office to see if she could get him a list of all cops in the city named Eric. Out of thirty-two thousand, there had to be at least a couple of hundred. One night, with a stack of file cards, he and Bob went through all the names until they came to Eric Washburn, a black cop in the Seventy-seventh Precinct. Washburn was one of the men who had tried to cast suspicion on them at times.

The whole affair seemed messy. The fact that Washburn was one of their own colleagues was bad enough. To go after another cop on criminal charges was a violation of an unwritten code of the Police Department—"Thou shalt not rat on a fellow officer." Worse yet, Washburn happened to be black.

"We'd better go see the captain," Dave said.

Levitan put them in touch with the Confidential Investigating Unit of Internal Affairs. "Well," Dave observed, "this is the first time we've ever had anything to do with these people when they weren't looking to hook *us* up on something." They were brought in to see Captain Nick Zirpolo, head of the Internal Affairs Division of Brooklyn North. While they were telling their story to Zirpolo, the phone rang. It was Captain Levitan.

"Yes?" Zirpolo said into the phone. "Sure, come on down." He hung up and looked at Dave and Bob. "Your captain wants to see me," he said. "Wait outside."

Levitan went inside to see Captain Zirpolo. When the private conversation was over and Levitan had gone, Zirpolo asked Dave and Bob to come back in.

"I've just had a very, very good conversation with your commanding officer," he said. "And he leads me to believe that you're the two most competent police officers in the city of New York. So I'm telling you this—I'm assigning two superior officers, one lieutenant and one sergeant, to work for you. Their first names are Steve and John, and that's how you'll address them from this point on. They'll do anything you say. This investigation is yours. I want any means necessary used, and I'll back you a hundred percent."

We've heard this before, Dave thought, but he seems to mean it.

The lieutenant and the sergeant, Steve and John, were brought in and introductions were made by Zirpolo on a first-name basis. "You do as they say," Zirpolo told the officers. "Is that understood?" For a few moments, there was silence in the room.

"Understood," the lieutenant said.

"Okay," Zirpolo went on. "Let's take it from here."

What are we supposed to do with these two superior officers? Dave wondered. None of our informers will talk in front of them. The best thing to do is send them out on dead ends, keep them busy going in circles. Keep them out of our way.

They were all in Dave's car, driving around the precinct. Whenever Dave saw an informer he would tell the lieutenant and the sergeant to go somewhere else. Slowly, the information came in. They went to Debra and gave her a description of Eric Washburn. It fit one of the three men. Then one of the informers said that a man they had arrested once before was one of the other cops.

"Wait a minute," Dave said. "We never arrested a cop before."

"Well, you arrested him."

"Who?"

"Jesse Bowles."

"Jesse Bowles? He ain't a cop."

"Well, he was one of the guys that robbed Jerry and Debra. They also robbed two brothers, Anthony and Randolph."

"What's their last name?"

"I dunno."

Using at least seventy informers in Bedford-Stuyvesant, Dave and Bob came up with the fact that Anthony and Randolph Morris, two brothers who were dealing in drugs, had been robbed by the same three men who said they were cops.

Finding the Morris brothers was no easy task. And getting them to talk freely was even more difficult. Eventually the Morris brothers confirmed that they had been robbed by three men, one of whom was Jesse Bowles, who had claimed to be policemen. The descriptions matched those given by Debra.

While the lieutenant and the sergeant from the Confidential Investigating Unit were following up more dead-end leads, Dave and Bob debated whether to go right to Jesse Bowles' apartment and confront him. Jesse had spent some time in jail because of them, and he probably would not be very cordial—especially if he was guilty. On top of that, Dave and Bob had been instructed not to go see him and tip their hand.

"There's no other way," Dave said when he and Bob were alone. "Let's try it our way. If it blows up on us, it blows up. If the whole case falls apart or something, we'll go out and be steelworkers. But if we don't go and see Jesse Bowles, we're gonna be at a standstill."

So they went. Dave stood at the door and, deciding that it would be too polite to knock, he kicked it open. Jesse was resting on his bed. He jumped up, startled.

"You can't kick my door in," Jesse said.

"Why not?"

"That's illegal, man!"

"Well, Jesse, we did it. Now what?"

"What do you want?"

"Jesse, we know about everything, man," said Dave, half bluffing. "We know about you, and Eric, and your other pal. We know you went up to Jerry's place and took off his wife, man. We know you hit Anthony and Randolph Morris in the park. We got you for a lot of stickups, Jesse. And when we get hold of Eric, he's gonna give you right up. We got complainants, names, dates, everything.

"Listen," he went on, "the fact that we collared you once before might mean something to us. Let's put it this way—if you cooperate with us, we might feel that we owe you something. We might give you an opportunity to get yourself out of this thing."

"How?" Jesse said.

"By having you as a material witness rather than as a defendant. We got all the information on you, and what we might do is pretend that we don't know any of it, and let you become the state's witness. So you can testify against your co-conspirators, and that would take the weight off you."

Much of what Dave was saying went over Jesse's head. Jesse distrusted Bob for some reason, and it took a while before he relaxed. Finally he blurted out that Eric Washburn, a cop in the Seventy-seventh Precinct who also used drugs, was involved. And a third party named Booker Kendric. The three of them would go to junkies' apartments and rob them, using Eric's shield and gun. When they had robbed the Morris brothers in Prospect Park, they had picked up two more guns to use.

Jesse was willing to make complete statements on tape at Nick Zirpolo's office. Dave and Bob brought him in.

On the tapes, Jesse said that he and Washburn and Kendric had robbed the Morris brothers not once but twice. After the first time. The two brothers had armed themselves with guns so that it wouldn't happen again. Unfortunately for the Morris brothers, however, they were caught off guard by the same three men. And the guns were taken.

Jesse also stated for the record that Eric Washburn had robbed various places up in Harlem. To commit robberies was one thing; but when the perpetrator was a cop, the potential for trouble multiplied. Not only would drug addicts and pushers be arming themselves against all cops, but the cop himself would become more dangerous. To avoid being caught, he would have no hesitation about killing one of his colleagues.

Jesse made statements for the district attorney as well. The D.A. then wanted Jerry and Debra to come in and testify as complainants. Dave and Bob were sent out to find them, but they had moved again. Nobody at St. Mark's Place knew where they had gone. Once again, Dave and Bob hunted up informers, junkies, relatives, anybody who might be able to help. A few days later they found Jerry and Debra, who came in and made statements.

Now Dave and Bob had to find the Morris brothers, who also

were suddenly missing. They discovered that Randolph Morris had been arrested since they had seen him. Dave and Bob managed to get him released from jail so he could make a statement.

The next step was to obtain a warrant for Eric Washburn's arrest.

They sat in the car at midnight, outside Patrolman Washburn's home in Brooklyn. Several other cars were on the stakeout as well. Dave lit a cigarette, imagining what it would be like to be in Washburn's place. To go after a cop was almost the same as going against yourself or a relative; no matter what the reasons, it seemed a kind of betrayal. Well, Dave thought, this guy betrayed the rest of us when he started hitting those places.

They watched Washburn go into the building. A superior officer was on hand to make the arrest. He may be guilty on criminal charges, but the Department wants him first. They suspend him, then cut him loose. Cut his ties and throw him to the D.A.'s office.

Twenty cops went to the door, knocked, and barged inside to arrest Washburn for robbery. Then the cops started searching the place. The lieutenant said to Dave, "Why don't you look around?"

I really don't want to find anything, Dave thought. Getting him for the robberies is bad enough. Now we might find the guns and maybe some of his drugs. Why hook him up more than we have to?

He and Bob went through everything. In one of the closets, in a shoe-polish can, Dave found one envelope of heroin. It fell out of the can to the floor and Dave stepped on it. Holy shit, Dave thought, why couldn't the guy have kept his own place clean? If locking him up will save another cop's life, then we've succeeded. Why embarrass this guy further by letting everyone know he deals in drugs?

Both Bob and the lieutenant had seen the envelope fall. The other cops were still searching. "I'm not gonna say anything," the lieutenant said to Bob, "but we don't know who else saw it. Let's be reasonable. It's your move."

Dave saw Bob staring at him. He took his foot away and picked up the small packet of heroin. The charge would be robbery and possession of drugs.

Eric Washburn admitted that the third man was Booker Kendric. They got a warrant to search his apartment and came up with a .38 automatic, foreign-made, loaded. Shortly afterward they arrested Kendric.

"If anything'll get you into the detective bureau," Captain Zirpolo told them, "this'll do it."

Maybe, Dave thought; but this wasn't the way we wanted it to happen. Dave and Bob hadn't slept for four days, and the whole experience was making them feel even more depressed and tired. Maybe arresting a police officer shows that we're dedicated, but it's nothing we want to brag about.

27

Bob Hantz sat in the front passenger seat of the parked car while Dave, behind the wheel, turned around to talk to Anthony and Randolph Morris. The brothers had agreed to give Dave and Bob tips on drug pushers and even help set up arrests. They seemed uncomfortable about it, though, and as Bob listened to the conversation, he too grew uneasy, without knowing why.

"The guy's name is Reggie," one of the brothers was saying to Dave. "A big supplier, man."

Bob wondered why they would be so eager to give up such an important heroin seller. After all, these guys are still on junk and they need their connection. What do they hope to gain? It might be a trap, for all we know.

Possibly Dave was having the same thoughts; now he was changing plans in midstream, backing off. "Let's wait on that. But we'll do something else."

"How about that guy Nickie we told you was doing stuff?"

"Yeah," Dave said. "Okay, we'll take that."

Bob continued to listen in silence. Why isn't Dave consulting me? Or at least glancing at me to see if I approve? Sure, I'll probably go along; but the least he can do is give the appearance of asking my approval.

Their agreement had always been that Dave would come up with the initial plan of action. Unless Bob came up with a better solution, he would accept it. The point was that Dave always consulted him, asked for his criticism. That was their clear understanding.

"Okay," Dave was saying. "Let's go."

"Wait a minute," Bob said. "Hold on, Dave. I think this thing smells, man. I want to talk it over first."

"Hey, Bobby! Don't fuck with me, man! You got a better way to do it?"

He looked at Dave and felt his own face burning. "We're not going ahead with this one," he said.

Dave glared at him. "This is *it*, Bob, whether you like it or not!"

Bob took a deep breath, held it a moment, then let it out slowly. "Well, you're not going to do it with me." He opened the car door, got out, slammed it, and walked away. His head was throbbing. He kept walking without looking back, his thoughts all jumbled—and then he cursed, quickening his pace, determined not to give in.

"Don't worry," Dave insisted. "My partner always covers me. He never lets me down."

Bob was at the station house when he heard there had been a "ten-thirteen, shots fired" involving Dave, and he wanted to crawl into a shell. When Dave came in with two prisoners and confiscated weapons, Bob looked at him but said nothing. Dave walked past him and upstairs to the squad room.

He's mad, too, Bob thought. Well, shit, all he had to do was consult me. He didn't have to change our plans right in front of those guys. Now he's waiting for me to give in and apologize.

Dave came back downstairs. Bob looked at him again and watched his partner walk out on the way to court. Well, that's it. Damn, we go all this time without a hitch. One thing comes up, and we're not even speaking.

At four o'clock Bob left the station house. The next day, when he returned to work, he discovered that Dave had called in to say he was taking a few weeks' vacation.

It was the late spring of 1971, more than three years since Dave had joined the police force. The best thing about the experience so far was the teamwork he had developed with Bob; yet here they were, like a pair of adolescents, moping around. He'll never give in, Dave thought; but neither will I.

The silence had gone on for two weeks. Bob had been working, just going through the motions. Dave had stayed home, thinking about the future. During his most reckless flights of imagination, he could see himself as the Police Commissioner of New York City—although he felt that he didn't have enough class even for assignments that required being polite and well-mannered. But despite the lack of a college education, he knew he could take on any job in law enforcement if he wanted to. Sometimes his mind drifted off and there he was, the head of the F.B.I., or at least its number one man in the field . . .

What he had to do now, he thought, was to get into the Detective Division. He had been told that all the complaints and investigations were holding both him and Bob back; up to now, none of the accusations against them had been substantiated. So what was the problem? Was narcotics work too "controversial"?

He decided to act, and made an appointment to see the new Police Commissioner, Patrick V. Murphy. On May 5, 1971, he went in for a personal interview. He told Murphy that the borough commander, the division commander, the captain, and every other boss had been telling him and Bob that they'd become detectives in short order.

"Do you know if there's a specific problem holding things up?" Dave asked.

"No," Murphy said. "I've heard that you're both very good cops, but also very controversial. That's all I know. But those commanding officers have no right to say you'll become detectives. I'm trying to get my commanders to stop saying things like that. To me," Murphy went on, "the most important job is out there in the street, in uniform, on patrol. Some cops feel it's a reward to become a detective. It might be, but it's hurting me to take my best men and make detectives out of them. The better you are, the more I want you in uniform, out there in the street."

Dave acknowledged his point, but said that he felt he would be more effective as a detective. Even as a patrolman, he had made nearly three hundred felony arrests so far with his partner, Bob Hantz, and about a hundred misdemeanor collars.

"I can't help being impressed by that record," Murphy nodded. "What bothers me is when other officers think they know what the next person is going to do, and they build up false hopes."

Dave thanked him and left. As he went through Murphy's outer office, a lieutenant came over and said, "Greenberg, you and Hantz'll be detectives by Friday. No doubt about it."

Bob Hantz picked up the phone, dialed, and waited. It rang twice and he heard Irene's voice at the other end.

"Hello?"

"Hey, what's new?"

"Bobby! Where've you been?"

"Nowhere. Is Dave around?"

"He's out right now. Why don't you come over here? Come for dinner. Bobby, all he does when he comes home is ask if you've called. But he won't pick up the phone and call you. Come over for dinner—"

"We should talk it out. It was stupid."

"Of course it was. The whole thing is crazy! You've worked together more than three years, and you let one little thing ruin it all. Bobby, he doesn't even *want* to go back to work, not with another partner. Come on over to the house. He should be home soon."

"Okay. Listen, Irene—thanks."

"Thanks for what? See you tonight."

It's so simple, Bob thought. I'm the one who has to give in. Take that first step, to keep us going.

They were on their way to the captain's office. Dave was sure that Levitan's request for a meeting had to do with a promotion to the Detective Division or maybe in the narcotics field. A lot of recommendations had been made on their behalf in recent weeks and months; besides, the Commissioner himself had promised to do something.

They walked into the captain's office and Levitan asked them to sit down. "As you know," he told them, "I'll be leaving in a few days to become a deputy inspector. I want you to know that you two have had a great deal to do with my promotion—if for no other reason than the fact that you've kept our arrest record so high. You've had to take a lot of static from everybody—and I know that the Washburn arrest didn't exactly earn you a lot of new friendships around here. In my book, you two guys are great. And completely honest."

Okay, Dave thought; the preliminaries are over. Now comes the good news about our promotion.

"Having said all that," Levitan went on, "I have to tell you that yesterday, two men from the Knapp Commission came here to the precinct, and you're under investigation."

The Knapp Commission, created by Mayor Lindsay the year before to look into police corruption in New York City, was a separate agency outside the Police Department.

"What for?" Dave asked.

"I don't know. The only specific thing they mentioned was the Hayes brothers shooting. They subpoenaed all my record books for the whole precinct from July of 1969 to August of 1970. And they want all your memo books for the same period of time."

"What is it, a joke?"

"Well, I have no idea what they think they'll find," the captain said. He warned them that it was probably a serious investigation. It would mean that any thoughts of promotion would have to wait. Even Commissioner Murphy would have to back away from his recommendation until this was over. He couldn't promote a pair of patrolmen if there was even the remotest possibility that they would be charged with corruption.

"So send them your memo books," Levitan said. "As a deputy inspector, I'll still be plugging for you. I hope the Knapp thing doesn't hinder your work. I'd advise some caution."

"Just the opposite," Dave said. "Our way is to hit 'em even harder. It's the only way we know."

28

They sat on a rooftop at two thirty in the morning, peering through binoculars across Troy Avenue at the Soul Black Castle luncheonette. For a store that was closed, it was extremely busy.

"Man," Dave said, "every junkie in the world is showing up. No question that this guy is doing some heavy drugs. This is one collar we've got to make."

The luncheonette was three doors down from the Aloha Bar, which Dave and Bob had raided several times in the past weeks. Over the summer they had been part of the new Anti-Crime Patrol in the precinct, wearing plainclothes and beards and operating on their own for the new captain, Emile Racine. The arrests had continued to pile up, although no new word about promotions had come.

"I wonder when this traffic is going to slow down," Dave was saying, referring to the junkies who were pouring in and out of the Soul Black Castle at this hour of the morning. Their information was that the proprietor, John Quick, was selling cocaine and heroin. Moreover, he was armed and could be expected to open fire, and there was one other man with him who carried a shotgun. No stoolie had been willing to help Dave and Bob get this man, for fear he would kill anyone who crossed him.

At four in the morning, Dave and Bob climbed down from the roof. They moved quickly across Troy Avenue to the luncheonette and started banging on the door. "Police!" Dave hollered, and he saw John Quick walking toward them, a gun stuck in his belt. They flashed their shields through the glass. Quick squinted, saw the badges, turned around, and ran to the back of the store. Bob lifted his foot up and smashed the wood on the door, cracking the lock off and shattering the glass.

They stood in the doorway for a moment. The counter ran along the right side of the store, front to back. John Quick was running into the back room, straight ahead. Dave yelled, "Freeze! Don't turn around!"

At the same time, Bob ducked and crept behind the counter, sneaking down the length of the store toward the back. If someone else was carrying a gun, Bob hoped to be there to surprise him.

Dave held his gun on John Quick, who still hadn't turned around. All right, Dave thought, but there must be another guy in the back room. John Quick's hand was moving toward a gun stuck in his waist. "If you move one more inch," Dave warned, "I'll blow you away. Now put your hands up in the air."

As Quick went to do so, the second man appeared in the doorway of the back room and told him, "Get out of my way!" Quick stepped to the side and Dave faced a double-barreled sawed-off shotgun. Behind the counter, Bob grabbed a huge metal pot of brown oatmeal and slammed it, upside down, over the man's head. Temporarily blinded, the man dropped his shotgun to the floor.

They found quantities of heroin and cocaine all over the back room. They had John Quick's fully loaded .32-caliber automatic and his partner's sawed-off shotgun. On the way out, they drew a sign on a large piece of cardboard—"This Is a Raided Premise. Stay Out"—and attached it to the door.

"Hey, listen," Quick said, "can we talk this over?"

"What do you mean?" Dave said.

"Hey, man, I got some money. I'll give you what I have, but I can get you a lot more, too."

"Well," Dave said, "maybe we can do something. But the thing is, we have to okay it with our captain. But I'm pretty sure he'll go along with it. We'll take you in and let you talk to him."

Dave could hardly keep from laughing as they drove the two prisoners back to the station house. Bob had picked up his thoughts; there was no need for them to discuss it. We got the collars, Dave mused, and now bribery! And what a beautiful way to do something for Racine! Not only is this a way of showing him that we're honest, but it'll give *him* something to show people. We'll let the captain himself make an arrest!

They walked into the station house with Quick and his partner, and Dave winked at the officer on the desk. The officer, knowing Greenberg and Hantz well enough by now, was not insulted when they walked past him to the back room.

Dave figured that Bob should watch the prisoners while he went to see Captain Racine. Just then he heard Bob say, "Listen, I'll watch the prisoners. You go see the Old Man."

The captain's door was closed. "He's busy," the desk officer said.

"Fine," Dave answered, going straight to the door and opening it.

Captain Racine was meeting with three of his officers. He looked up and saw Dave. "One second," he said to Dave. "Uh, listen," he told the others, "you'll have to excuse me a minute. Something important just came up."

The officers got up and left Racine's office.

"Come in, Dave. What's up?"

"Listen, you got a minute?"

"Certainly."

"Fine. Let me go get Bobby, and we'll get somebody to watch the two prisoners we have."

Dave returned to the back room and asked one of the cops to watch the two prisoners. Then he and Bob walked into the captain's office.

"Okay," Dave said, "the guys want to pay us off. They got a few hundred dollars on them, but we'd like *you* to get paid also."

Racine just stared, not knowing for sure what was going on.

As Dave explained, he would stop from time to time, waiting for Racine to reply. The captain would say, "Are you through?" "No," Dave would answer, and go on explaining. By this time, Captain Racine was not sure whether they were fooling with him or being serious.

"And that's it," Dave said at last. "We're going to go out and bring him in here. And you're going to tell him that okay, you accept."

"What?"

"Right," Dave said. "When we bring him into your office, you're going to say, 'How much?' As a matter of fact, when he makes his first offer, say to him, 'That's not enough.' Got it?"

Dave could see that the captain's mind was reeling, wondering what was happening.

"Okay," Dave went on. "So we bring him in here, and he makes an offer. I know he's got three or four hundred dollars, so the first offer he makes, say, 'No, you'll have to do better than that.' If he comes up with more, take it and then say to him, 'Well, how about my men?' Let's cover at least the three hundred dollars that we know he has. But, Cap, if that's not enough, get an I.O.U. for the rest."

Captain Racine just nodded, bewildered.

They brought John Quick in. Dave closed the door. "This is Captain Racine. Captain, this is John Quick. Mr. Quick has something to say to you, Cap."

The captain seemed to sense what was happening. A faint smile flashed across his face. John Quick was glancing at Dave, as if to ask what it was he should say.

"Don't worry," Dave told him. "Tell the captain what you told us."

"Oh, yeah," Quick said. "Well, I'd like to get along with everybody. You know, man, I'm all right, I know all the boys. I'd like to take care of you, so we can get rid of this."

Captain Racine was about to say something, but Bob cut him off. "Well, how?" Now the captain knew what was going on; they were coaching him as things went along.

John Quick pulled a hundred-dollar bill out of his pocket and placed it on the desk. "That's for you," he told Racine.

"You're going to have to do better than that," Racine said. "What have you got there, anyway?"

"A hundred dollars," Quick said. Then he reached into his pocket again and took out another one, placing it on the desk beside the first.

"That's good," Captain Racine said. "But what do I have to do for this?"

"Well," Quick replied, "you have to tell the men it's all right to cut me loose. Everything is all right—take care of business."

Warming up, Racine leaned forward and said, "What you just told me is that you're giving me two hundred-dollar bills!" Apparently the captain had figured that Dave and Bob were wired with miniature recorders. They were not wired, but Racine was playing it as if the whole conversation were going on tape, so that everything had to be brought out. "You're telling me," he went on, "that these two one-hundred-dollar bills are for me to tell my men not to lock you up—or to lock you up, but to make sure that you don't get convicted. Is that what you're telling me, Mr. Quick?"

John Quick looked over at Dave, as if to ask what sort of a weird captain this was.

"Go on," Dave told him. "He's the captain, man. Tell him."

"Yes, Captain," said Quick.

"Well," Racine said, "that's fine, but what about my men? These two one-hundred-dollar bills are for me."

Quick reached into his pocket and took out still another hundred-dollar bill.

"Yes," Racine said, making sure the nonexistent tape recorders got the additional facts. "What is that?"

"Another one hundred dollars," Quick said. For some reason he had begun to speak the same way as the captain. "That's for your men."

Dave and Bob could no longer keep from laughing. They turned around, trying to muffle it.

"Okay, Cap," Dave said, his eyes watering from the laughter, "is everything satisfactory?"

"It is?" Racine asked.

"Yes, isn't it?"

"Oh, yes! Sure," Racine said, rising and shaking John Quick's hand. "Okay, I'll take care of everything, Mr. Quick."

They led the prisoner outside and asked another cop to watch him a moment. Then they went back into the captain's office.

"Okay," Racine said. "Close that door. Now, what are we up to?"

"Well, Cap," Dave said, "the fact of the matter is that a bribe was just committed. You're holding the evidence. I wouldn't get my fingerprints on it, if I were you. You're making an arrest for bribery."

Racine looked puzzled again. "Who am I locking up?"

"Me and Bob."

"What?"

"No," Dave said, laughing, "you're locking up the other guy. Mr. Quick. Let it be known that this is a first! The captain of a precinct, a commanding officer, is making an arrest for bribery!"

The captain was laughing along with him. "It already sounds exciting," Racine said. "You must have a reason for it."

"Well, Cap, what's the biggest thing going these days? What's in the news most of all?"

"Uh, bribery."

"Right. Me and Bob make bribery collars all the time," Dave lied. "It's not going to do us any good, but I imagine that it would do you some good."

"Well, what do I do?"

"You don't have to do anything. Just remember everything that was said. Bobby and I will book the guy. We'll take him down to court and all, and we'll get the D.A.'s office to set up the interviews and have you come down at your convenience. You'll testify at the grand jury and we'll commit the guy. But there's one thing—we're not telling him yet."

"What do you mean?"

"As far as he's concerned, the fix is in. Let him keep thinking that way. We got him on the other charges, and we'll add the bribery at the arraignment. It won't hurt him, one way or the other."

"You're on," Racine said.

The prisoners were booked on charges of illegal possession of drugs and weapons, and Dave also wrote in the charge of bribery against John Quick. There was no entrapment involved, since Quick had instigated the bribe down the line. The desk officer read off the first two charges, but when he came to "bribery" he stopped short and looked up at Dave, who shook his head as a signal for him to read no further.

They took the unsuspecting Quick and his partner down to court. He went before the probation interviewer, who began asking him the usual questions. "Where do you live?"

"Hey," Quick said, "don't worry about it. You don't need all that. Everything's taken care of."

Then he was interviewed by the Legal Aid attorney.

"It's all right," Quick said, winking. "Don't worry about it, everything's taken care of."

Dave and Bob drew up the complaint in the D.A.'s office. They got the prisoners out of the cell and brought them before the judge for arraignment. Many of the defendants on hand were Quick's friends, so he smiled at them.

If we were really going along with this bribe, Dave thought, we'd be locked up on the spot. The guy's making it so obvious! Everybody in this courtroom is probably swearing that we've taken money from the guy.

They went up before the bench. The Legal Aid attorney looked at Quick and said, "What should I tell the judge?"

"Don't worry about it, don't worry about it."

"Your Honor," the assistant district attorney said, "due to the gravity of the charges, the people request twenty-five thousand dollars' bail."

John Quick's face broke into a big smile. As far as he knew, it was all a charade and everyone, including the judge, was in on it. He looked at Dave and Bob, winking at them again. They returned the wink.

The judge looked down at the papers, saw the charge of bribery, and announced, "Mr. District Attorney, I think twenty-five thousand dollars is very minimal bail. How about making it thirty-five thousand?"

"*What!*" the Legal Aid attorney shouted.

"You can't do that!" John Quick echoed. "Everything's been taken care of, Judge! The fix is in! The fix is in!"

The judge, his face reddening as the courtroom filled with laughter, rapped his gavel and arraigned John Quick, who realized for the first time that he was being charged with bribery.

It was September, and Dave was disgusted. Four months had gone by since he had seen Commissioner Murphy. He felt like resigning. What else could he do to get promoted? Bob convinced him they should write a letter. They got one of the college-educated cops in the precinct to type it up while they dictated to him, hoping that he would phrase their ideas a little better:

September 13, 1971

From: Patrolmen David Greenberg, #27306, and Robert Hantz, #27318, 77th Precinct.

To: Police Commissioner (Direct).

Subject: TO ASCERTAIN REASON FOR FAILURE TO RECEIVE PROMOTION TO THE GRADE OF DETECTIVE.

1. On May 5, 1971, during a personal interview with you, it was conveyed to the undersigned that a promotion to the grade of detective was forthcoming in the immediate future. It is apparent to the undersigned that due to the lapse of time, this directive has been overlooked or rescinded.

2. Inasmuch as your reply to this communication will weigh heavily on our decision to remain as police officers or pursue another means of employment, we feel that the following facts should be revealed:

a) During the last three years, we have made approximately 400 arrests, consisting of approximately 300 felonies, and our conviction rate, including pleas of guilty to lesser charges accepted by the district attorney's office, is approximately 90 percent. These arrests include:

1. The mortal wounding of two drug pushers (the Hayes brothers) who attempted to take our lives.

2. The arrest of a patrolman (Eric Washburn) assigned to the 77th Precinct, with two others, in connection with armed robberies and possession of drugs.

3. The arrest and conviction of three men armed with sawed-off shotguns who attempted to assassinate us.

4. The arrest of one person who attempted to assassinate Patrolman Greenberg at his residence.

5. The arrest and conviction of one person who also attempted to take our lives (firing a shot at Patrolman Hantz in a car).

6. Arrested one person (John Quick) for possession of dangerous weapons, drugs, and bribery.

7. It has been brought to the attention of the commanding officer, 77th Precinct, and ourselves that due to our activity, a reward has been posted in writing to anyone succeeding in killing us.

Dave wondered if they should add more. In recent months he had gotten his hat shot off in broad daylight; he had received forty stitches in his upper arm after being stabbed by a bayonet; a glass door had broken, nearly severing his hand at the wrist. Bob had almost killed himself crawling across a cable that had snapped, slamming him against a fire escape four stories up. Dave had hung for an hour by a rope, inside a dumbwaiter. He had hidden inside a huge old baby carriage, with a blanket over him, to make undercover arrests. Bob had dressed up as a woman one time. They had posed as mailmen, as elevator operators, and as members of the Board of Health, often using makeup from a theatrical store. There was so damn much they could put down in this letter . . .

"Fuck it," Dave said. "Let's just include the awards."

3. The following Medals and Citations have been awarded to us:

> Steuben Association Medal of Valor
> Pulaski Association Medal
> Two (2) Medals of Merit
> Two (2) Honorable Mentions
> Two (2) Commendations
> Six (6) Meritorious Awards
> Thirty-six (36) Excellent Police Duty Awards

We are also members of the Honor Legion.

Then they dictated the wind-up:

4. It is our understanding, on the basis of hearsay, that the possibility exists that we are being slighted for promotion, which you have already designated for us, out of fear of bad publicity in light of investigations being conducted by various agencies.

It is our belief that all allegations are being made by people whom we have arrested, or people that are associated with those we have arrested; and that they are trying to have us removed, in order to reconvene their illegal activities.

It is also our belief that, considering the amount of attempts on our lives, the time and devotion extended to the Department, we should have earned your confidence. And that promotion to the grade of detective should be forthcoming in spite of the investigations being conducted. We assure you that any allegations will be unsubstantiated.

In effect, they were accusing Commissioner Murphy of being afraid of controversy. A week later, his office called with a message that he wanted to see them.

Commissioner Patrick Murphy sat behind his desk with their letter in his hands.

"To put it as plainly as we can," Dave said, "we're down to the wire. We figure that before we walk out of here, it's one of two things—we get made detectives, or we resign. That's what we tried to say in that letter.

"We know we're controversial," he went on. "But we're saying, Fine, we don't care. If somebody thinks we've done something wrong, let him step forward and arrest us. Otherwise, promote us."

"Would you accept a plainclothes position strictly in narcotics work?" the Commissioner said.

"Well," Dave answered, "in order for you to offer us that position, you must think we're that good. And if you think we're that good, then why won't you give us what *we* want, rather than be afraid of publicity?"

"You'll have to understand something," Murphy said. "I'm a public administrator. And you're telling me that you're under investigation. Now, what if I promoted you and subsequently you get put under arrest? That would be political suicide on my part. And I have to answer to the Mayor and everyone else. But let me say this much—at such time that I feel that I'm willing to risk it, then there isn't anyone who can prevent me from promoting you."

"What does it take to convince you?" Bob said. "Put it out where we can see it."

"We've even locked up a cop," Dave added.

"Don't tell me about arresting a cop for doing something wrong," Murphy snapped. "That's your job! That's what you're supposed to do."

Dave was shamed by the Commissioner's sincerity. This Murphy must believe in what he's doing; he's not just trying to be a publicity hound with his war on corruption. What can I say?

The discussion went around and around. Yes, they also had made a bribery arrest. And narcotics, and guns, and stolen cars.

"If you felt there was any truth to these investigations of us," Dave said, "you would suspend us! You wouldn't let us run around with a badge and a gun, thinking that something's going to come of these investigations. And we don't stop working just because we're being investigated. So why would you stop our promotion for that reason?"

"Well," Murphy said, "the truth is, the Chief of Detectives doesn't want you. He turned you down."

Dave wondered why. "Well, listen, who's the Commissioner, you or the Chief of Detectives?"

"I have the last say, of course. I'm very, very interested in the two of you. And I'm going to look into it further. I'm going to have you reevaluated. And if I see fit, then there isn't anyone who's going to stop me."

"No good," Dave replied. "It's been months since I saw you the first time. Nothing's changed. Here's my shield."

He and Bob stood up and dropped their shields on Murphy's desk. As they headed for the door, Murphy called, "Say, what did you mean by this paragraph here?"

They turned around. Murphy was standing now, and they had to come closer to see which paragraph he meant. It was a ploy to keep them in the room, one that Murphy used several times over the next hour.

At last the Commissioner said, "Look, you can resign if you want to. I can't give you a 'yes' answer right now. I need some more time. If you feel you can trust me, then hang in there. Wait it out."

He means it, Dave thought. He doesn't want us to throw in the towel. He really can't promote us, because of the position he might be in. But he wants to keep on fighting. He knows what we're going through—he won't give in, but he's on our side.

Before leaving, Dave and Bob picked up their shields.

"I have the feeling he knows something," Dave said afterward. "He held something back. When he asked us to wait, it was as if he knew something was coming. Maybe one final test, to see how we come out of it."

"What are you talking about?"

"I don't know," Dave said. "It's just a feeling I got."

Bob walked into the Seventy-seventh Precinct House in the afternoon, his mind on how long it would be before Dave exploded and handed in his badge. Every other day he threatened to resign. Dave gave everything he had, without fear of the consequences, and he expected no less in return. Right now he was getting a lot less.

"Hantz!" the switchboard operator called. "You had a call."

"Any message?"

"No, he'll call back at sixteen hundred."

"Fine."

At exactly four o'clock, the call came in. "Hantz here."

"Hi, Bob."

"Hi. Who's this?"

"Ed."

"Ed?"

"Yeah, Ed Droge. I'm a cop."

"Oh," Bob said. He had no idea who Ed Droge was. "Hi, Ed."

"How's Dave?"

"Fine, Ed. Dave's fine."

"Listen, I got something going. Are you interested?"

Who is this guy, Bob wondered. "What have you got going?" he asked, thinking that it might be some information about a drug pusher.

"Well, if you're interested, call me back at seven o'clock. I'll give you a number."

"Look, this is kind of ambiguous. Would you mind telling me what you're talking about?"

"I don't want to talk about it over the telephone, but I can tell you that you two are the only guys who I have any confidence in. If anybody can do it, you guys can do it."

Well, Bob thought, it's got to be a hit. He's setting us up with a narcotics arrest. A house connection. If it's legit, the guy is making a very nice gesture.

"Okay, Ed. Any particular place?"

"Yeah, I'll give you the number."

Bob wrote down the telephone number.

"Phone me back at seven o'clock," Droge said.

"Will do," Bob said, hanging up. I must know that guy from somewhere, he thought. In court? Well, he's on a first-name basis with us, so I suppose it'll come to me soon.

Three hours later, off duty, Bob called the number. The phone at the other end rang twice and Droge answered it. "Listen," he said, "I'll tell you what I got. I'm not in the sector any more."

Bob's mind was racing. "You're not in the sector. Are you in the Seventy-seventh Precinct?"

"No, in the Eighty."

"Okay, go ahead."

"Here's the situation. I got a friend. The friend's doing some business. And he would like me to cover him, but since I'm not in the sector, I can't do it. He would like a truck to go through the precinct, and he wants to know that the truck is going to be covered."

"He doesn't want anybody to bother the truck?"

"Right."

"Ed, what's the truck got?"

"I don't want to rap over the telephone," Droge said, and just then Bob heard a clicking noise. "What's that?"

"I guess my phone is faulty," Bob said.

"Wait a minute. I don't want to talk over the phone, I—"

"Ed, hold on. I can't do any business with you if I don't know what I'm doing."

This is coming down all wrong, he thought. Have to get in touch with Dave. He could be getting the same phone call, for all I know.

"Listen," Droge said. "The guy's running narcotics."

"The guy's running a narcotics truck through the precinct?"

"Yeah."

"Go on," Bob said.

"The guy is willing to offer five hundred dollars to let the truck clear your sector."

Wait a minute, Bob thought. We haven't had a sector for a long stretch now. The whole borough of Brooklyn knows that Dave and I are in civilian clothes. This guy says he's in the Eightieth Precinct, right next to us, and he doesn't know we don't have a sector?

"Ed, I've been dealing in narcotics a long time. My partner and I have tried to do a bang-up job. And we're supposed to let a narcotics truck go through our precinct? Would you do it?"

"This is a personal friend of mine, and I'm asking you two guys for a personal favor."

"Let me call you back," Bob said.

"Okay. I'll be waiting."

Bob hung up. This was a live one.

29

"Eddie Droge," Dave said. "That's the guy who was in our Criminal Investigation Course."

Bob had been on a first-name basis with Droge during those four weeks. Only now did he remember that Eddie's last name was Droge. As Bob remembered it, Droge was about twenty-eight. He had gone out to lunch with him a lot, flipped coins together in the hall before class. The guy almost forced himself on me. Said he was having troubles with his wife. Wanted to know what bars I frequented, how close Dave and I were. Asked about the collars we'd made. In a way, I felt sorry for him. But he was pushy—came on too strong, for a guy who professed to have an inferiority complex. Dave wrote him off as insignificant.

"Listen," Dave said, "first of all, the guy's a bum. If it is Droge, and I'm not even sure of that, he's got no right to call us and make an offer like that. If he knows anything about us, he knows that the last thing in the world we'd do is run protection for a drug ring. Second of all, Bobby, we've got to give up the guy no matter who he is. If it is him—and even if he was a friend of yours—it might be a setup. In all probability, his phone was wired."

"You know something?" Bob said. "I heard a click at his end, but the guy was trying to imply that *I* was wired. He acted all panicky, said he didn't want to talk over the phone."

"Bullshit. The guy had to be wired and throwing the weight over to you. Look, he was your friend. We could turn him down and leave it at that, but we're supposed to report it. We could get locked up for not turning him in. Whoever it is, he's putting us in a bad position. It's probably not even Eddie Droge. It's somebody using his name, trying to set us up. The best thing to do is get in touch with Internal Affairs. Or let the Old Man know what's going on, so he doesn't think we're going over his head."

Dave considered all the possibilities. It could be that Internal Affairs itself is trying to trap us, set us up. Or it might be an organization that wants to deal drugs but has to get rid of us. The best way to do that would be to set us up with an operation and then call the police and say that we're being paid off to let that truck go through.

"It's a tough situation," he said. "I hate to get another cop in trouble just because of a phone call. I mean, we could get out of it just by saying no. But then again, with all this weight coming down on us, and everybody out to get us, I can't see us taking a fall for someone else. Especially when there's so many possibilities. We're in a position where we can't just do nothing."

They called Captain Racine.

"We're involved in something very touchy," Bob said. "Could be a cop involved. We're taking the proper procedure, though."

"Don't say any more. You handle it as you see best."

The guy really has faith in us, Dave thought.

In the courthouse they met with Captain Nick Zirpolo of the Confidential Investigating Unit of Internal Affairs. Certainly he would know if his own bosses were instigating the bribe.

They told Zirpolo about the call. "This is too big for me," Zirpolo said when they had finished. "I have no way of knowing if Internal Affairs is trying to set you up, but if they are, you've blown it by talking to me. If it isn't I.A.D., at least you'll have the right coverage."

They agreed to follow his instructions—in effect, go to work for Internal Affairs on this case. Later, at the Seventy-seventh Precinct station house, they met with Internal Affairs agents. Bob was told to call Eddie Droge again; this time the phone was wired. He and Dave were in the captain's office with the I.A.D. agents. The tape recorder was running.

"Hi," Droge said. "Listen, I don't want to do much talking on the telephone, but the deal is still on. Five hundred dollars to let the truck go through."

"Ed, do you take me for a fool?" Bob asked. Everyone in the

office looked at him as if he had just blown the whole operation. Only Dave was smiling. "Ed? I asked you, do you take me for a fool?"

"No. Of course not."

"Well, I want to ask you a question. You're talking about a truck. You're not talking about a car, but something big. Which means the guy has to be carrying an awful lot of narcotics. And you have the audacity to throw me and my partner a bone of five hundred dollars?"

"How much do you want?"

"It has nothing to do with what we want. *You* called *me*, Ed. Right?"

"Yeah."

"Okay, then. What is this, Macy's bargain basement? We're not here to bargain. Call the shot, and let's stop bullshitting and get down to business."

"All right. How about fifteen hundred?"

"Is that apiece?" Bob asked.

"I'll tell you what. I'll discuss it with my man. Why don't we meet tonight?"

"Fine," Bob said.

"You pick the spot," Droge said.

Bob looked at the others in the room. "Well, let me think of a good place to meet," he said, gesturing for somebody to give him a suggestion. One of the Internal Affairs men wrote "Market Diner—12th Ave., Manhattan" on a piece of paper. Bob glanced at it and shrugged. The Market Diner? I wouldn't even know how to explain where it is. He shot a second look around the room. This time a sergeant wrote down another address on a piece of paper, but Bob shook his head again.

"Eddie? Listen," Bob said, "I'm not familiar with where you're living now or anything."

"I'm over on Bay Parkway."

"Okay, Ed, *you* pick the spot."

"How about the Green Tearoom on Eighty-sixth Street, just off Bay Parkway?"

"Say it again, Ed. I didn't quite hear you."

Droge repeated the address.

"Any particular time?" Bob asked.

"How about eight o'clock tonight?"

"All right. You have no qualms about me bringing my partner, do you?"

"No, no. Bring him."

"And you'll bring your friend? The guy with the truck?"

"Well, I don't know about that," Droge said.

"Okay, I'll tell you—if you're not going to bring your friend, do me a favor and at least bring the money."

"Jesus, man, you don't waste any time."

"When you have debts, baby, you have debts. You ought to know that. If you want to do some business, do it with the money in your pocket. You'll have it?"

"Yeah," Droge said. "I'll have it."

"Okay, Ed. We'll meet you."

When Bob hung up, the tape was played back. Then he and Dave excused themselves from the office and went to the men's room to talk.

"Well," Dave said, "now at least we've eliminated the possibility that Internal Affairs is trying to set us up. Do you think the guy is really Droge?"

"I think so, but there's still a chance that it's somebody else."

"Maybe the D.A.'s office is trying to set us up," Dave said. "Or a narcotics operation out to get us. As far as these Internal Affairs guys are concerned, it's just a crooked cop trying to get us on the pad."

From the precinct house they were taken to the Internal Affairs headquarters to be wired for sound. They had been through this routine before and it had blown up in their faces, so neither one of them took it too seriously. The first thing they did at the I.A.D. office was to lie down on couches to take naps.

The deputy inspectors, chief inspectors, captains, lieutenants, and sergeants were all somewhat nervous. "Listen," someone said, "this is very important! I don't know if you understand what's going on here! You can't go to sleep!"

"It's four o'clock in the afternoon," Bob said. "We've got until eight."

"Wait a minute," a senior officer broke in. "Sit up and listen, because this is the way it's going to happen. First you—"

"Stop!" Dave told him. "I don't know what you have to say about how it's gonna happen, but it's *not* gonna happen that way. *You* need *us*. As far as I'm concerned, you have everything. We've cooperated with you as far as we're supposed to. Now we're off duty. If you want us to continue assisting you, it's got to be *our* way. We just don't trust you! And it would really behoove you to get Captain Zirpolo and his men down here to work with us, inasmuch as we do trust them."

"We can't do that."

"Okay. If we have to work with you, then you have to do it our way. We've been in the position more than once of relying on someone else, and we ended up almost getting killed."

"I think we can come to some sort of compromise."

"Fine," Dave said. "First thing you do is wake us up in an hour. We're going to take a nap."

Within a few minutes, they were talked out of prolonging their nap. "The first thing we want you to do," they were told, "is empty your pockets."

Dave and Bob looked at each other. "What did you say?" Dave asked.

"Empty your pockets and take off your shoes."

"You're forgetting something," Dave said. *"We* came to *you.* You didn't come to us!"

"That's right," Bob said. "Don't intimidate me by telling me to empty my pockets. What right do you have to count my money? If we do this, it's only because we have nothing to hide. I don't want you thinking that *we're* the bad guys, even though we came to you in the first place. Now, do we understand that?"

"Yes! Yes!" came the replies. Dave and Bob gave over their money and took off their shoes.

"Who's gonna hold the wire?" someone asked.

"It doesn't matter who holds the wire," Bob said.

"Droge called you and referred to you as Bob, so you carry the wire. We're going to tape it to your chest. But we'll have to shave it first."

"Shave what?"

"Your chest."

Bob looked around the room a moment, and then he began to

laugh. "This is a circus! I can't *believe* this. Why would I want to shave my chest?"

"So the tape won't stick to it."

"I am not shaving my chest. I went along with the shoes-off-the-feet routine, and I emptied my pockets. But I'm not going to shave my chest. And besides that, give me a receipt for the money."

"A receipt?"

"Damn right," Dave said. "You're not taking our money off us without giving us a receipt for it."

"Okay. Yes, sir."

Now an officer said, "We'll have three plainclothesmen, the inspector, and—"

"Hold it," Bob said. "Will you excuse us a minute?" He and Dave went out to the hall. "Dave, I'm not doing this."

"I don't care," Dave said. "Let's go back and tell 'em it's got to be our way or nothing."

When they walked back in, Bob told everyone, "If we do this, we're going to do it our way. I'm not jeopardizing Dave, and he's not jeopardizing me. And if we're not here to jeopardize each other, you people certainly are not gonna jeopardize us."

"You have my solemn word," the lieutenant said, "that you will handle this investigation *any way* you want to. Except for two stipulations."

"Stipulations?"

"The object of this investigation is to get as much information as we can about organized crime. You are to find out who Droge is working for. After you find out who's fronting it, you are *not* to bust him under any circumstances. The reason is to obtain as much information as we possibly can."

Another officer added, "And, fellas, this'll put you in the detective bureau for sure. What're you laughing about?"

"Nothing," Dave said, rubbing his eyes. "It's just that we've heard that before."

The Internal Affairs people agreed to have no cops inside the Green Tearoom during the operation. Dave and Bob agreed that they would not make an arrest. Everybody shook hands.

Bob was wired with two devices, a miniphone-recorder and a

transmitter. He and Dave decided that if they got to the restaurant before Droge did, Bob would sit with his back to the door. Dave would be able to see Droge come in, and he would lead him to the seat next to himself, facing Bob, so the guy would be speaking right into the microphone.

"Remember," they were told, "Bob's equipment includes a transmitter to every radio car in the area. We'll have seven or eight cars involved. Keep us posted as to every step you take, since there won't be any cops on the scene."

As they were leaving the room, the lieutenant added, "From now on, keep in sight at all times."

"Where's your men's room?" Dave asked.

"In there."

Dave and Bob went inside to wash their hands. An officer followed them inside. Suddenly Dave walked out and ran to the exit door of the building. The officer, who was supposed to keep them both in sight, dashed into the hall. "Help! One of them's gone! Help!"

The officer ran to the main office for reinforcements. Bob came out to the hall and heard Dave's whistle. He turned, saw his partner at the exit door, and they both went out to Dave's car. The entire Internal Affairs staff was in a panic trying to find them.

"There they are! In the car!"

An officer came running over. Dave looked up at him and said, "Hey, are you guys with us? We're gonna be late!"

"Don't do that to us again!"

"Do what? We went to the men's room and got in the car, just like we said we were going to do."

The officer ignored the remark. "Sergeant! Would you ride with them, please?"

The sergeant got in the back seat, and they pulled away from the curb, followed by several other cars carrying men involved in the operation.

As the procession headed toward the Green Tearoom in Brooklyn, Dave repeatedly broke loose and lost the cars behind him. He and Bob kept speaking into the transmitter Bob was wearing, relaying new information; and the sergeant in the back seat, now in a panic, leaned over Bob's shoulder and yelled,

"Don't worry about it, everything's under control! I'll give you our exact location! It's—"

By the time they arrived, the procession behind them was scattered all over Brooklyn.

Dave parked the car. As he and Bob walked down the sidewalk to the Green Tearoom, they spoke for the benefit of all the agents listening in.

"We are now commencing with our step-by-step report," Dave said. "We are heading for the Green Tearoom."

"We are now opening the door," Bob said.

"Stepping inside."

"Step by step."

"Bob has just stuck his left foot into the restaurant."

"One male at cash register, pressing button number ten."

"We are in—repeat, *in*—the Green Tearoom."

"Dave just blew his nose."

There were only seven or eight customers in the restaurant. Odd, Dave thought—this place is usually mobbed. They went down to the last booth. Droge was nowhere in sight, and nobody else was waving to them. They sat down, Bob with his back to the door and Dave across the table from him. A waitress came to the table, and they asked for menus.

Bob sat by the aisle, watching his partner's face. Dave nodded. Someone had come into the restaurant. No question about it—Eddie Droge.

Dave stood up and gestured to Droge, who came toward him down the aisle. Droge was wearing a sports jacket, which was strange; they had never seen him, on or off duty, wearing a tie or jacket. Dave reached out to shake his hand. "Hey, how're you doing, Eddie? How's everything?" As they shook hands, Dave noticed that there were wires inside Droge's sleeve. Who the hell is *he* working for, he wondered.

Dave sat down again, pulling Droge onto the seat beside him. Eddie and Bob shook hands across the table.

Suddenly Dave noticed that Bob's collar had opened, revealing the white tape on his chest. He tried to distract Droge's attention from Bob. Then he gave a hand signal and Bob quickly closed his collar. Now, Dave thought, I've got to signal Bob that Droge is wired! Who is Droge working for? The F.B.I.? The D.A.'s office? No matter who it is, we're being framed by somebody!

The waitress came back and they ordered dinner. Bob quietly pulled out his gun and held it in his lap underneath the table.

Dave and Bob had no way of knowing that Ed Droge was working as an undercover agent for the Knapp Commission. Charged with investigating police corruption in the city, the Commission itself had instigated the bribe offer to them. At this moment outside the Green Tearoom, Internal Affairs officers were literally bumping into Knapp Commission agents.

A Knapp agent and an Internal Affairs agent passed each other on the sidewalk. They went twenty feet in opposite directions, stopped, and looked around at each other. Then they walked back to confer.

"Hey," the Knapp agent said, "what are you doing here?"

"We got an operation going."

"Yeah? So do we!"

"Where's your operation?"

"In the Green Tearoom. Where's your operation?"

"Same place."

"Who do you got?" the Knapp agent asked.

"We got some cop who's trying to bribe two of our boys."

"Yeah? Well, we got two of your boys trying to *take* a bribe."

"Who's your guy?"

"Eddie Droge. Who're your boys?"

"Greenberg and Hantz."

"Uh, listen—we got a little problem, here. Eddie Droge is working for us," the Knapp agent said.

"Well, that's good. Greenberg and Hantz are working for *us.*"

"Hey, Eddie," Dave was saying inside the Tearoom, "how's that chick you were with?"

He was trying to avoid the subject of the narcotics truck and the money, and to embarrass Droge instead. After all, he thought, anything we say will go on his tape as well as ours. He must be working for the Commissioner's office or something.

"I heard your wife almost found out about her," Dave went on. "And hey, I hear you've been making a lot of money on the side."

Droge was visibly nervous, obviously not wanting all this to go on his tape recorder.

Dave looked up and saw the Internal Affairs lieutenant striding into the restaurant. He tapped the table, and Bob looked over his shoulder. Bob moved over so the lieutenant could sit beside him.

"The operation is terminated," the lieutenant said.

Dave squinted at him. "The operation is terminated?"

"Yes," the lieutenant said. "Don't say another word."

Dave nodded toward Droge. "Who?"

"Knapp Commission," the lieutenant replied.

"Fine," Dave murmured.

The lieutenant stood. "Let's go outside and we'll take care of everything."

"Hey," Dave said. "Later, man. We ordered dinner. When we get done, we'll go."

By now it had dawned on Eddie Droge that Dave and Bob were working for Internal Affairs, and that they were not going to be arrested. Chances were better that they might beat him up or kill him on the spot for having tried to frame them. He started to rise, intending to leave with the lieutenant. Dave grabbed him by the arm and pulled him back into the booth.

"Eddie," Dave said, "you just ordered dinner!"

The lieutenant stood there for a moment. "All right," he said, turning around and leaving the restaurant. The waitress came with the food.

"Eddie," Bob said, "there's no panic. Relax."

"Yeah," Dave added. "You were just doing your job."

Droge looked at them. "You wired?"

"Yeah," Bob said. "You, too?"

"Yeah."

"Let's be a man about this, Eddie," Bob said. "Turn your recorder off."

"Will you do the same?"

"Sure!" Bob said.

Droge reached under his jacket and shut off his recording machine. Dave and Bob heard the click. Then Bob reached under his shirt, but only pretended to turn off his device. The three of them began eating dinner.

"Eddie," Bob said, "who're you working for?"

"Knapp."

"Eddie, is there anything personal?"

"Yeah," Dave said. "Why us, Ed? I mean, why would you set us up like that?"

"I mean," Bob continued, "what is the purpose of this, Eddie? I mean, you were such a nice guy in school and all. What made you do this?"

They poured it on, patronizing, sarcastic, until Droge blurted out, "I *told* those people! I *told* them they were going up the wrong tree."

"What tree, Eddie?"

Droge told them the Knapp Commission had put him into the Criminal Investigations Course just so he could get next to them. The operation had already been going on for several months! No wonder Murphy couldn't promote us, Dave thought. The Knapp Commission was all set to get us!

"Eddie," Bob repeated, "was it something personal?"

"No! I told those people that you guys were clean."

"Eddie—why are you here?"

"I had no choice."

"What do you mean?" Bob pressed him.

"Well, I—I can't talk."

"Okay Then write it down on a goddamn napkin! You don't have to speak. Write it down on a piece of paper!"

Droge took out a pencil, then hesitated.

"All right," Bob said. "You're sure it wasn't personal?"

"No, not personal."

"How much money did they give you, Eddie?"

"They gave me five hundred."

"Were the bills marked?"

"No."

"That's good," Bob said, picking up the three checks for the meal. Dave knocked Droge off the seat and onto the floor, and then Bob threw the checks in his face. "That's good," Bob went on, "because you just bought dinner. Pay the checks, motherfucker!"

As they walked out, every customer in the restaurant got up and followed, leaving unfinished meals on the counters and tables. All went to pay their checks. All were Knapp Commission plants—not only the customers, but the man pushing the broom, the counter man, the grill man, and the waitress.

Outside, there were cameras on rooftops across the street from the Green Tearoom. Dozens of agents were milling around, comparing notes. The crowd included representatives of the Knapp Commission, Internal Affairs, the F.B.I., the Police Commissioner's Confidential Investigating Unit, the D.A.'s office, and even the Internal Revenue Service. Aside from the members of Internal Affairs, they all were under the impression that Greenberg and Hantz had been caught accepting a bribe.

Dave and Bob were told to return to the Internal Affairs office in Brooklyn for a debriefing.

"This is really something," Dave said as they drove back. "There was a bribe attempt made—entrapment. By the Knapp Commission! Whoever's in charge of the Knapp Commission is guilty of conspiracy to commit bribery! Why in the world would they go through all this trouble to get *us*? What have we done, man, to make those people want to lock us up so badly? If we didn't say anything about the phone call, if we'd just said no and been honest, we could've been locked up for not reporting it! And if we had met Droge on our own to see what he wanted, we would've been locked up for accepting a bribe. We had no way to turn! We were just lucky we didn't pursue this all on our own and try to make the arrest. Any other way, we'd have been locked up."

Sydney Cooper, chief of Inspectional Services, responsible for all anticorruption efforts in the Police Department and therefore in charge of Internal Affairs, had been notified by the district attorney's office that two policemen would be brought in under arrest for accepting a bribe. There had not been time to tell him that the operation had backfired. Nor had he been informed that the two policemen in question had been working for *him* and had caught the Knapp Commission instead. Cooper was waiting at the Internal Affairs office for the two "guilty" cops to arrive.

Dave and Bob, wearing beards and dungarees, walked in and approached Cooper. "Are these the two cops?" he asked. Before anyone had a chance to answer, Cooper yelled, *"Fucking hippie cops!"* and spat in Bob Hantz's face.

Bob wiped it off, and then he and Dave lunged at Cooper. Two officers stepped in front of the chief and backed him into the elevator, closing the door. Dave was nearly blind with fury, swinging wildly and yelling. Several men jumped both him and Bob, to hold them back. When he had calmed down, someone handed him his gun, telling him he had drawn it.

"Will you two take the stairs up to the office, now?"

"It'll be a cold day in hell, baby, before I walk up those stairs!" Bob roared. "You get that elevator for us!"

They rode up and emerged outside Sydney Cooper's office, only to be greeted by a big crowd of Internal Affairs agents, members of the D.A.'s office, and cops.

"What the hell are we doing here?" Dave said to no one in particular.

"You have to go through a debriefing now."

"Hey, take your fucking debriefing, and take that degenerate that has no hair on his head, and stick it all up your ass!"

Dave and Bob started to walk out. One of the Internal Affairs men called, "Wait a minute! You can't do that! You have to understand! He had no idea what happened, and—"

"Who is he?"

"Sydney Cooper, the chief of investigation."

"Well, how come he's the fucking chief and he don't know what's going on?"

"We didn't tell him."

"Listen," Dave said, "we don't want to have any more to do with you guys. It went as far as it can go, and we're leaving."

"What's it going to take to get you guys to cooperate?"

"Our gold shields," Dave said. "Get somebody up here with them right now. Make us detectives and we'll talk. Otherwise, we're going home."

"Why?"

"We want to know why it is that out of thirty thousand cops to try and frame, they chose us. And something else—we're placing Michael Armstrong, chief counsel of the Knapp Commission, and Eddie Droge under arrest! Where are they?"

"They're right here," someone said.

Armstrong and Droge were brought in.

"You're under arrest!" Dave told them.

"What for?"

"Bribery!"

The district attorney came in and said, "That's right, they committed bribery. We'll have to book them."

"No," said one of the Internal Affairs officers. "No further action at this time, as far as arrests are concerned."

"Hey," Dave shouted, "Wait a minute! We want these guys locked up! They committed a bribery!"

"Well, listen, an investigation is pending. I guarantee you, we'll submit everything to the grand jury, and the indictments will be handed down against them."

"You sure about that?"

"Yeah."

Satisfied, Dave and Bob walked into Sydney Cooper's office and sat down.

"Sit up straight!" Cooper ordered. "I'm a chief!"

"Where are the Indians?" Bob muttered.

What did you say?

"Never mind," Dave answered. He and Bob stood up, took out their police shields, and dropped them on the desk. "You're nothing," Dave said. "We quit." As they started for the door, two of Cooper's men blocked it.

"Are we under arrest?"

"Of course not!" Cooper yelled. "You're not under arrest! I just didn't understand what was happening when you came in downstairs. You'll have to excuse that. I wasn't aware—"

"Are we under arrest?"

"No, I—"

"Well, if we're not under arrest, we're leaving now."

"You can't leave now! We need your cooperation in ascertaining what happened!"

"That's fine," Dave said, "but we're not cops any more. We just resigned. And we're leaving. The only way we'll stay here is if you tell us we're under arrest."

"We'll have to hold you for investigation."

"Hold us for investigation? We want an attorney."

"Don't give me that shit! You can't have any attorney! You're working for *me*, and I won't let any fucking attorney in here!"

"Fine. We won't answer any questions."

"Look, sit down, and—"

"The first thing I want from you," Bob said, "is an apology."

"I don't give any apologies," Cooper said.

"Let's go, Dave. When you apologize as a gentleman," Bob told Cooper, "then we'll talk."

A deputy inspector came into Cooper's office and told Dave, "We have one order—and that's to see that you two men are happy when you leave here."

"Okay," Dave said. "We'll take our gold shields now. That's the only way we're going to be happy."

"We can't arrange that now."

"Fine," Dave told the inspector. "We have an appointment with the press. We think the public should know about what just went on."

"Wait a minute! Listen, you have to understand something. This is an investigation that's still being conducted, and this being made public might—"

"What do you want?"

"We want you to talk to the chief, and to put everything on tape. But I guarantee you—you'll have your gold shields in a week."

"Great," Dave said. "Now we want an attorney."

It was already past midnight when an attorney for the police union arrived and obtained an apology from Cooper. Dave and Bob then went inside and told him what had happened.

In November, Dave and Bob were summoned to Police Headquarters for their promotion. They were told to bring their medals and citations, and some of the illegal weapons they had confiscated. A morning press conference was planned, with Commissioner Murphy presiding. All the men in the Seventy-seventh Precinct extended congratulations. Captain Racine, who had received word that he would be promoted soon, went to headquarters with them. It was a big moment.

When they showed up, the promotion had been canceled. No explanation.

"I've had it," Dave said. "They're playing their games again. They have another investigation going. They're not going to promote us. It's time to get out."

He and Bob were in a bar, drinking and trying to sort out what had happened. They held no grudge against Eddie Droge. The Knapp Commission had previously apprehended him committing a crime, and he had been used. According to their information, it was Sydney Cooper who was now stopping their promotion, claiming they were still under investigation.

"I'm going to stick it out," Bob said. "I know I'm not going anywhere, but there's a future in it for me—maybe not the one we could have had, together, but at least there's something."

The next day, Dave wrote up an application to resign from the police force. Then he went to Florida, alone, to forget.

Returning from Florida after two weeks, he thought he might go back to steelwork full time. Or hang out a shingle and become a private investigator. Go out as a civilian and make narcotics arrests on the side—really show up the system. When he ran out of money, he would think of something else.

He walked into the house and slumped down in a chair. "There's a little bit of a problem," Irene told him.

"What do you mean?"

"Well, Bob is involved. Seems he's in trouble."

"Yeah? How come?"

"I'm not sure, but it stems from this," she said, handing him a recent copy of the *Daily News:*

COPS NET FIVE IN DRUG FACTORY SHOOTOUT

Police Commissioner Murphy's anticrime section returned its first dividends in Brooklyn early yesterday as five police officers arrested five persons they said were involved in a drug factory operation on Fulton Street.

The multiple arrests evolved from what first seemed a street disturbance. It ended after a four-block chase, in which several shots were fired.

Dave called Bob immediately. "Hey, I'm back. What's the trouble?"

"It's crazy," Bob said. "I was with four other guys. We made the arrest. And then one of the women we locked up announces that somebody took thirty-five hundred dollars from her! As far as everybody's concerned, all five of us are going to be locked up. Only thing is, the chick says it was a black guy. Obviously, it's not me. There were two black guys on the anticrime team with us. But nobody's doing any talking, so all five of us are taking the weight."

"Well, look, Bobby—give it to me straight. Far as I'm concerned, you might have given up completely and started taking advantage of the job—thinking maybe you can get rich quick or something. So give me the truth, man. Did you make something on this deal? Did something come down the way it's not supposed to?"

"Dave, that thing was as legitimate as ever! I don't know what happened. I thought we did a good job, but we're all getting hung!"

"Okay, man. It looks like I'm going back to work."

"What do you mean?"

"Stay loose. I'm going to see what I can do."

From what Dave was able to find out on his own, the accusation that some money had been taken could not be substantiated. He did learn that some sort of investigation was proceeding in the rackets section of the district attorney's office. He'd have to find some excuse to go up there and snoop around. Well, he thought, how about the promise we got that there would be a grand jury hearing on the Knapp Commission incident involving Eddie Droge? Another promise broken—but why not use that as an excuse?

So he went to the D.A.'s office, ostensibly to inquire when a grand jury hearing might be held. While he was there, he walked around, looking for any evidence of the supposedly top-secret investigation concerning Bob and the four other anticrime cops. On a desk, he saw one folder bearing the name of one of the cops. And before leaving, he overheard a conversation about the investigation. The same cop's name—Tony Lewis—was mentioned. Apparently one of the cops had taken a gun from somebody during the arrest at the drug factory. Instead of confiscating the weapon, the cop had returned it to the owner.

Dave went to see Tony Lewis on his own. He could hardly believe that a cop would take advantage of four of his colleagues by doing something wrong behind their backs and then, once he had been caught, allowing them all to remain under suspicion.

Dave confronted Lewis at the Seventy-seventh Precinct. "Is it true you took a gun away from someone during that arrest and then returned it to him the following day?"

"What?"

"Look," Dave said, "I'm making a statement to you. What do you have to say to it?"

"All right. Yes, I did do that. But how did you know about it? Does anyone else know about it?"

"Just tell me something," Dave went on. "Which of the other cops knew about it besides you?"

"None of them. Just two guys—not cops."

"Let me tell you something," Dave said. "You're going to be locked up, man."

"Does anybody else know about it?"

"Hey, you're telling me that only two guys knew about it. Then how did I find out?"

"I don't know."

"Well," Dave said, "the D.A. knows about it. And with what I have to tell him, you're going to be locked up. You took advantage of those guys, and you deserve to get what you're getting. But that's not even the reason I'm turning you in. I'm turning you in because right now it comes down to you or my partner. And, baby, I don't care if your name is Jesus Christ—if it comes down to you or him who gets hung, it's you."

Dave went back to the D.A.'s office and told them that he had obtained an admission about the gun from Tony Lewis.

"But in order for me to testify," Dave said, "you have to be willing to give up the rest of your investigation." At first the D.A.'s men refused, threatening repercussions against Dave. "Threaten me for whatever you want," he told them. "But I'm getting out of the job anyway, and you can't hurt me."

The argument went on and on, until the D.A.'s office conceded that there was no case against anyone, for anything, without Dave's testimony. All the district attorney had was a partial case against Lewis—a statement by the owner of the gun that Lewis had returned it to him. Dave's testimony would clinch it.

On the understanding that all further action against Bob and the other cops would be dropped, Dave testified before the grand jury. But then the D.A.'s office wanted to know how Dave had found out about its investigation. "Tell us who your informer was," an assistant district attorney said.

"Informer?"

"That's right. This was a confidential investigation. No one outside our office knew about it. You had to have inside information."

Dave glared at him. "Five minutes ago, you people were on your hands and knees, begging me to help you! And now, after I do help you, you're trying to nail me for knowing what I was talking about!"

"You have an informer working in our office, and we want to know who it is."

"If I had an informer and I don't want to tell you who it is, what would you do?"

"We'd subpoena you to the grand jury, and have you testify under oath. And if you perjure yourself, we'd lock you up."

Dave thought about this a moment. "Okay," he said. "Here goes, fellas. I have an informer. But I don't want to tell you who it is."

"You do have one?"

"Yup."

"Well, then, you'd better tell us who it is."

"Nope."

"Then we'll take you before a grand jury."

"I guess you'd better. That's the only way you're going to get me to tell you who my informer is. Put me under oath."

They cursed him out but Dave was smiling.

Dave and Bob were standing outside the courtroom where the grand jury was sitting.

"I'm gonna tell 'em everything," Dave said.

"I'd like to be there with you," Bob told him.

"Hey, Bobby, listen—I'm getting out of the job, man. You're not. Why give them a reason to come after you even more than they have? Let me go in there. You can't say any more about all of it than I can. You can only corroborate it. When the jury decides to investigate my statement, then you can be subpoenaed. But right now, it's not necessary."

"Okay, man—give 'em hell."

Inside, Dave was told to identify his "informer" within the D.A.'s office. "I'm requesting permission of the foreman to let me answer the question put forth by the D.A. in my own words," Dave said. "I believe this request is necessary, inasmuch as what I have to say will concern a number of his supervisors and associates and therefore I believe he will attempt to censor my testimony."

"Go ahead," he was told.

"I also believe this jury might feel that further investigation is necessary concerning the incidents in my testimony. And I would like you to know that I'm willing, and I might add, anxious, to cooperate."

"Proceed."

"It is my belief that there is a great deal of not only lax security but also incompetence and concealing of facts on the part of the D.A.'s office," Dave said, launching into an account of the shooting of the Hayes brothers in Coney Island. He related how he and Bob had gone to the D.A.'s office for assistance, and how there had been only one miniphone for the two of them. "It didn't operate anyway," he said. "And there was no coverage with manpower, either. Ordinarily, when there is a life lost due to action taken by police, the matter is presented before a grand jury. But in this case, where *two* lives were lost, it was never presented. The reason was, I believe, to conceal blundering and poor supervision."

The members of the grand jury were leaning forward, listening to every word.

"Another incident," he said, "was what I believe to be a moral crime committed by the D.A.'s office. My partner and I went to the D.A. in connection with a bribe offer made by a suspended judge," he went on, describing the Vinny Rose–Arthur Graham encounter. "Once again," he said, "the incident was not presented to a grand jury. And the reason, I believe, was to keep from involving the D.A.'s office in any scandal or bad publicity."

Next Dave turned to the recent Knapp Commission incident involving Eddie Droge. "This was another episode in which the D.A.'s office did not take the proper action," he said. "It was an attempt by the Knapp Commission to apprehend my partner and myself in the commission of a crime which *they themselves committed.*"

Dave told about the call from Ed Droge to Bob, offering five hundred dollars to go on the pad; and about how they had gone directly to Internal Affairs about it. "We expressed to the district attorney our desire to have this incident brought before a grand jury, inasmuch as there was a crime committed by Patrolman Droge, that of bribery, and by members of the Knapp Commission. We were assured by the D.A. that this would happen. It never did."

The grand jury proceeded to question Dave about what he had said so far. Two hours later the hearing took up the matter of his alleged informer within the D.A.'s office. He began with an account of how he had gone there and had walked around, seeing the folder with Patrolman Tony Lewis's name on it and overhearing a conversation. "I then left and asked persons I'm familiar with in the street for any information concerning Lewis. I learned that he had taken a gun and returned it. I then investigated further, which included interrogating Lewis, when admissions were made. I informed the investigating officer of the statement I had obtained and was requested by the D.A.'s office to appear at the grand jury. I was told that there was no case without my testimony. So I testified, and an indictment against Lewis was obtained. Then they wanted to know who my informer was.

"The truth is, I *don't have* an informer in the D.A.'s office. I deliberately lied, but only for the purpose of being able to be brought before this grand jury, so I could tell you what should have been told to grand juries previously. So on the record, right now, I'm stating that I have no informer. It was only due to the laxity of the district attorney's office itself that I was able to walk in and learn that an investigation of Lewis and the others was taking place. And if it hadn't been for me finding out, they never would have made the arrest that was necessary to begin with. I lied to them, *not* under oath, so I could *get* under oath and tell you all that I've said. And that's all I have to say."

The grand jury began applauding, and as Dave turned to leave, they gave him a standing ovation.

Dave stopped his resignation procedure before it was too late; the Internal Affairs Division was now trying to close out all its cases against him and Bob, because they were going to be promoted.

On February 17, 1972, Dave and Bob were called and told to appear the following morning at the Police Commissioner's office. Once again they were ordered to bring some of their confiscated weapons to be displayed at the press conference.

"I almost feel like not going," Dave said. "I sure as hell don't want another rehearsal."

But they showed up as scheduled, having told no one at the precinct about it this time.

"There'll be a press conference at eleven o'clock," a lieutenant said. "Television cameras, the works. Before you go in there, I want to go over some of the questions that are sure to be asked—and I'll tell you what answers should be given."

Dave looked at the lieutenant a moment. "Listen," he said, "the only reason we had to wait so long to get here is because we wouldn't go along with what you're telling us to do right now. You don't have to promote us if you don't want to. And you don't have to do it publicly, either, if you don't want to. But if it is done publicly, and if they ask us questions, *we're* going to give them the answers."

The lieutenant conferred with his colleagues a moment; then he returned, smiling. "Okay. It's all yours."

Various police officials, including Commissioner Murphy, walked into the room at headquarters and shook hands with Dave and Bob. When Sydney Cooper came in and extended his hand, they withdrew theirs. "You lucky sons of bitches," he said.

The scene was unusual, to say the least. Seldom, if ever, had two patrolmen been promoted and transferred together in a special ceremony at headquarters, with the Commissioner presiding and TV cameras whirring. Murphy was up front, wearing a dark suit and looking quite solemn at the microphones. Flanking him were two young cops, wearing beards. Dave was wearing his red and white Batman T-shirt; Bob had on a white turtleneck sweater. Guns were strapped to their shoulders. On the table before them was an assortment of pistols, revolvers, rifles, shotguns, knives.

"Guns and narcotics are the instruments of death in our society," Commissioner Murphy observed. "These men being promoted today to detectives third grade have waged their own war on crime in our city. They are men of great imagination, efficiency, integrity, and bravery. Every officer in the Department should try to emulate their actions."

Murphy pinned on their new gold shields. The reporters began asking questions. What in their backgrounds might have led them to achieve such phenomenal success as officers of the law?

"Well," Dave Greenberg said, "actually I always wanted to get into this field—as a criminal."

Bob Hantz grinned. "At one point," he said, "I sort of wanted to be a burglar."

31

Dave Greenberg left the house early. He drove over the bridge to Brooklyn, through the streets of Bedford-Stuyvesant, toward the station house of the Seventy-ninth Precinct. It was his first day as a detective, assigned with Bob Hantz to the Robbery Squad in the Thirteenth Division.

Today they would begin again, just four years after meeting each other at the Academy. They had made a grand total of six hundred arrests, gained a conviction rate of better than ninety percent, collected nearly two hundred illegal weapons, survived twenty-six major investigations, appeared fifty-one times in front of the Civilian Complaint Review Board, earned forty-three citations apiece, foiled attempts against their lives. They had beaten the system—played the game, but in their own way.

As Dave parked his car, he thought of the headlines the day before: GOLD BADGES FOR BATMAN AND ROBIN: MURPHY PROMOTES DYNAMIC DUO; PAIR OF SUPERCOPS EARN SUPER STATUS. Not bad, Dave chuckled to himself; not bad.

He walked into the old station house and upstairs toward the squad room. Bob was at the top of the stairs. Something was wrong.

"What is it, man?"

"Heavy," Bob said. "We've been put on separate teams. With opposite shifts."

"We're not working together? Split up?"

"Right. The lieutenant says we don't have enough experience."

Dave Greenberg hesitated. Then he slapped Bob on the shoulder and together they walked into the squad room.

"Don't worry," Dave said. "I've got a plan . . ."